The Horse

Judging — Breeding — Feeding
Management — Selling

An unusual head and neck study of the famous Greyhound 1:55$\frac{1}{4}$, the champion trotting horse of all time. Photo by J. A. McClasky.

THE

HORSE

Judging – Breeding – Feeding
Management – Selling

D. J. KAYS

Professor, Department of Animal Science
Ohio State University

NEW YORK *A. S. Barnes & Company* TORONTO

To My Wife

who urged me to keep on keeping on

Look back at our struggle for freedom,
  Trace our present day's strength to its source;
And you'll find that man's pathway to glory
  Is strewn with the bones of a horse.
                                        —ANONYMOUS

Preface

In this book on horse production I have undertaken to present a balanced discussion of the many problems connected with it—judging, breeding, feeding, miscellaneous management, and marketing and selling. I have tried to make these discussions as informative and practical as possible, repeating wherever my experience as a teacher has shown me that repetition is necessary to drive an important point home to the student. The numerous illustrations have been selected with care; it is hoped that the accompanying legends will be interesting and informational.

Although it is primarily a text for courses in horse production offered at the college level, as a reference the book should be useful to all teachers of vocational agriculture and to 4–H Club leaders everywhere. The latter groups will find the chapters on judging especially helpful. Horsemen interested in all the areas of horse production will also find much of value.

In preparing this book I have drawn freely from the works of many authorities, notably Akers, *Drivers Up*, Beeman, *Veterinary Obstetrics and Zootechnics*, Craig, *Common Diseases of Farm Animals*, Gabaux and Barrier, *The Exterior of the Horse*, Gay, *Productive Horse Husbandry*, Hervey, *The American Trotter*, Holmes, *The Principles and Practice of Horse Shoeing*, Kilpatrick, *My Seventy Years with Clydesdales*, Lungwitz and Adams, *Horse Shoeing*, Morrison, *Feeds and Feeding*, Peckinpah, *The Appaloosa Horse*, Sanders and Dinsmore, *A History of the Percheron Horse*, Sisson, *The Anatomy of the Domestic Animals*, Susanne (Emily Ellen Scharf), *Famous Saddle Horses*, and Wall, *Practical Light Horse Breeding*. I also owe a debt to The American Horse Shows Association, to the *Chicago Horseman*, publishers of *Care and Training of Trotters and Pacers*, and to Ransom Publishing Company, publishers of *Who's Who and Where in Horsedom*. My thanks to the authors and publishers of copyrighted works for their generous permission to make use of any material I needed.

Several chapters in the text discuss the results of feeding experiments. For much of these data I am indebted to Edmonds, *Feeding Purebred Draft Fillies*, Ahlgren, *The Pasture Problem*, and Walker and Hackleman, *Five Steps in Pasture Improvement*. In the chapter on horse parasites I owe a similar debt to Dr. Frank Thorp, Jr., and Dr. Robert Graham, of the University of Illinois, authors of *Common Parasites of Horses*. Other pamphlets or breed publications that I have found especially helpful include the Fort

Riley Cavalry School's *Horsemanship and Horsemastership;* Conley, *4–H Light Horses,* and Rooks and Jackson, *Light Horses,* both published under the auspices of the Iowa Horse and Mule Breeders' Association; Michaelis and Denhardt's pamphlet on the Quarter Horse: *Who He Is and What He Is;* The United States Trotting Association's *Trotting and Pacing Guide* and *Standardbred Sport;* and pamphlets published by the Horse and Mule Association of America, especially *Horses and Riders.*

The various breed associations have supplied me with statistics from their registries, statistics which show what has happened to horses in the last fifty years. These organizations include the American Hackney Horse Society, American Quarter Horse Association, American Saddle Horse Breeders Association, American Shetland Pony Club, American Shire Horse Association, American Suffolk Horse Association, Belgian Draft Horse Corporation of America, Clydesdale Breeders Association of the United States, The Jockey Club Thoroughbred Registry, Morgan Horse Club, Palomino Horse Breeders Association of America, Percheron Horse Association of America, Tennessee Walking Horse Breeders Association, and The United States Trotting Association.

The editors of many of the breed publications have been kind enough to search out and send me information that I could not find elsewhere. For their kindness I am heavily indebted to the editors of *The Horseman and Fair World, The Harness Horse, The Thoroughbred Record, The American Horseman, Saddle and Bridle,* and *The National Horseman.*

Two well-known teachers of equitation—Mrs. Annie Lawson Cowgill of Milan, Missouri, and Miss Nona Rutland of New Orleans, Louisiana—have been generous with their suggestions concerning the material on equitation.

The excellence of many of the drawings is largely due to the painstaking care of the Campus Charts Service of The Ohio State University, which prepared them from my rough sketches. When original prints were unavailable I have relied on the technical skill of Mr. George Wolfram of the Photography Department of the University, under whose direction new photographs were made.

D. J. K.

Columbus, Ohio
January, 1953

Table of Contents

List of Illustrations

1

The Horse Business–
Then and Now

Man and His Horse through the Centuries

"Prehistoric man dwelling in earth's huge caverns has preserved a record of the most notable achievement of his age, of the noblest conquest ever made by man over the brute creation. Upon the walls of his subterranean home, carved in the imperishable rock, amid rude sketches of mastodons, of cave bears, of reindeers and other objects of his dread or of the chase, again and yet again man draws the picture of a bridled horse.

"Before kingdoms were conceived, before social order was known, before tribal law was recognized, horse and man proclaim the coming civilization. The domestic tools of the earliest agriculturalists and the weapons of the first warriors are ornamented with the head of the haltered horse.

"Man freely confesses his obligation to his horse. Freely he manifests his love and affection for his horse. Every noble attribute man possesses is found in its perfection in his horse.

"Throughout the ages man has proudly likened himself unto his horse; has gladly lived with him under the same tent as a companion on his journeys; cheerfully toiled with him as a servant in the fields; hunted with him as his comrade; raced with him as the fleetest beast afoot; fought with him as his truest and fiercest ally; died and been buried with him, begging with his last breath that his horse be sculptured on his tomb.

"Together they have endured the privations and hardships of toil; together they have shared the defeats, the spoils and the victories of war.

"Together they shall enjoy the fruits of their labors and together they shall divide the honors of eternal peace."

This eulogy concerning the horse was written by Mr. George Wentworth, formerly of The Union Stock Yards in Chicago. In these few words Mr. Wentworth has made clearly articulate the contributions which horses have made to men throughout the centuries.

Changes during the Last Three Decades

In 1924 I spent twelve weeks in the city of Boston working for the Horse and Mule Association of America. In the course of my assignment, which was to study costs incident to the delivery of merchandise, I called on all types of firms—the many that were making all deliveries with horse-drawn equipment, concerns that were using motor equipment only, and those that were using both types of equipment.

One day I dropped into the offices of the Massachusetts Society for Prevention of Cruelty to Animals. When I left the offices of this organization that day, I had a generous supply of circulars and pamphlets which had been published under the auspices of the society.

That night as I was thumbing through some of these pamphlets my attention was arrested particularly by one article. As I recall, one statement in it was to this effect: "More astounding than the mushroom growth of the automobile city of Detroit and more astounding than the kaleidoscopic growth of the rubber city of Akron, is the spirit of a people, whose desire it is to have a car for everybody and a road upon which to drive that car everywhere."

Then the writer of this article wrapped the robes of prophecy about himself when he said: "It is this same spirit of a people that places the saturation point in the automobile industry coincident with eternity."

Well, the motor business expanded steadily from the year 1924, when this article was written, until the hard times in 1929 and the early thirties, when the curve of expansion in the motorized vehicle industry turned downward. But since those difficult years, the motor business has expanded rather steadily and the horse business has receded.

With the coming of World War II, motor manufacturing made tremendous strides. Our young men who participated in the war were taught to fly through the sky and shoot down. They also learned how to dive beneath

On October 9, 1889, at Terre Haute, Indiana, the famous Axtell, hitched to a high-wheeled sulky, trotted a mile in 2:12, lowering the world's record for three-year-old trotters. On the evening of that day a syndicate of breeders bought Axtell from his owner, Mr. Charles Williams, for $105,000, a record price up to that time for a trotter or a pacer.
Currier & Ives.

Greyhound 1:55¼, the world's champion trotter, making his last public appearance during the Grand Circuit Race meeting at Delaware, Ohio, September 17, 1947. R. C. Flanery driving. Photograph courtesy Mr. R. C. Flanery.

the sea and shoot up. Motors for use in every area of human activity were given unusual impetus. Hence today motors are so highly perfected that they are as indispensable in times of war as they have long been in times of peace. The streets of our cities are so cluttered with automobiles that a pedestrian cannot cross without the aid of a traffic light or the whistle of a traffic policeman. It is not too much to say that motors are so thick that the first noise that a baby in his cradle hears, when he is old enough to understand anything, is the sound of a motor purring in his ears. The situation has changed so much in the last thirty years that today we have more automobiles in the United States than we have telephones.

Work horses, heavy harness horses, and road horses have been hit the hardest. Today, it can be said truthfully, the work horse business is a vanishing industry. On many work horse markets, not only old horses but many young horses are going to the killers at three cents a pound. In Ohio today, there are more farms without any work horses than there are farms with them. Vocational and 4-H Club judging contests in Ohio no longer feature any classes for horses. However, the coaches of judging teams at the intercollegiate judging contest at Chicago in 1952 included two classes of draft horses as a feature of their judging contest. At Ft. Worth, at the American Royal at Kansas City, and at the Denver Livestock Show, the students judging contests feature classes of Quarter Horses. On the Chicago horse market in 1916, during the First World War, the dealers handled in excess of 193,290 head. In 1950, only 246 head of horses went through the Chicago market. These figures were taken from the annual report of The Union Stock Yards Company of Chicago.

In the case of heavy harness horses and roadsters, the only demand for them is from the people who patronize the shows. As a consequence, the demand for such horses today is limited in comparison to the demand in the heyday of the business. City planning boards, when they lay out a park, provide bridle trails for saddle horses but no roads for high-stepping, heavy harness horses. And, of course, the automobiles have driven the road horses off the public highways.

The only horse that has been kicked upstairs by the great tidal wave of motor development is the saddle horse. Here are a few reasons why: Automobiles have increased the number of people who have hands with soft palms, they have increased the amount of fat which folks have deposited at their waistlines, and they have increased the number of people who pant audibly when they reach the top of a flight of stairs. So, for the sake of healthful exercise, there are more people riding horseback in this country today than ever in the history of the business.

In 1926, Bowen Rigging Company of Boston had two five-horse hitches working in the heart of the congested, frequent-stop territory in old downtown Boston. Today, on the streets of our large cities, most horse-drawn vehicles have been replaced by motor trucks. Photograph courtesy Bowen Rigging Company.

Virginia Dawn 245684—first prize four-year-old and grand champion Percheron mare, Chicago International, 1948. This mare includes in her make-up many of the characteristics sought in the best representatives of the breed. She was bred and exhibited by Mr. Frank C. Rathje of Palatine, Illinois. The peak year for registration of Percherons in the United States was 1917, with a total registration that year of 10,508 head. In the year 1950, Percheron registrations in the United States had dwindled to 149 head. These figures show how much the draft horse business has been affected by motor trucks and tractors. Photograph courtesy J. F. Abernathy.

The Shows as Evidence of a Wide Interest in Horses

At the shows, local, state, and national, there are more women and children riding horses than ever before. To attract the little tots four to six years of age, the shows are featuring lead-pony classes, which are well patronized.

Then, too, the shows are providing a great many pleasure classes, equitation classes, amateur classes, and owner-to-ride classes. These classes are very well filled at shows all over this country. In addition to the classes mentioned are the stock horse classes, Palomino classes, cutting horse classes, Quarter Horse classes, and the parade classes—ample testimony that more people are riding horses in this country today than ever before.

On a judging assignment in a western state in the autumn of 1950, I attended a bridle trail breakfast. Of the 120 people present, 85 had ridden horseback that morning. In the late winter of 1951, I talked to a banquet group of the Mahoning County Saddle Horse Breeders Association at Youngstown, Ohio. One hundred and fifty horse enthusiasts were present. Such gatherings are by no means unusual and are additional testimony that thousands of people in this country today still believe that "there isn't anything so good for the inside of a man as the outside of a horse."

Equitation Projects at Colleges and Universities

The directors of the physical education departments in our colleges and universities are beginning to think about the advantages of an equitation project as a feature of their physical education programs for students. Pioneers in this movement are Stephens College and Christian College, both at Columbia, Missouri. For years Miss Annie Lawson was in charge of the equitation work at Stephens, which under her leadership expanded and popularized its equitation program so much among the students that today college authorities everywhere regard Stephens College as an outstanding leader in equitation work. Under Miss Shirley Drew, Miss Lawson's successor, the equitation work has gone steadily forward.

Part of the equitation plant at Stephens is a big riding arena, a building which would adorn any campus and be an addition to the physical plant of any county or state fair grounds in this country. The main stable, of brick construction, houses thirty-two head of saddle horses. Other barns house eighteen head, but the main barn is about the last word in modern con-

A group of jennets in a pose which furnishes an unusual opportunity to study the head and neck features of this species. This photograph was taken on the farm of Mr. T. J. Moss, near St. Louis, Missouri. The same thing has happened to the work mule that has happened to the work horse: the mule business has rapidly become a vanishing industry. The Standard Jack and Jennet Registry of America reports only 32 registrations for 1950.
Photograph courtesy J. F. Abernathy.

veniences and accommodations, featuring roomy, comfortable stalls, tack room, lockers, shower room, toilets, and a small classroom.

In 1951, when I last visited Stephens, classes were being conducted not only in the main arena but in the three outside arenas.

I watched the instructional work for beginners, for intermediates, and for advanced students. In addition to instruction in the riding of three-gaited and five-gaited horses, students were being taught to ride hunters and jumpers. The completeness of the physical plant and the fine teaching staff explain why girls from all over the United States enroll for the equitation work at Stephens College.

When the equitation project at The Ohio State University actually got under way, in the fall quarter of 1946, 35 girls were enrolled. Since that time, including the fall quarter of 1952, there have been 1049 girls enrolled in the equitation classes at Ohio State. At the present time at The Ohio State

University equitation classes are scheduled 9–12 A.M. and 1–4 P.M. five days a week. There are ten equitation horses for classroom work daily. The animal husbandry department feeds, waters, and cleans out after the horses, takes care of the tack and has the responsibility of having them ready for all classroom sessions. Each girl pays a quarterly fee of $20. The physical education department pays the instructional costs as well as the feed and labor costs incident to carrying on this project.

At the present time in this country, thirty-eight universities or senior colleges in twenty-three different states feature courses in equitation as part of their physical education programs.

Questions

1. What phase of horse production has been most adversely affected by the great tidal wave of motor development in this country? Why?

2. What phase of horse production has been least affected as a result of motor vehicle expansion? Why?

3. What is the chief source of demand today for heavy harness horses and roadsters? Why?

4. What proof do present-day shows furnish of a keen and increasing interest in saddle horses?

5. What evidence of student interest in riding is furnished at the present time by the physical education departments of colleges and universities in the United States?

6. Compare the total number of horses and mules in the United States during the peak days of the business with the total number of horses and mules today.

2

The Field of Horse Production

Introductory Statement

For purposes of discussion, the problems in the field of horse production may be grouped under the following subheadings: Judging, Breeding, Feeding, Miscellaneous Management, and Marketing or Selling. The success or failure of the horse breeder may be accounted for in any one of these areas.

Judging

Faulty judgment in the selection of foundation stock may account for disappointment right from the beginning. It is most important, therefore, that the prospective breeder of both grade and purebred horses be as thoroughly informed as possible before he spends any money for foundation stock.

Breeding

The progeny which results from the first matings of the foundation stock may be disappointing. Sometimes the beginner, in defense of his judgment when he purchased his foundation stock, may repeat the matings in a futile attempt to get the sort of progeny which he insists should result from the matings of his choice. The progeny always proves or disproves the wis-

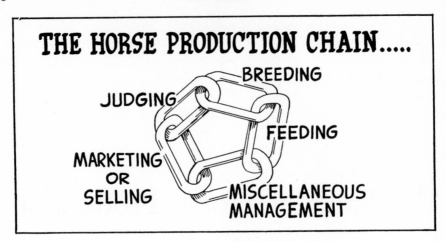

THE HORSE PRODUCTION CHAIN.....

BREEDING

JUDGING

FEEDING

MARKETING
OR
SELLING

MISCELLANEOUS
MANAGEMENT

"For," said the deacon, "it's mighty plain,
That the weakest link must stand the strain;
And the way to fix it, I'm not in jest,
Is to make that link as strong as the rest."

dom of the matings, but it is costly to repeat matings that have produced
disappointing results.

Feeding

A good pedigree gives a purebred animal the right kind of identity. But
to those engaged in the horse business a good pedigree, important as it may
be, is not an absolute guarantee of good results. The very best-bred animals
must be well fed if maximum results are to be forthcoming to the breeder
whose money is invested.

Miscellaneous Management

Faulty management and disappointing results team up together in the
livestock business. To paraphrase a statement quoted in the final chapter: "If
you want to be disappointed in the horse business, buy horses which have
had better care than you intend to give them." Too often men who launch
purebred livestock projects make the mistake of purchasing high-priced
livestock before competent men are hired to take care of them. In such instances the venture is usually disappointing.

Selling

A primary purpose of the purebred herd or flock is to produce sires
whose offspring will maintain or actually improve the levels of excellence

already reached in commercial herds and flocks. This statement is as true of the horse business as it is of every other phase of the livestock business.

Therefore the stallion selected for use upon both grade and purebred mares should have in his make-up the characteristics which buyers insist upon as well-marked features in his get. If such stallions are used, the difficulties incident to selling the progeny will be reduced to a minimum. Never in the history of the horse business has the market been glutted by good ones. The supply of top horses has never exceeded the demand because the best ones have always sold themselves.

Questions

1. Name the five links in the Horse Production Chain.
2. Why is judging important as one of the links in the production chain?
3. Why is breeding important as one link in the chain?
4. Why is feeding so important a link?
5. Discuss faulty versus sound management as a link in the chain.
6. Discuss the individuality of the stallion as a factor of importance incident to the sale of his get.

3

Features in Horse Make-Up

The Relationship of Form to Function

The Head

In all types of horses, the size of the head should be in proportion to the size of the body. As in other animals, the proportions of the head are considered a rather accurate index of the body proportions. Therefore, in judging horses one should always keep in mind the importance of balanced conformation.

In the case of foals, yearlings, and two-year-olds, a big head balanced in its proportions is an indication of growthiness and outcome. Of course, the terms "too big" and "too small," as applied to the head of any horse, are used advisedly. The head should not be so big that it appears coarse and plain and common. It should be big, with refinement as one of its essential features.

The small pony type of head in draft foals and yearlings is undesired because such heads are correlated with a tendency toward too early maturity, failure to grow out properly, and a consequent lack of size.

Therefore, in judging horses, the big coarse head in the case of all kinds of light-leg horses and the small pony type of head in the case of draft horses should receive sharp penalty. Somewhere between these two extremes discriminating judges make their choice.

The head of the drafter is rarely too large. A rule among draft horse men is that a drafter's head should not be so large but that a collar which will fit the horse can be slipped on over it.

The Features of the Head

Soundness of the head in all its features is a primary qualification in horses of all types. This requirement is emphasized in the market, in the show ring, and in the stud. Buyers of horses for these purposes are imperative in their demands for soundness. But the buyers for show and the buyers in quest of foundation stock also emphasize some features of the head which are of little interest from the standpoint of the open market.

Roadsters, saddlers, heavy harness horses, and all types of pleasure and show horses must be "breedy"—smart and trim about their heads and fronts —if they are to please the people who patronize the shows.

In all types of horses intended for breeding purposes, masculinity and femininity are important features of the head. Long, narrow heads with deeply dished faces or ugly Roman noses are undesirable because of their plainness. Width between the eyes and width of muzzle and jaws are taken to indicate capacity and growth possibilities. Straight-faced horses are preferred to the dished-faced and Roman-nosed types.

The Ears

The size, length, set, direction, and movements of the ear are important. Extremes in size of ear detract from the appearance of the head. The medium-sized ear, with proportions that help dress up the head, make the facial expression the most pleasing. Ears that are long, thick, and heavy— "mulish"—in their proportions make the head look plain. Ears that are short result in displeasing proportions. Such ears, however, are usually associated with the chunky type of horse, thick, closely and evenly made, and of prompt energetic manner on the move. A medium-sized ear, clean-cut in design, that shows the blood vessels clearly outstanding is characteristic of all horses in whose make-up quality and finish are well-marked features.

Set or location of the ear in no small way determines the beauty of the head. Ears set pretty well apart, not too low down over the eyes or too far back on the poll of the head, contribute to good looks. Ears set too low make a horse appear plain and unintelligent. Set too far back, they cause a horse to look sour and sulky, especially if such ears are accompanied by a Roman nose.

If the ears are carried in semihorizontal position, that is, if a horse drops his ears sideways, he is said to be lop-eared. Lop ears always make a head look common.

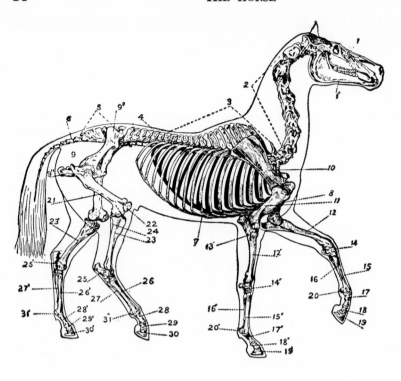

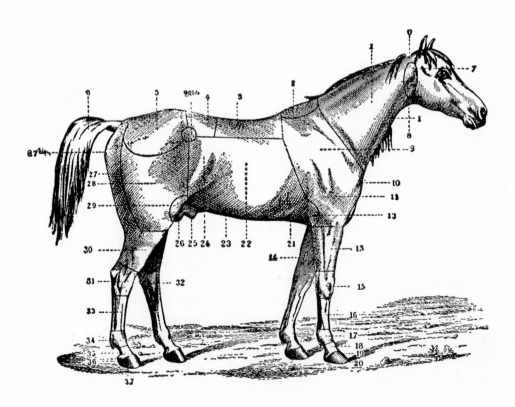

Opposite, upper: *Skeleton of the horse, showing the vertebral arch and the bone columns, one pair of the legs supporting, the alternate pair partially flexed, in a stride.* 1, bones of the head; 1', lower jaw; 2, cervical vertebrae; 3, dorsal vertebrae; 4, lumbar vertebrae; 5, sacral vertebrae (sacrum); 6, coccygeal vertebrae; 7, ribs; 8, sternum (breastbone); 9, pelvis; 9', ilium; 9", ischium; 10, scapula (shoulder blade); 11, humerus; 12, radius; 13, ulna; 14, carpus (knee); 15, large metacarpal bone (cannon); 16, small metacarpal bones (splint bones); 17, first phalanx (long pastern); 18, second phalanx (short pastern); 19, pedal bone (hoof bone); 20, proximal sesamoid bones; 21, femur; 22, patella (knee-pan or -cap and stifle joint); 23, tibia; 24, fibula; 25, tarsus (hock); 26, large metatarsal bone (cannon); 27, small metatarsals (splint bones); 28, first phalanx (long pastern); 29, second phalanx (short pastern); 30, pedal bone (coffin bone); 31, proximal sesamoid bones. *This illustration does not show the navicular bone, either front or rear legs. Other illustrations in this chapter show the location of the navicular or distal sesamoid bone.*
From Gay, *Productive Horse Husbandry,* courtesy J. B. Lippincott Company.

Lower: *A scorecard terminology study of the horse. Regions of the horse seen in profile.* 0, poll, or nape of the neck; 1, neck; 1', jugular gutter; 2, withers; 3, back; 4, loins; 5, croup; 6, tail; 7, throttle, or throat latch; 8, throat; 9, shoulder; 10, point of the shoulder; 11, arm; 12, elbow; 13, forearm; 14, chestnut; 15, knee; 16, cannon; 17, fetlock; 18, pastern; 19, coronet; 20, foot; 21, xiphoid region; 22, ribs; 23, abdomen; 24, flank; 25, sheath; 26, testicles; 27, buttock; 27, bisection of buttock; 28, thigh; 28, bisection of haunch; 29, stifle; 30, leg; 31, hock; 32, chestnut; 33, canon; 34, fetlock; 35, pastern; 36, coronet; 37, foot. From Gay, *Productive Horse Husbandry,* courtesy J. B. Lippincott Company.

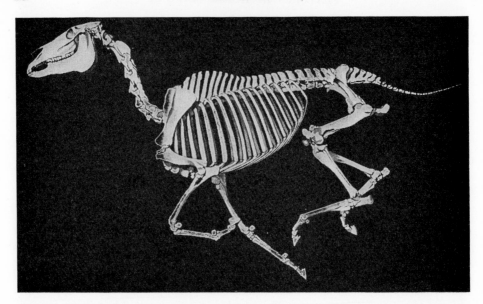

The famous American race horse Sysonby, showing action and sequence of hoofbeats at the run. This illustration shows plainly the way in which the bones act as levers as the hind legs are drawn up beneath the body, and moved forward again preparatory to straightening out and propelling the horse forward with a long stride typical of great running horses. The run is a rapid, three-beat gait in which a hind foot makes the first beat in the series, the other hind foot and diagonal fore foot make the second beat simultaneously, the remaining fore foot makes the third beat; then the body is projected clear of the ground and a hind foot makes the first beat in a new series. Photograph courtesy American Museum of Natural History.

The direction and movements of the ear are important considerations. Horses that carry their ears at an angle of about 45 degrees with the axis of the head are directing their ears in pleasing fashion. Horses at work or posed and set for inspection always look well with their ears so directed. Such direction of the ears brings out the beauty of the head and results in a pleasing countenance.

The movements of the ear are indications of temperament. Ears kept in a constant state of unrest may indicate nervous temperament, impaired eyesight, or even total blindness. Motionless ears are indications of a slow, lazy, sluggish, phlegmatic disposition.

The set and carriage of the ear is most important in all types of light-leg horses for pleasure and show purposes, where finish and dressiness about the front contribute to good looks. In general, the ears are satisfactory if of proportionate size, properly set and directed, clean-cut and trim in appearance, with a minimum of long coarse hair protruding from the inside and fringing the borders.

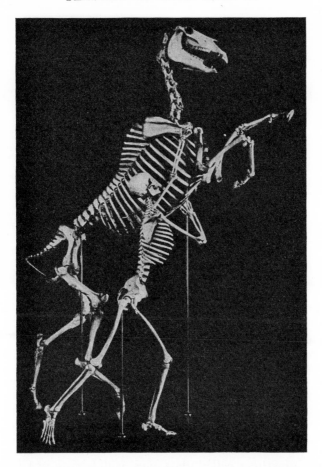

This illustration pictures clearly the skeletal structure of the horse and the man and shows how bones act as levers in supporting and propelling the body. The hock joint in the horse is the counterpart of the ankle joint in man. The knee joint in the horse is the counterpart of the wrist in man. The tuber calcis, the short bone protruding at the rear of the hock joint, like the heel in man, is the lever upon which the muscles act to lift the body upward and forward. Photograph courtesy American Museum of Natural History.

The Eyes

Big, full, prominent eyes, of a dark, rich hazel color are desired in all types of horses. Eyes that are distinctly blue are considered weak eyes because such color is associated with eye unsoundness. In buying horses or in judging horses the examination of the eyes is a first consideration. This is because blindness seriously depreciates value on the open market, and in the show ring constitutes a disqualification. This is true of stallions, mares, or geldings. Therefore eyes that are characterized by clearness, deep coloration, and intensity of reflection are preferred.

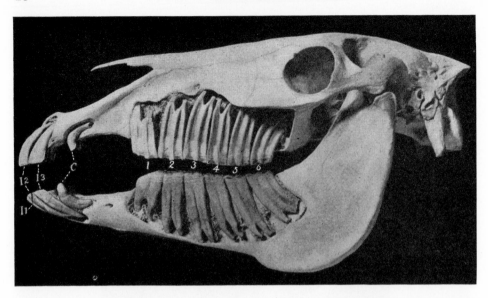

Skull of adult horse, sculptured to show embedded parts of teeth. The jaws are separated for the sake of clearness. I1, I2, I3, incisor teeth; C, canines. The cheek teeth are num-bered without reference to the first premolar teeth (wolf teeth), which are not present in this specimen. This is the skull of a stallion or gelding, for the canine teeth are present. In the case of stallions and geldings, the bars of the mouth (the interdental space) extend from the canine teeth to the premolars. The lower jaw is hinged. Sometimes it protrudes beyond the lower limits of the upper jaw and the defect is termed "monkey mouth." Sometimes the lower jaw recedes and the defect is termed "parrot mouth." The distal extremities—the incisor teeth—of upper and lower jaw should meet evenly. From Sisson, *The Anatomy of the Domestic Animals,* courtesy W. B. Saunders Company.

Walleyes, sometimes called glass eyes, watch eyes, or Clydesdale eyes, are those in which the iris is of a pearly white color, destitute of pigment. Such eyes are objectionable on the basis of looks, but nevertheless are func-tional and are not considered disqualifications.

The bovine eye is one characterized by excessive convexity. Its bulging tendency has resulted in the name "popeyed." Such eyes are objectionable because they depreciate good looks and predispose to myopia or nearsight-edness. Horses having such eyes quite commonly shy.

"Pig's-eye" is the term applied if the eye is too small, narrow, and squinty. Such eyes usually have thick eyelids and are commonly associated with coarseness and a sluggish, phlegmatic temperament.

The Nostrils

Good-sized nasal passages are considered indications of good breathing apparatus throughout. Small nostrils, on the other hand, are usually asso-ciated with short, flat ribs and consequently a chest that lacks capacity.

Just as the color of skin in sheep is an indication of health, so is the color of the mucous membrane or lining of the nostrils in horses. In buying horses, therefore, it is a good plan to examine the nostrils. The normal nostril discharge is transparent, resulting from the continuous discharge of tears. It is also odorless. Colored discharges of any kind from the nostril suggest sickness or disease.

The normal nostril should be large, the skin clear, the mucous membrane rosy at rest, more or less deep red after exercise, the liquid discharged should be clear and transparent, the breath should be odorless or at least not unpleasant, and breathing should be noiseless. The nostrils should be large because the nasal passages are the only avenues of air intake to the lungs.

The Mouth

The jaws of the mouth should meet evenly. Protruding or receding lower jaws—synonyms of monkey mouths or parrot mouths—are undesirable because they are unsightly and may also interfere with eating and good doing ability.

The parts of the mouth are the lips, the teeth and the gums, the bars, the lingual canal, the tongue, and the palate.

The lips, like the jaws, should meet evenly. They function as organs necessary to the prehension of food and also aid in mastication. The lower lip in part supports the bit and the impulses or directions of the bit are in a degree received by it.

To avoid a continuous escape of saliva the lips should meet closely. This is not always possible if the head is reined too high or if the lower lip is actually paralyzed. In the first case, the lower lip drops down after becoming tired by the unnatural position of the head. In the second case, in addition to difficulty in the prehension of food, the appearance is unsightly. Unilateral paralysis draws the lip to one side. Bilateral paralysis causes the lip to drop on both sides and become pendulous. This defect may be congenital but usually it is acquired.

Some horses have the annoying habit of lip slapping or beating the lower lip against the upper by a series of convulsive movements. Usually it is a vice of idleness.

The Teeth

The teeth are classified as incisors, canines, and molars. They are organs of mastication. Age is estimated by inspection of the incisors.

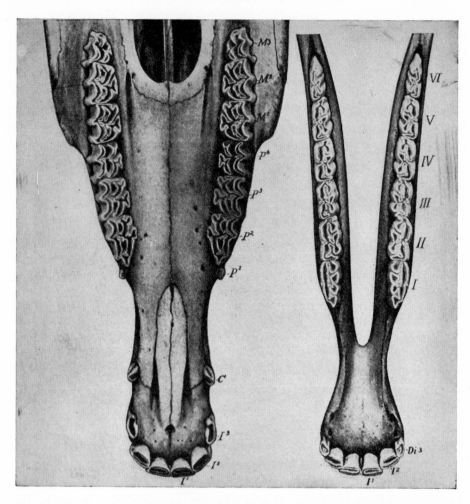

Left: *Upper teeth of horse about four and a half years old.* I1, I2, I3, *permanent incisors;* C, *canine teeth or tushes;* p1, *small vestiges of premolar teeth known as "wolf teeth";* P2, P3, P4, *true premolars;* M1, M2, M3, *true molars. A typical rising five-year-old mouth.*

Right: *Lower teeth of horse four years old.* I1 *and* I2, *middle and intermediate permanent incisors.* Di3, *deciduous or baby incisors.* I, II, III, *premolars;* IV, V, VI, *molar teeth. The interdental space, incisors to first premolars, is known as the bars of the lower jaw. The bit rests here when in proper position.* From Sisson, *The Anatomy of the Domestic Animals,* courtesy W. B. Saunders Company.

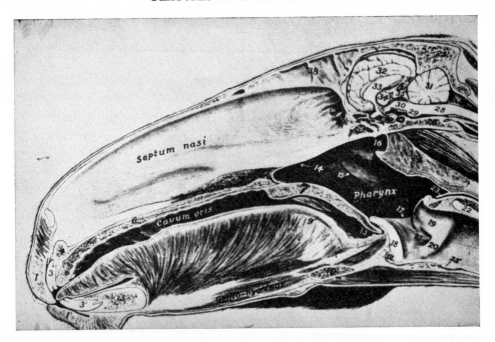

Sagittal section of head of horse. This illustration shows why horses do not breathe through their mouths as do cattle, sheep, swine, and dogs. The soft palate is a musculo-membranous curtain which separates the cavity of the mouth from that of the pharynx except during swallowing. The soft palate is greatly developed in horses, its average length, measured medially, being about six inches. Its length and contact with the epiglottis, plus the fact that the horse does not have voluntary control of his soft palate, may account for the fact that, in horses, mouth breathing does not occur under normal conditions and for the fact that when a horse vomits the ejected matter escapes usually through the nasal cavity. This explains why horses even on the hottest days, at the end of a race or at work in the field, do not run their tongues out. The air supply for horses is furnished through their nasal cavities. They inhale and exhale through their nose. Study especially the following: 6, hard palate; 7, soft palate; 13, the epiglottic space; 18, the epiglottis. Note the relative positions of the soft palate, the trachea, and the esophagus. From Sisson, The Anatomy of the Domestic Animals, courtesy W. B. Saunders Company.

The bars of the mouth occupy the space on each side of the lower jaw between the incisor and the premolar teeth or between the canine and the first molar teeth. The bars are covered only with mucous membrane.

In the mare the canines, or tushes, are undeveloped, and the bars extend from the corner incisors to the molars. In stallions and geldings, however, they are developed; hence the bars of the mouth are shorter, extending only from the canines to the molars.

It is against the bars of the mouth that bit pressure is brought to bear in the control of horses by the reins. Horses are said to be hard-mouthed when the mucous membrane of the bars becomes toughened and thickened and the sensibility of the mouth is deadened because of the calloused condition of the bars.

The lingual canal is the space between the branches of the lower jaw in which the tongue is situated.

The tongue is an organ of prehension, mastication, gustation, and deglutition. It is located in the lingual canal and practically fills the mouth when the jaws are in proper position. The tongue helps to support the bit and, like the lower lip, receives impressions from the reins.

Some horses have the vice of doubling the free end of the tongue backward and placing it over the bit. This can be prevented by a tight curb chain to prevent the shifting of the bit in the mouth. Other horses, called tongue lollers, let the tongue hang, or dangle from the mouth, whether at work or at rest. Especially designed bits quite successfully correct this vice.

The hard palate forms the anterior or superior wall of the oral cavity. It is limited in front by the incisor teeth and in the back by the attachment of the soft palate.

Sometimes the hard palate becomes congested and inflamed, pouches and projects downward below the edges or tables of the incisor teeth and interferes seriously with mastication. This condition is termed "lampas," commonly but incorrectly called "lampers." Horses thus afflicted will go off feed until the tissues recede to normal position.

The Neck

The anterior limits of the neck are the poll, the parotid region, and the throat. The posterior limits are the withers, the shoulders, and the breast.

In all types of horses, proportionate length of neck is desired. Cleancutness about the throat and width between the mandibles of the lower jaw indicate minimum interference with the wind passages. Crest of neck in both mares and stallions is needed to break up the plainness that always accompanies a neck which is straight along the top.

"Arch" and "crest of neck" are synonymous terms. In mares the neck is not so strongly crested as in stallions. The neck of the mare is leaner, less bulging, not so heavily muscled. Its proportions suggest femininity, broodiness, and maternal refinement. In stallions, the crest of neck is stronger because of height and thickness. The lateral muscles of the neck are more bulging. Such bulky muscling contributes to the masculine make-up of the stallion front.

Mares are said to be strong-fronted, too strong, or "studdy" about their fronts when their head and neck suggest stallion proportions. Stallions are dubbed weak-fronted, gelding-fronted, or mare-fronted when they lack typical stallion proportions of head and neck. Stallionlike features, style, and boldness of carriage should characterize the stallion front.

THE FORM OF THE NECK   The neck is straight when the superior border from the poll of the head to the withers approaches a straight line. The neck is arched when the superior border is convex from poll to withers. "Swan-neck" is the term applied when the anterior portion of the neck is strongly convex and the whole neck imitates in form and carriage that of the bird from which it takes its name.

"Ewe-necked" is the term used when the superior border of the neck shows a distinct depression just in front of the withers. The ewe-neck is the reverse of the form desired; hence horsemen refer to it by the expression "set on upside down."

"Lop-neck," "fallen neck," and "broken crest" are terms applied when the crest of the neck becomes invaded with adipose tissue, resulting in so much weight that the neck cannot sustain itself and it breaks over or falls to one side.

Ewe-necks and broken crests are unsightly and undesired. The straight neck always means a plain front because arch or crest of neck is needed to make the front look imposing and attractive. Therefore crest of neck is demanded in all types of horses where impressive fronts are a requirement.

Length of neck is an important consideration and varies with the type of horse in question. Length is one of the outstanding features of the swan type of neck which characterizes gaited saddlers. More or less shaped like a letter S, this type of neck, although long, places the weight of the head closer to the body, thereby enabling a saddler in action to shift the weight from the front end rearward to his hind legs. This lightens the forehand and contributes to the finish of the horse's performance.

Proportionate length of neck is required in all horses, because long muscles mean more contraction, and this in turn results in a longer, more sweeping stride of the fore foot. The swan necks of saddlers therefore have two advantages. The long muscling makes possible grace and brilliancy on the move and permits rapidity and extended action of the fore legs. At the same time, the S design brings the head close to the body and lightens the forehand.

Short necks, bulky, thick, and staggy in proportions, are undesirable in saddle horses because they mean a lack of suppleness and mobility. Quite commonly a short neck makes a horse heavy-headed and less subject to control. In race horses, short, bulky necks mean short elevator muscles in the shoulders and less length of stride.

Thick, bulky necks are least objectionable in draft horses, because they do most of their work at slow paces and can use to advantage the weight that comes from big, heavy muscles. Such necks are not desired in light harness

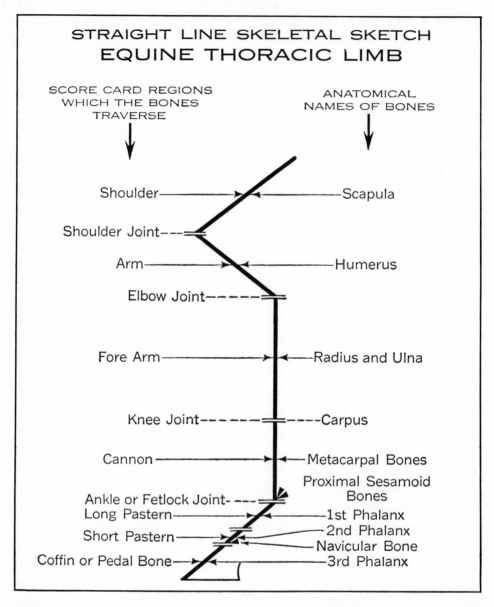

STRAIGHT LINE SKELETAL SKETCH
EQUINE THORACIC LIMB

SCORE CARD REGIONS
WHICH THE BONES
TRAVERSE

ANATOMICAL
NAMES OF BONES

Shoulder————————Scapula

Shoulder Joint———

Arm————————Humerus

Elbow Joint—————

Fore Arm————————Radius and Ulna

Knee Joint———————Carpus

Cannon————————Metacarpal Bones

Proximal Sesamoid
Bones

Ankle or Fetlock Joint————
Long Pastern————————1st Phalanx
Short Pastern————————2nd Phalanx
Navicular Bone
Coffin or Pedal Bone————————3rd Phalanx

horses, heavy harness horses, or saddlers. They contribute to plainness of make-up and depreciate performance.

The Withers

These comprise the region between the two shoulders on top, behind the crest of the neck, and in front of the back. The height of a horse is measured from the highest point of the withers to the ground. Equine stature is stated in hands and inches, four inches constituting a hand.

Withers that are fairly prominent are desired because they ensure maximum length of spinal and shoulder muscles, also a longer stride to the fore foot. Horses with low, thick, rounding withers which lack definition move out awkwardly and clumsily in front. Such horses are usually low-headed, too heavy on the bit, predisposed to forge and interfere, and unfit for movement at rapid paces.

"Mutton withers" is the term applied to coarse, flat, rounding conformation over the shoulder top. In saddle horses such withers are objectionable, not only because they affect performance but also because they fail to provide a good seat for the saddle and do not furnish the proper purchase for the saddle upon the back. Consequently it is difficult to keep a saddle in place.

The Back

The back is limited in front by the withers, behind by the loin, and laterally by the ribs. In saddlers it is the part of the top which receives the weight of the rider. In all horses its function is to transmit to the front end of the body the efforts of propulsion which are communicated to it from the back legs through the loin.

A straight back of proportionate length is most desired. It is always a sign of strength and provides for the greatest freedom of movement of the legs. A convex back is termed a "roach back." Such backs are shorter than straight backs and do not permit sufficient extension and flexion of the legs in taking long and rapid strides. Roach backs and long legs are a combination which results in forging.

The back that is concave or hollow is referred to as sagging or as a swayback. It is objectionable because it depreciates appearance and suggests weakness. The short, straight back supported by ribs that are well sprung, long, and deep provides a middle that has ample breathing and digestive space. Such proportions indicate good wind as well as good feeding and staying qualities. Short, flat ribs are characteristic of horses that are poor feeders and have poor wind and staying power as well as poor shipping qualities.

The Loin Region

The loin includes the portion of the top which extends from the last ribs to the hips. Short, heavy loin muscles are demanded because they furnish the chief means of support for the lumbar vertebrae. Shortness of the loin is necessary to the best functioning of this part in the transmission of power from the hind legs forward.

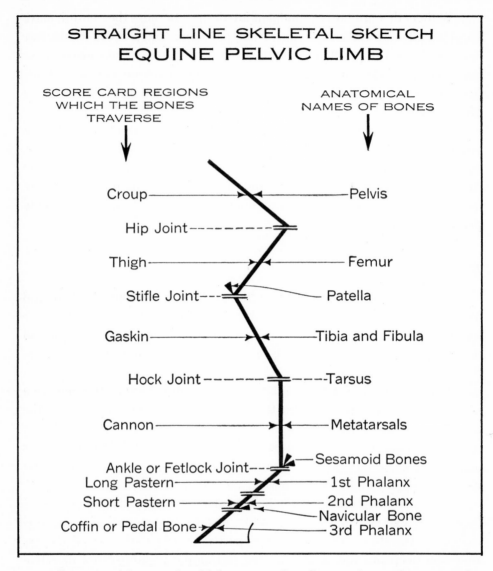

STRAIGHT LINE SKELETAL SKETCH
EQUINE PELVIC LIMB

All types of horses should have an abundance of muscling over the loin. "Coupled up good and close" describes ideal muscling on the loin. Horses that break across the top in front of the hips and that are long, narrow, and weak in loin conformation are spoken of as being slack in their coupling. Other terms applied are light over the kidney, long in the coupling, wasp-waisted. Quite commonly such horses are long-middled, shallow-middled, racy-middled, short in the back rib, cut up in the flank or hound-gutted.

The Croup

This includes the region from the hips back to the tailhead. In direction, the croup may be too steep, it may be too nearly level, or it may even incline upward from hips to tail. If a horse is too steep in the croup, the top line looks plain. Furthermore, the steep croup tends to displace the hind legs too far forward beneath the body, causing them to bear too much of the body weight. If the croup is too nearly horizontal or is set up a bit at the tail-head, the hind legs are displaced rearward. In the latter case the back is not so well supported because the front and rear bases are spread farther apart.

The croup should carry the width as uniformly as possible from the hips rearward. "Goose-rumped" is the term applied to horses that taper from the hips to the tailhead, displaying peakedness and angularity in this region. Horsemen like to see the croups of their horses deeply creased. They associate this feature with heavy muscling and with easy-keeping and good feeding qualities.

The Flanks

To give balance to the middle, horses of all types should be deep in the fore and rear flanks. Depth of flank in front and behind contributes to the draftiness of conformation. The best flanks are seen in horses that are well fleshed and highly fitted.

The flank movements, which are indicative of a horse's wind and breathing, should be slow and regular without any signs of jerkiness. The normal number of movements when at rest is twelve to fourteen a minute.

Age and physical condition are factors causing a variation in the number of flank movements. Excessive flank movement is quite commonly called panting. A horse that is easily winded and stays winded a long time is narrow in his chest, shallow in his rib, and cut up in his flank.

The Breast

The breast is limited above by the inferior border of the neck, behind by the axillae or armpits, and on the sides by the arms.

Proportionate width is demanded in all types of horses. Too much width, even in draft horses, where width is greatly emphasized as a feature in conformation, constitutes a real defect. When the front legs are set too far out on the corners, a rolling, rocking, laboring, ungainly gait results. With front legs so placed, horses are unfit for work at speed. This is the reason why the draft horse, whose business is to work at slow paces, can be proportionately wider in front.

The narrow-breasted horse whose front legs appear to have the same point of junction to the body is spoken of as being pinched or too close in front. A narrow breast commonly accompanies a lack of muscling and constitution.

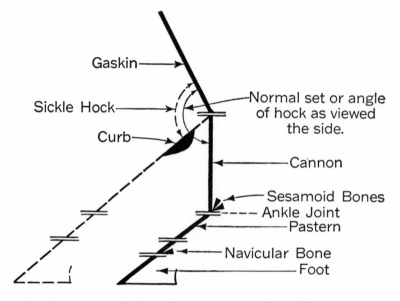

WHY ARE SICKLE HOCKS OBJECTIONABLE IN HORSES?

Gaskin

Sickle Hock

Normal set or angle of hock as viewed the side.

Curb

Cannon

Sesamoid Bones

Ankle Joint

Pastern

Navicular Bone

Foot

Sickle hocks result in displacing the hind feet so far forward beneath the body that there is a predisposition to curbiness.

The Chest

The chest or thorax, the bony frame which houses the important organs of circulation and respiration, functions in three important ways: it protects the organs of circulation and respiration; it serves as one of the most important parts of the respiratory equipment; and it serves as a base of attachment for many muscles that function in locomotion.

Height, width, and length of chest are important features. Height is measured from the summit of the withers to the floor of the chest. Width is the transverse dimension. Length or depth is measured from front to rear. This dimension is taken from the angle of the shoulder to the middle of the last rib. Length of chest depends upon the distances between the ribs and upon the projection of the ribs backward.

Backward projection of the ribs makes it possible for a horse to have a short back or top and still have a long or deep chest. The measure of the projection of the ribs backward gives the measure of the projection of the ribs forward during inspiration.

The arch of rib, the depth of rib, the distances between the ribs, and their degree of projection backward are all features which contribute to chest capacity. Ribs that are flat, short, close together, and slightly inclined rearward diminish chest capacity and are objectionable.

The Shoulder

The scapula is the skeletal base of the shoulder. The chief duties of the fore legs are to support weight, to preserve the stability and balance of the body, to aid the hind legs in propelling the body forward, and to resist the injurious effect of wear and tear on their own structures. Listed below are reasons why the shoulders should be long and sloping, rather than short, straight, and steep.

1. A long, sloping shoulder makes possible a greater extension of the forearm.

2. The front leg can be raised higher, allowing the stride to be fully completed before the foot strikes the ground.

3. A long shoulder gives power and strength to the swing of the fore foot.

4. A long, sloping shoulder contributes to ease, freedom, and style of action.

5. Long, sloping shoulders help to disperse the evil effects of concussion.

STRAIGHT SHOULDERS, ON THE OTHER HAND, ARE OBJECTIONABLE FOR SEVERAL REASONS:

1. They depreciate looks.

2. They are commonly accompanied by short, straight pasterns, resulting in a stilty set to the front leg, a conformation predisposing to shorter steps and harder concussions.

3. Straight shoulders do not furnish so desirable a collar bed.

4. Straight shoulders retard the rotation of the scapula, and horses commonly work their front legs with less freedom. Shoulders are sometimes referred to as pegged when shoulder action seems retarded rather than free.

The Arm

The humerus traverses the arm region. To permit a sufficient extent and rapidity of action of the thoracic limb, the bone of the arm should be short in comparison with that of the shoulder.

If the length of the arm be excessive in comparison with the shoulder,

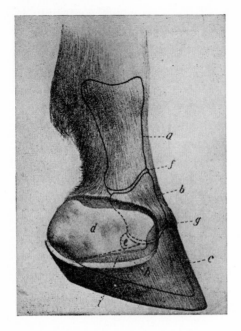

Digit of horse showing surface relations of bones and joints. From Sisson, *The Anatomy of the Domestic Animals,* courtesy W. B. Saunders Company.

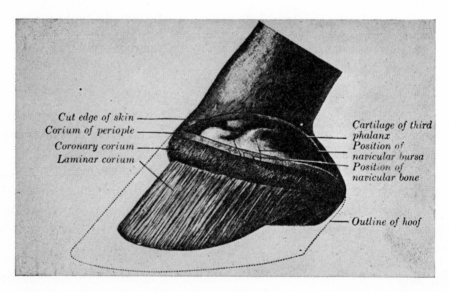

Lateral view of foot of horse after removal of hoof and part of the skin. From Sisson, *The Anatomy of the Domestic Animals,* courtesy W. B. Saunders Company.

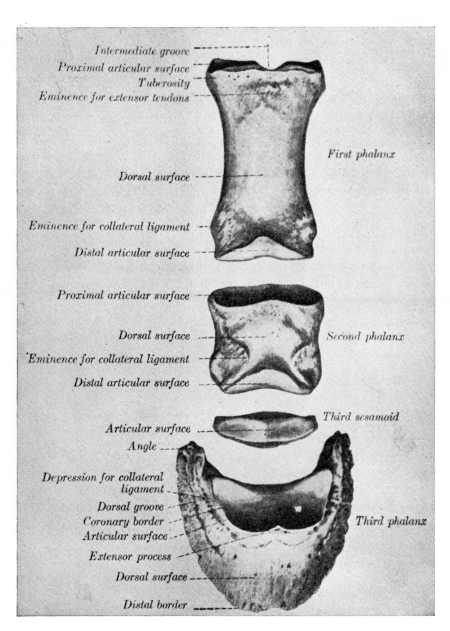

Intermediate groove

Proximal articular surface

Tuberosity

Eminence for extensor tendons

First phalanx

Dorsal surface

Eminence for collateral ligament

Distal articular surface

Proximal articular surface

Dorsal surface

Second phalanx

Eminence for collateral ligament

Distal articular surface

Articular surface

Third sesamoid

Angle

Depression for collateral ligament

Dorsal groove

Coronary border

Third phalanx

Articular surface

Extensor process

Dorsal surface

Distal border

Phalanges and distal sesamoid of horse, dorsal aspect. From Sisson, *The Anatomy of the Domestic Animals,* courtesy W. B. Saunders Company.

especially if the shoulder be short and straight, the foot will cover less ground at a single stride, and action will not be so reachy, free, and easy.

A long shoulder, a short arm, plus a long forearm makes possible maximum extension of stride and speed. The arm should operate in a plane parallel to the plane occupied by the horse's body. If the arm deviates inward too much, a horse will stand toe-wide at the ground. If the arm deviates outward too much, a horse will stand toe-narrow or pigeon-toed.

The Forearm

This is the name given to the region between elbow and knee joints. Length of stride depends very largely upon the length of the forearm because the forearm carries the knee forward and upward. Hence the longer the forearm, the longer the stride.

Short forearms in comparison with the cannon regions are objectionable because they result in shorter strides. They augment height rather than extension as a feature of the stride. Long forearms and short cannons not only favor speed but contribute to stability on feet and legs. The knees are brought closer to the ground, making the support of the body easier during contact.

A heavily muscled forearm is most appropriate in draft horses. Slender, "weedy" forearms in drafters are correlated with angularity of appearance throughout and a general lack of draftiness.

The Chestnuts

These are semihorny formations varying in size with the type of horse in question. On the front legs they are located upon the inside face of the forearm a few inches above the knee. On the hind legs they are located on the lower inside face of the hock. They are not nearly so well developed in light-leg types as in draft horses. They are thought to be the rudiments of the internal digit which once characterized the species.

The Knee

This joint should be wide, thick, deep, and clean-cut in outline, properly placed and directed. Thickness of the knee is measured from side to side, width from front to rear. Width and thickness are desirable features because they increase the supporting area of the joint and furnish a more stable support for the body.

To distribute wear and tear properly, the knee must be correctly placed. If the joint breaks or deviates forward, a horse is termed knee-sprung, over

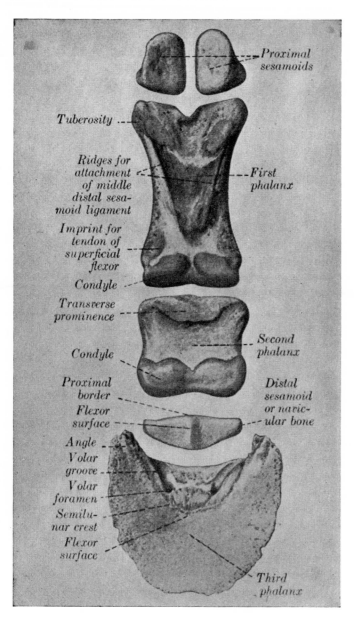

Digital bones of fore limb of horse, volar aspect. From Sisson, *The Anatomy of the Domestic Animals*, courtesy W. B. Saunders Company.

on the knees, easy on the knees, or buck-kneed. If length of toe accompanies this knee-sprung conformation, there is a strong disposition to stub the toes, stumble, and fall.

If horses stand back on their knees, they are termed calf-kneed. Such horses on the move usually bring their feet down hard, increasing concussion. Furthermore, a calf-kneed horse stands and goes up hill all the time.

If knees break inward, they are termed knock-kneed. If his knees break outward, a horse is said to be bow-kneed or to stand open in his knees.

The Hind Leg and the Front Leg Compared

The arm of the front leg corresponds to the thigh of the hind leg. The femur is the anatomical base of the thigh. The elbow, the forearm, and the knee of the front leg are the counterparts of the stifle, the gaskin, and the hock behind. Heavy muscling through thigh, stifle, and gaskin is demanded. The hind legs are the propellers; hence this muscle requirement.

Horses that are turned out a trifle in the set of the stifle are preferred. This permits maximum extension of the hind leg, augments freedom of action, and turns the hocks inward beneath the body, permitting a horse to work his hocks close together and go collectedly. The gaskin should equal the forearm in length and, like the forearm, should be heavily muscled.

The Hock Joint

The hock joint is referred to as the pivot of action in a horse. It plays an important part in propulsion and aids in the work of decreasing and dispersing the evil effects of concussion. It is called the pivot of action because it is the region upon which the extensor muscles concentrate their propulsive efforts. As the feet carrying the body forward at a great rate of speed strike the ground it is mostly upon the hock joint that the reaction from locomotion bears. It is the hock joint that bears the burden of the weight when a horse rears from the ground.

The hock joint presents a satisfactory make-up when it is clearly outlined, appears lean in quality, is wide and deep in its proportions, is well opened as viewed from the side, and is properly directed as viewed from the rear. A hock is lean and dry in appearance when its prominences and depressions are well marked and when the skin is fine and close fitting.

In the preferred direction of the hock joint as viewed from the rear the points of the hocks are slightly deviated inward. In some breeds, the Clydesdale, for example, the hocks typically deviate inward at their points. The hind cannons occupy parallel planes. The hind toes turn slightly outward.

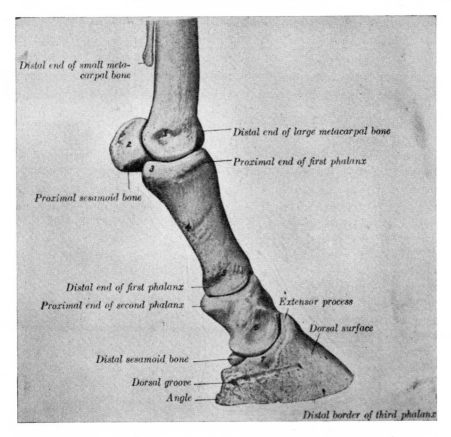

*Distal end of small meta-
carpal bone*

Distal end of large metacarpal bone

Proximal end of first phalanx

Proximal sesamoid bone

Distal end of first phalanx
Proximal end of second phalanx

Extensor process

Dorsal surface

Distal sesamoid bone

Dorsal groove

Angle

Distal border of third phalanx

Skeleton of digit and distal part of metacarpus of horse. From Sisson, *The Anatomy of the Domestic Animals,* courtesy W. B. Saunders Company.

This position on the hind legs permits the Clydesdales as a breed to work their hocks close together and to go collectedly.

Horses that stand with the points of the hocks turned inward and base-wide at the ground are termed cow-hocked. Horses with hocks that turn outward are dubbed open in the hocks. Such hocks predispose to a twisting, rotating action on the move and are also termed rotating hocks.

If the angle formed by the hock as viewed from the side is too acute, a horse is called crooked in his hocks, is said to have too much set to the hocks or is called sickle-hocked. If hocks are rounding on the back side they are called curby or saber-hocked. A hock may lack set and be too straight. This condition is objectionable because it tends to shorten the stride. Improper set of the hock joint results in improper distribution of body weight and predisposes to early unsoundness of the part.

The cannon region extends from knee and hock to fetlock joints. The three bones, one large and two small, which traverse each front cannon are the metacarpals. The small metacarpals are commonly termed "splint bones."

The three corresponding bones in each of the rear cannons are the metatarsals. In general form and arrangement, the metacarpals and the metatarsals resemble each other rather closely. The metatarsals, however, are longer.

The size of the cannons depends not only upon the size of the metacarpal or metatarsal bones, but also upon the size and the set of the tendons that traverse the region. Horses that are constricted, "chopped away," or "tied in" beneath the knee are criticized by horsemen as lacking bone. Bone is an indication of substance and contributes to ruggedness and draftiness of make-up. Furthermore, big cannon bones and strong, well-set tendons are required to furnish ample support to knees and hocks. Clean-cutness and definition should characterize the cannons. Round, meaty cannons suggest staleness, secondhandedness, and a lack of quality.

The Fetlock Joint

The fetlock joint is the connecting link between cannon and pastern bones. It functions as an elastic support of the body weight and aids greatly in dispersing concussion.

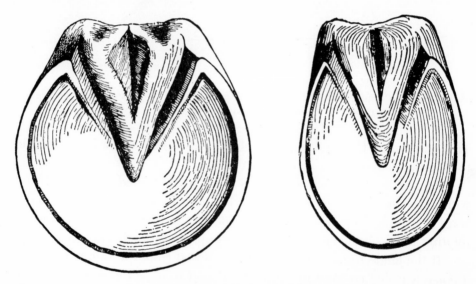

A wide fore hoof and a narrow fore hoof. From Lungwitz and Adams, *Horse Shoeing*, courtesy J. B. Lippincott Company.

Ankles set well back on springy pasterns are desired. Straight, stilty ankles mean hard concussions. They also predispose to knuckling or cocked ankles. "Up on the ankles" and "over on the ankles" are terms referring to the same conformation of this joint. Clean-cut fetlock joints are desired in all types of horses. Thick, coarse, round ankle joints characterized primarily by fullness rather than leanness contribute to the plainness and coarseness of the underpinning.

Feather, Footlock, Ergot

"Feather" is the term given to the hair which fringes the posterior border of the cannon and fetlock joints. Among the draft breeds Clydes and Shires have it in greatest abundance; hence they are termed the "feather-legged" breeds.

The footlock refers to the tuft of hairs which grows from the posterior base of the fetlock. This tuft surrounds and hides from view the ergot, a semi-horny projection which protrudes from the posterior base of the fetlock joints. Usually it is completely surrounded by the footlock.

The Pasterns

Springy length and set of pasterns are primary requirements in both light and heavy horses. Extremely long, low pasterns are weak pasterns. Such pasterns in company with shallow heels characterize horses that are termed "coon-footed." Short, straight pasterns increase concussion, augment stilty action, and rob the gait of spring and freedom, important features of the stride.

Straight pasterns and small, boxy feet with their narrow heels and their straight, upright hoof walls hasten the formation of sidebones. The pasterns serve as a base of attachment for extensor and flexor tendons; hence they function in locomotion as agents of extension and flexion. Snap, as a feature of the stride, is due in no small part to the working of the pastern joints.

The Foot

Three bones constitute the bony base of a horse's foot about which the other supporting structures are arranged. The largest one of these bones is the pedal bone, resembling in shape a miniature foot and so porous in structure as to resemble pumice stone in appearance and density.

The navicular bone is the smallest of the three bones of the foot. It is located at the posterior junction of the pedal and coronary bone, resting slightly on the pedal bone, but held in place largely by the deep flexor tendon.

The third bone, called the short pastern or coronary bone, belongs partly to the foot and partly to the leg.

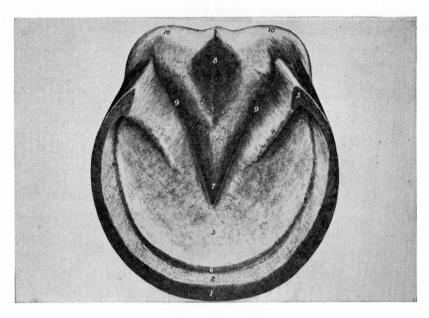

Right fore hoof of horse, ground surface. From Sisson, *The Anatomy of the Domestic Animals,* courtesy W. B. Saunders Company.

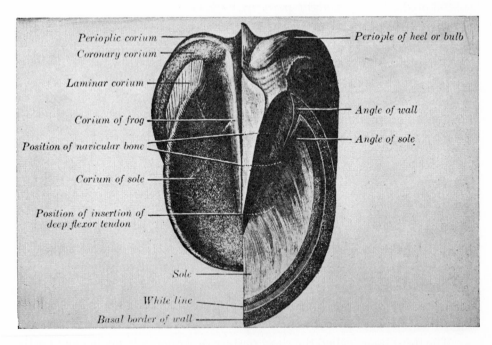

Ground surface after removal of half of hoof to show corium. From Sisson, *The Anatomy of the Domestic Animals,* courtesy W. B. Saunders Company.

The pedal bone is located mainly toward the anterior and lateral portions of the foot, the back portion of the foot containing but very little pedal bone. In this posterior portion of the foot, the deficiency of pedal bone is made up by the introduction of two large plates of cartilage. The presence of these lateral plates of cartilage in this region is due to the lateral movements which the foot is called upon to perform. These movements could not take place if the pedal bone in extent completely filled the hoof wall within which it fits.

The pedal bone is not placed parallel to the ground, but it fits within the hoof, with the toe slightly lower than the heel.

The Foot Joint

The foot joint is formed by the articulation of the three bones, pedal, navicular, and coronary.

FUNCTIONS OF THE NAVICULAR BONE   The navicular bone increases the articulatory surface of the pedal bone and supplies or provides a yielding articulation, thus saving a direct concussion and lessening wear and tear on the structures. It is not held in place by ligaments alone. Its chief support is the flexor tendon. A close fit occurs between the tendon and the bone, a synovial apparatus or bursa between them preventing friction.

Held in place largely by the flexor tendon, the navicular bone is permitted to function as a yielding articulation. To this ability to function as a yielding joint is due in large degree the springiness of stride which features a horse's gait. If the navicular bone fails to function properly, a short, stilty, peggy gait results.

Lateral Cartilages

Attached to each wing of the pedal bone is a large, curved plate of cartilage. In extent it reaches upward beyond the coronary band, extends backward to the heel, and in forward location embraces two thirds of the lateral circumference of the foot. These cartilages function in the following ways:

1. They form a yielding and elastic wall to the sensitive foot.

2. The elastic movements of these cartilages assist the circulation of the blood in the foot.

3. They render the internal foot elastic and permit a change in shape which occurs under the influence of the weight of the body. The weight bears upon the frog and this in turn presses upon the bars of the foot. The pressure on the frog is also transmitted to the plantar cushion, which likewise

flattens and spreads under pressure. Both of these factors cause the cartilages to bulge slightly outward.

When these elastic cartilages ossify their function is destroyed and lameness may occur. When sidebones result in lameness, however, there are usually other defects of the feet accompanying the sidebones which help to account for the lameness. If lameness occurs, the pressure which causes it may be due to the compression of the sensitive laminae between the ossified cartilages and a contracted hoof wall at heel and quarters.

Causes of Sidebones

1. Concussion. Sidebones are thus common accompaniments of straight shoulders, short pasterns, and narrow, contracted feet. This combination of characteristics increases concussion.

2. Improper shoeing. The feet may not be allowed to spread and expand at the heels normally because a shoe that is too small or one in which the nail holes are punched too far back holds the heels in too rigid position.

3. Treads from other animals or treads inflicted by the animal itself with the calks of an opposite shoe.

4. Dropping the pole or the shafts of a vehicle carelessly upon the hoof head.

5. In severe cases of laminitis, ossification of the cartilages may result.

Plantar Cushion

This is a fibrofatty mass located in the posterior part of the foot between the lateral cartilages and filling in completely the hollow of the heels. Its inferior face is a complete counterpart of the face of the frog above which it lies. The back portion of the cushion is softer than the front, where at its apex it is dense and fibrous.

The Hoof Wall

The division of the hoof wall into toe, quarters, and heels is for convenience of reference and discussion only; no natural division exists. On the outside of the wall, at the point of junction of hair and hoof proper, is a rim of rather soft, nonpigmented horn known as the periople. It functions in cementing the skin to the hoof and in providing the wall with a thin covering resembling a light coat of varnish, which prevents undue evaporation from the horn.

The wall is thickest and longest at the toe, thinnest and shortest at the heel. Thickness of hoof wall at toe and quarters is necessary because of the wear at these points. Thinness of the wall at the heels makes the foot yielding instead of a rigid, horny box.

At the heels, the wall is inflected and continued beneath the foot as the bars. They extend forward, forming a V-shaped structure to receive the frog.

The wall, therefore, is an incomplete circle of horn designed to provide and permit spread at the heels. The bars give the wall additional strength as a supporter of weight and prevent a rupture between the wall and the frog during the expansive movements of the foot. They afford a solid bearing to the back portion of the foot.

The Sole

This portion of every normal foot is concave. The sole of a hind foot is more concave than that of a fore foot. This concavity is proof that the general surface of the sole is not primarily to bear weight, although the thin edge of the sole in contact with the wall is a weight-bearing surface. The union between the sole and the wall is indicated by a white line which encircles the entire junction of sole and wall. The chief function of the horny sole is to afford protection to the sensitive parts above.

The Frog

The foot pad or frog is a semisoft elastic structure, shaped somewhat like a pyramid and molded or fashioned upon the surface of the plantar cushion. The horn of the frog contains more moisture than any other portion of the foot, and it is this moisture, aided by the secretion of the glands of the plantar cushion, which explains the soft, fluctuating characteristics of the frog.

The depression on the undersurface of the frog is called the cleft of the frog. Above the cleft on the side of the frog next to the sensitive foot is a projection of horn known as the frog-stay or peak. This peak functions in preventing the displacement of the frog, it also acts as a wedge which is forced upward under pressure when the foot comes to the ground. It thereby exerts pressure on the plantar cushion, which bulges outward and assists in the expansion of the foot.

The frog-stay also stimulates the nerve endings in the plantar cushion, thereby permitting the frog to function as an organ of touch. The frog is an anticoncussion mechanism to prevent jar. In conjunction with the posterior wall the frog receives the impacts of the foot when it comes in contact with the ground. These impacts are imparted to the plantar cushion and through the lateral cartilages to the hoof wall, which expands.

Sometimes when a foot has been kept shod for a long period and the frog is kept off the ground too long, the part atrophies, the heels contract, the foot gets smaller, and the pad is rendered functionless.

The Anticoncussion Mechanism of the Foot

Several characteristics in the design of the equine foot tend to reduce wear and tear, batter and jar. When a horse is in standing position the weight carried on each fore foot is somewhat more than one fourth of the weight of the body. On the move, the weight borne by a single foot varies from half the weight on the trot or the pace, to the entire weight in certain phases of the canter, the rack, or the gallop. The mechanisms to save concussion and to protect the structures of the foot and the limb are as follows:

1. The yielding articulation in the pedal joint.

2. The increase in the width of the foot, known as expansion, when the feet are in contact with the ground.

3. The frog and the plantar cushion.

4. The slight descent of the pedal bone and the slight yielding tendency of the sole of the foot.

Questions

1. What is the objection to a pony head in young draft colts?

2. What do you understand by the term "lop-eared" as applied to horses?

3. Ears kept in a constant state of unrest may be indicative of what unsoundness in horses?

4. What is the meaning of the term "wall-eyed"?

5. What is the meaning of the term "monkey mouth"?

6. The tongue is defined as an organ of prehension, mastication, gustation, and deglutition. Give a synonym for each of these terms.

7. What is the difference in the bars of the mouth in mares and stallions?

8. What is meant by the terms "bovine eye" and "pig's eye" as applied to horses?

9. Define the term "myopia."

10. Why should the nostrils of a horse be large?

11. Describe the normal discharge from a horse's nostrils.

12. What is the meaning of the term "parrot mouth" as applied to horses?

13. What is the lingual canal?

14. What is a lip slapper?

15. What is meant by unilateral paralysis of the lower lip?

16. Define the bars of the mouth.

17. What is a tongue loller?

18. What is the hard palate?

19. Define the term "lampas."

20. What is a ewe-necked horse?

21. When is the term "staggy" applicable to the neck of a mare?

22. What is the meaning of the term "lop-neck"?

23. Name two advantages of the long swanlike type of neck in saddle horses.

24. Short necks are least objectionable in what type of horse?

25. In terms of the equine skeleton locate the withers of a horse.

26. What are the advantages of high, sharp withers?

27. What are the disadvantages of low, rounding withers?

28. What is the meaning of the term "mutton withers"?

29. In terms of the skeleton define the back region of a horse.

30. Give a synonym for the term "convex back."

31. Give a synonym for the term "concave back."

32. List the features that contribute to a good middle in any type of horse or pony.

33. In terms of the skeleton define the loin of a horse.

34. Give a synonym for the term "loin."

35. Why should the loin in all horses be short and strong?

36. When is the term "wasp-waisted" applicable to horses?

37. What is the meaning of the term "hound-gutted"?

38. In terms of the skeleton define the limits of the croup.

39. What are the objections to a croup that is too steep?

40. What is the meaning of the term "goose-rumped"?

41. Explain how the flank movements may be indicative of a horse's wind or breathing.

42. In terms of the skeleton define the limits of the breast of a horse.

43. Distinguish in the meaning of the terms "breast" and "chest."

44. List a synonym of the term "chest."

45. What advantages in the conformational design of a horse are due to the backward projection of the ribs and the oblique angle of junction, instead of a right-angled junction of the ribs with the spinal column?

46. What bone forms the skeletal base of the shoulder region?

47. Name several reasons why the shoulder of a horse should be long and sloping.

48. State several reasons why straight shoulders are objectionable.

49. What bone traverses the arm region of a horse?

50. In terms of the skeleton, define the limits of the forearm.

51. Explain how a long forearm augments the length of stride.

52. What are the chestnuts as features of horse make-up?

53. Locate the chestnuts on both the front and the rear legs.

54. What is the anatomical name for the knee joint?

55. Give two synonyms for the term "buck-kneed."

56. Give a synonym for the term "back at the knees."

57. What is an objection to a buck-kneed horse?

58. State an objection to calf-knees.

59. What bone furnishes the anatomical base for the thigh?

60. The elbow, the forearm, and the knee of the front leg are the counterparts of what features of the hind leg?

61. What is the anatomical name for the hock joint?

62. When is the term "cow-hocked" applicable to the set of a horse's hind legs?

63. If a horse's hocks as viewed from the side have too much set to them, what descriptive term is applicable?

64. What is the objection to sickle hocks?

65. What is a curb?

66. What is the objection to a position on the hind legs where the points of the hocks turn outward?

67. Name the bones which traverse the cannon regions of the front legs.

68. What are the splint bones?

69. Name the bones which traverse the cannon regions of the hind legs.

70. Name a synonym for fetlock joint.

71. Why should the ankles be set well back on long, sloping pasterns?

72. What is a cocked ankle?

73. What is meant by the term "feather" as applied to horses?

74. Name the "feather-legged" breeds of draft horses.

75. What is the footlock?

76. Define the term "ergot."

77. What are the objections to short, straight pasterns in horses?

78. When is the term "coon-footed" applicable to horses?

79. What three bones constitute the bony base of a horse's foot?

80. Give a synonym for pedal bone.

81. Locate the navicular bone.

82. Name the bones that constitute the foot joint.

83. State the functions of the navicular bone.

84. Describe and locate the lateral cartilages.

85. List the functions of the lateral cartilages.

86. Define the term "sidebone."

87. List the common causes of sidebones.

88. Define, locate, and discuss the function of the plantar cushion.

89. Name the divisions of the hoof wall of a horse's foot.

90. Define the term "periople" and state its functions.

91. Tell why the hoof wall is thickest at the toe.

92. Tell why the hoof wall is thinnest at the heels.

93. Define the white line.

94. Define the bars of the foot.

95. Is the ground surface of the sole of the normal foot concave or convex? Why?

96. Is the hoof wall or the sole of the foot designed primarily to support weight? Why?

97. What is the chief function of the horny sole of a horse's foot?

98. Define the frog as a feature of the horse's foot. State its chief function.

99. What is the frog-stay? State its function.

100. Name the mechanisms which save concussion, and help to protect the foot and limb of a horse when in motion.

4

Utility the Basis

for the Classification

of Horses

The author of a bulletin entitled "Market Classes and Grades of Horses and Mules," a publication prepared many years ago at the University of Illinois, made the following statement in his opening paragraph: "Horses on the open market are classified according to their jobs."

Utility—the use to which a horse is put, the job at which he works— is therefore the basis for the market classification of all horses.

Since horse judging consists largely of a study of the relationship of form to function and since a horse's value is based largely upon what he can do, it is most important that we as students of horses have an intelligent understanding of the relationship between form and function.

Some structural features in the make-up of the horse place definite limits upon his usefulness in any specific field of service. Other structural features greatly enhance his usefulness in a specific field. In judging horses, therefore, we should keep in mind constantly this matter of relationship of form to function because horses have to do as they are designed to do.

Left: *The correct stand-ing position of the front leg as viewed from in front.*

Right: *The correct stand-ing position of the front leg as viewed from the side.*

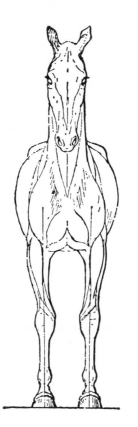

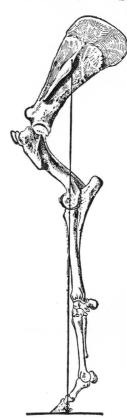

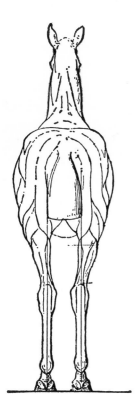

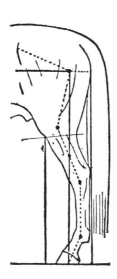

Left: *The correct standing position of the hind leg, viewed from the rear, as determined by the plumb line.*

Right: *The correct stand-ing position of the hind leg, viewed from the side, as determined by the plumb line.* Drawings from Ga-baux and Barrier, *The Ex-terior of the Horse.*

Examples of Correlated Features Involving the Relationship of Form and Function

1. The proportions of the head in all kinds of horses are a rather accurate index of the body proportions to be expected. That is to say, long, narrow heads are commonly correlated with long, shallow, narrow bodies.

2. Small heads in draft foals and yearlings are correlated with too early maturity and an ultimate lack of scale or size.

3. Long, sloping shoulders are correlated with long, sloping pasterns.

4. Short, straight shoulders are correlated with short, straight pasterns.

5. A small, narrow, squinty eye, known as pig's-eye in horses, is correlated with coarseness in quality and a lazy, sluggish, phlegmatic disposition.

6. A deeply creased croup as a feature in horses is correlated with easy-keeping, good-doing, and satisfactory feeding qualities.

Correlated Structural Features in Horse Make-Up Which Enhance Action

1. Long forearms as features of the front legs are correlated with long strides.

2. If horses stand toed straight away on their front feet, they are likely to have trueness of action or directness of stride.

3. Sloping shoulders and sloping pasterns are features of the front leg which are correlated with a springy stride.

4. When horses stand with the points of their hocks turned slightly inward, with their hind toes turned slightly outward, and with their hind cannon bones occupying parallel planes, their hocks will be carried close together instead of wide apart. Such a position on the hind legs is therefore correlated with collected action instead of spraddled action behind.

Correlated Structural Features in Horse Make-Up Which Predispose to Defective Gaits or to Unsoundness

1. The calf-kneed position on the front legs is a feature in horse make-up that is correlated with hard concussion of the feet at the completion of the

stride. That is, the calf-kneed position on the front legs tends to make a horse pounding-gaited on the move.

2. Low, rounding withers are features which are correlated with the defect in gait known as forging. Thick-withered horses commonly hang in the bridle, go low-headed, and handle their front legs awkwardly and clumsily.

3. The pigeon-toed position on the front feet is correlated with a defect in gait known as paddling or winging out.

4. The toe-wide or splay-footed position on the front feet is correlated with the defect in gait known as winging in or dishing.

5. If horses stand with the points of their hocks turned outward, this faulty position on the hind legs is correlated with a defect in stride known as limber hocks or rotating hocks.

6. Stilty ankles and pasterns are correlated with a stilty stride, hard concussions, and a predisposition to cocked ankles or even unsoundness at an early age.

7. Front legs, set way out on the corners of the body, constitute a structural defect which is correlated with rolling, laboring action in front.

8. Short, thick, bulky necks are features of saddle horse make-up which are correlated with a lack of suppleness and mobility of neck.

9. Short, straight shoulders and short forearms are features of the front legs that are correlated with short strides.

10. Buck knees and long toes are features of the front legs that are correlated with stumbling as a defect in action.

11. An extremely straight hock is a defect in position on the hind leg, as viewed from the side, which is correlated with the unsoundness known as stringiness or crampiness of the hind legs when the horse is on the move.

12. Nervous and continuous movements of the ears may be correlated with impaired eyesight or actual blindness.

13. Protruding, bulging, bovine eyes sometimes called pop-eyes are correlated with a defect in vision known as myopia, a synonym for near-sightedness.

14. Short, straight shoulders, short, straight pasterns, narrow, contracted heels are correlated with the unsoundness known as sidebones.

15. Long, low, weak pasterns and shallow heels are correlated with the unsoundness known as ringbone, a bony deposit or exostosis which appears on the pastern bones.

16. "Sickle hocks," a term which applies to hocks that have too much set as viewed from the side, are correlated with the hock unsoundness known as curbiness.

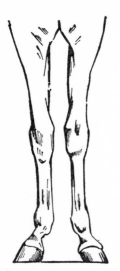 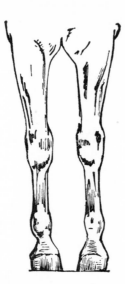 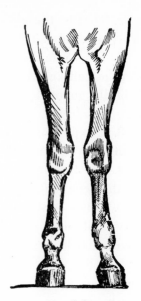

Base-narrow and splay-footed, or nigger-heeled, or toe-wide   *Toe-narrow or pigeon-toed*   *Knock-kneed*

From Gabaux and Barrier, *The Exterior of the Horse.*

 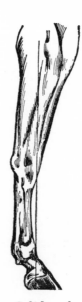 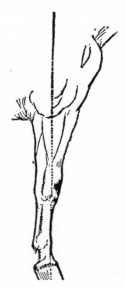

Knee-sprung or over on the knees   *Calf-kneed*   *Pastern too straight*

From Gabaux and Barrier, *The Exterior of the Horse.*

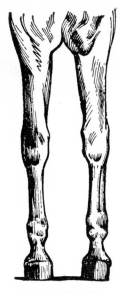

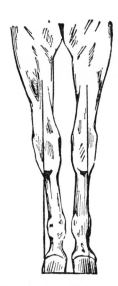
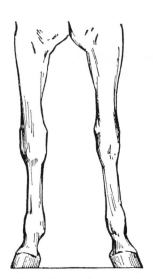

Bow-kneed   *Too close at the ground*   *Too wide at the ground*

From Gabaux and Barrier, *The Exterior of the Horse.*

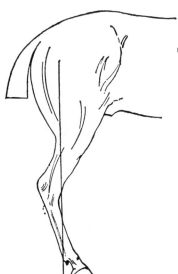
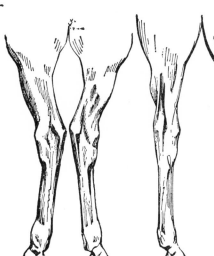
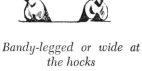

Bent, saber, or sickle hock   *Cow-hocked*   *Bandy-legged or wide at the hocks*

From Gabaux and Barrier, *The Exterior of the Horse.*

17. A thick, discolored, mucous discharge from a horse's nostrils is correlated with sickness or disease.

18. Very steep croups often accompanied by displacement of the hind legs too far forward beneath the body are correlated with sickle hocks and a predisposition to curbiness.

Way of Going Helps to Determine Function

The term "way of going" is self-defining. The pace refers to the rate at which a horse moves. Action implies flexion of knees and hocks.

The stride presents for study the following features:

1. Length, the distance from the point of breaking over to the point of contact of the same foot.

2. Directness or trueness, the line in which the foot is carried forward during the stride.

3. Rapidity or promptness, the time consumed in taking a single stride.

4. Power, the pulling force exerted at each stride.

5. Height, the degree to which the foot is elevated in the stride, indicated by the radius of the arc described.

6. Spring, the manner in which the weight is settled upon the supporting structures at the completion of the stride.

7. Regularity, the rhythmical precision with which each stride is taken in turn.

8. Balance, the ability of a horse to coordinate his action and go in form.

The Gaits

A gait is a term which refers to a definite way of going, characterized by distinctive features regularly executed.

The *walk* is a slow, flat-footed, four-beat gait; it is one of the most useful gaits, whether in harness or under saddle, if executed with snap and animation, as it should be.

The *trot* is a two-beat gait, in which the diagonal fore and hind legs act together. The rate of speed depends upon the horse. The road horse trot is a fast-stepping trot, characterized by the length and rapidity with which individual strides are accomplished, and is executed with an extreme degree of extension. The heavy harness horse trot and the hackney pony trot are high-stepping trots and are characterized by height and spring of stride, the

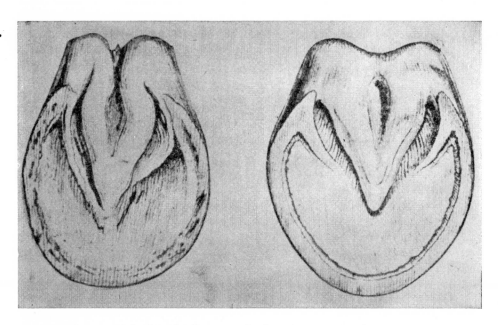

Contracted vs. wide heels. The figure on the left shows a foot that is narrow and con-tracted at the heel. The figure on the right shows a foot with ample width at the heel.
From Lungwitz and Adams, *Horse Shoeing*, courtesy J. B. Lippincott Company.

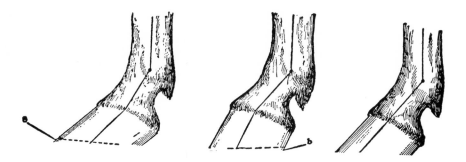

How the foot axis may be broken forward or backward by the trimming of the hoof wall.
Left: *An untrimmed hoof with an excess of horn* (a) *at the toe, which breaks the foot axis backward.* Middle: *An untrimmed hoof with an excess of horn* (b) *at the heel, which breaks the foot axis forward.* Right: *Hoof dressed and foot axis straightened by removing excess of horn below dotted lines in the two preceding illustrations.* From Gay, *Productive Horse Husbandry*, courtesy J. B. Lippincott Company.

horse setting himself, going collectedly, and executing each step with an extreme degree of flexion and the utmost precision.

The *pace* of the light harness horse is a rapid, two-beat gait in which the lateral fore and hind legs work together. It is characterized by the readiness with which pacers can get away at speed, a minimum of concussion, more or less side motion (pacers are sometimes called side-wheelers), the absence of much knee fold (although some pacers are trappy gaited), and the necessity for smooth, hard footing and easy draft for its execution.

It is difficult for most pacers to go in deep or heavy footing, such as fresh snow, sand, or mud, and they have a jerky, unsteady way of pulling a rig if any pull is necessary. The increased draft caused by an extra person up behind or a rough bit of road will swing most pacers into a trot if they can trot at all. Jogging down hill will force some trotters to pace, while an upgrade will set pacers to trotting. The pace is essentially more a speed gait than a road gait.

The *amble* is a lateral gait usually distinguished from the pace by being slower and more broken in cadence. It is not a show gait as is the stepping pace, which is the slow gait required of gaited saddlers in competition. The stepping pace is a lateral four-beat gait done under restraint in showy animated fashion, with the chin set and with the folding of knees and flexing of hocks which contributes to showiness of performance. There is a break in the impact of the feet on the same side of the body, thereby actually making the gait a stepping pace or a four-beat gait done at slow speed.

The *rack* is a fast, flashy, four-beat gait more clearly defined by the discarded name "single-foot." It is rarely executed voluntarily, but under compulsion of hand and heel and is characterized by quite a display of knee action and speed. While very pleasant to the rider, it takes a lot out of a horse and should therefore be called for with judgment and discretion.

The *gallop* is a fast, three-beat gait, in which two diagonal legs are paired, their single beat falling between the successive beats of the other two legs, the hind one of which makes the first beat of the three. A hind foot makes the first beat in the series, the other hind foot and diagonal fore foot make the second beat simultaneously and the remaining fore foot makes the third beat in the series. Then the body is projected clear of the ground and the hind foot makes the first beat in a new series.

The *canter* is a three-beat gait done under restraint. The sequence of the hoofbeats is the same as in the gallop. At the canter the weight of the horse is sustained mainly on the haunches or rear quarters, the forehand is lightened, the chin is set, and the gait is executed in a slow, animated, collected rhythmical way on either lead at command. In an arena, when a horse

A sharp contrast in draft horse type. The Belgian mare on the left is short-legged, deep-bodied, and thick-stifled, stands correctly on her legs, with sufficient muscle wrapped up in her hide to have balanced proportions, thin or fat. The gray gelding is too leggy, too shallow, and too narrow—a hard-keeping kind. Note also his straight ankles and pasterns.
Photograph courtesy Photography Department, The Ohio State University.

is cantering to the right, his right front leg should be in the lead. When he is cantering to the left, the left front leg should be in the lead.

If a horse cantering to the right is leading with his left front leg, he is guilty of a cross-legged canter. Such a canter is objectionable for two reasons: a cross-legged canter means a rough ride; and a horse that canters cross-legged is out of balance, is less securely braced on his feet, and therefore may stumble and fall.

The *running walk* is a slow single-foot or four-beat gait, with the break in the impact or rhythm occurring between diagonal fore and hind feet. In the stepping pace, which is also a slow, four-beat gait, the break in the impact occurs between lateral fore and rear feet.

Since the running walk is a gait that can be maintained all day, it is the business gait in the South and Southwest, where plantation horses are ridden extensively. It is good for six to eight miles an hour, with the greatest ease to both horse and rider. Walking horses, running walkers, plantation horses,

Miss Annatation 203115, a good type study in Percheron mares. Note her strong back, short coupling, heavy muscling, and rugged bone. Balanced in conformation, she stands on lean ankles, springy pasterns, big, shapely feet, all of which contribute to the correctness of her underpinning. Photograph courtesy Cook and Gormley.

plantation "nodders" (sometimes so called because these horses keep time to their paces by the nodding of their heads)—all these terms refer to the same type of horse. At the shows, plantation horses are required to do a flat-foot walk, a running walk, and a canter.

The *foxtrot* is a short, broken, nodding, somewhat uncollected trot, a gait sometimes used as a substitute for the running walk. It is rougher to ride and is therefore not as popular as the running walk, a gait which does contribute to the comfort of the rider.

Some Factors Which Determine the Way of Going

The factors determining a horse's way of going are either natural or acquired. The former consist of type, conformation, direction of leg and form of foot, and breeding. The latter are schooling, handling, and mechanical appliances.

Type

On account of the correlation between form and function, a horse must do as he is made to do. His capabilities in the way of performance will be limited in some respects and extended in others, according to the plan of his structure. A short, thick, low-set horse will have more power than speed, the reverse being equally true. A cobby horse has a trappy stride, while the stride of a tall, rangy horse is characterized by reach.

Conformation

A horse low in the forehand—that is, round and flat over the withers —is likely to forge because such horses move their front legs out poorly and the front feet get in the way of the rear feet. Long, rangy-bodied horses, slack in the coupling, usually have a tendency toward an uncoordinated way of going.

Direction of Leg and Form of Foot

The relation that the direction of the leg bears to the form of the foot is most intimate; each is an important factor in determining the directness of the stride. The form of the foot fixes the point at which the leg breaks over —the center of the toe, or the outer or inner quarter, depending upon whether the foot is symmetrical or the inner or outer quarter is higher.

The direction of the leg determines the course of the foot during its stride, whether advanced in a straight line or describing the arc of a circle inward or outward, dependent upon the deviation in the direction of the leg. The form of the foot and the direction of the leg are correlated, usually, so that their combined influence on the way of going may be considerable.

Some of the common deviations in the direction of the front leg are knee-sprung, calf-kneed, too straight or stilty, base-narrow, base-wide, nigger-heeled, pigeon-toed, knock-kneed, and bow-kneed.

Some common deviations in the set of the hind legs are too straight in the hocks, sickle-hocked, cow-hocked, bow-legged, or bowed in the hocks and turned out at the points of the hocks.

Breeding

Breeding has much to do with the particular gait at which a horse goes. Light harness foals—trotters and pacers—are bred to race in harness at the trot or at the pace. Hackney foals are bred to fold their knees, to flex their hocks, to go high, and to go in form. Thoroughbreds are bred to run. In each of these, the particular way of going is largely a matter of breeding and the urge or the instinct to go that way is almost as strong as it is for a field dog to point or for a game-bred rooster to battle.

Heredity

Type, conformation, direction of leg, and form of foot are all more or less hereditary characters and are associated with a corresponding instinct. A foal is not likely to be endowed by inheritance with an instinct to trot and at the same time inherit a structure which is adapted only to galloping.

Horses are occasionally seen, however, which, though bred properly, manifest a disposition to do what they are physically incapable of doing. Others seem structurally qualified for superior performance of some sort, but fall far short of doing anything remarkable because they apparently do not know how.

Hence we know that the highest order of performance can only be attained when the inherited instinctive tendencies are in line with the horse's inherited physical development.

Schooling

Horses, like men, reflect in their attainments, first, their inherent capabilities; and, second, what has been made of them. All of the graduates of an academic or a gymnasium course are not equals, either in their mental or in their physical accomplishments. Nor are all who have been deprived of any educational advantages destined to a common level or rank in society. Some may reach even a higher rung on the commercial or social ladder than will be reached by people who have had every educational opportunity.

An individual may owe his proficiency either to his opportunities or to his own particular abilities, or to a favorable combination of both. Only the highest type of education designed to realize strong natural aptitudes can develop an accomplished individual.

Hence it is hardly worth while to spend time and money to educate a colt in ways to which he is not adapted. It is a difficult, unsatisfactory task to school a born trotter as a gaited saddler or to school a gaited saddler as a heavy harness horse. Ample proof of the accuracy of this statement, reversed, is found in the earlier days of horse shows in this country. It was common to find single-minded horsemen resorting to all sorts of ingenious methods of preventing a horse from going high in order to make a trotter of him. They often gave up in despair and sacrificed him to the knowing buyer who, by changing tactics and schooling him along the line of action for which he had a strong inclination, finally turned him out a show horse of note. If, on the other hand, we take a natural characteristic and develop it by artificial means, we may expect results far in advance of what could otherwise be obtained.

No race horse or show horse of any class comes to his high degree of proficiency without an education. Not only must the trotter be trained to make him physically fit to race; he must actually be taught to step. The same is true of heavy harness horses, saddle horses, jumpers, and others. They may have the natural aptitude to begin with, but that is not sufficient to get the best out of them.

Handling

Handling is but the application of the schooling. It is painful to see a well-schooled saddle horse, to whom every little movement of hand or heel has a meaning, with some awkward man up, who is reaping the fruits of his ignorant handling in a ride that is most distressing, both to himself and to his mount; or to see a horse, on whom much effort has been spent in teaching him to flex his neck, knees, and hocks in a proud, collected, balanced, high way of going, put in light harness, with the omnipresent Kimball Jackson overdraw, and a heavy fisted driver up, who boasts of how fast the horse can step.

It is as essential that the handling be in accord with the schooling as that the schooling should follow the line of natural aptitude. The handling offers the stimulus; the schooling makes possible the response. Harmony between the two is therefore imperative.

There are individual differences in the methods of different handlers. Among all race and show riders or drivers, each fundamentally correct in his methods, there is always one who is capable of better results than the others.

Mechanical Appliances

Mechanical appliances are chiefly accessories to the handling and schooling of horses. They consist of the bit, shoes, weight, and hopples.

BIT   The bit is for purposes of control and also for the use of the rider to indicate to the horse the gait required.

SHOES   The style of the shoe and the dressing of the foot for its application have considerable influence on the way of going. By shortening or length-

A COMPARISON OF TROTTERS
AND PACERS IN ACTION

*The top photograph shows a
trotter in motion. If a trotter
forges or speedy-cuts himself,
legs on the same side of the
body are guilty of interference. If a pacer forges or
speedy-cuts himself, diagonal
legs are guilty of interference.*
Photographs courtesy *Horseman and Fair World* and
Department of Photography,
The Ohio State University.

ening the toe, the breaking over is either facilitated or retarded, with a consequent shortening or lengthening of the stride; by raising or lowering the
inner or outer quarter, the point at which breaking over takes place may be
regulated within limits.

WEIGHT   By putting weight on or by taking weight off the foot, the
stride may be lengthened or shortened, heightened or lowered. Weight may
be secured either by permitting an abnormal growth of the foot itself or
by adding it to the shoe. Weight fixed at the toe promotes extension on the
principle of the pendulum, the weight coming into play toward the end of the
stride to carry the foot out.

On the other hand, weight well back in the shoe, toward the heel, is
believed to be conducive to action by calling for extra flexion in order to lift
the foot. Whatever alterations are made in the matter of shoeing or weight-
ing must be gradual in order not to unbalance the horse in his stride.

HOPPLES   By uniting a hind leg and a fore leg by means of hopples, a
horse is held to his stride and prevented from breaking, mixing, or going any
other gait. The straps are crossed or straight, depending upon whether the

Creation's King 2663, Hackney pony stallion, demonstrates knee and hock action requirements for Hackney ponies. This pony was the grand champion Hackney pony at the Chicago International in 1949. Owned and shown by Heyl Pony Farm, Washington, Illinois. Harley Heyl driving. Photograph by Freudy Photos, courtesy Mr. Heyl.

horse trots or paces. Hopples about the pasterns are sometimes put on harness horses to develop action. "Rattlers" or links of light chain are often fastened about the pasterns of saddle horses in training to increase both knee and hock action. Weighted boots are also used to enhance action.

Going Surface

Although not of a mechanical nature, the character of the surface on which the horse steps has a marked influence on the kind of stride he takes. As a general rule, heavy, soft, or deep going causes a high stride, while a hard, smooth surface is more conducive to speed. Of the speed horses, trotters and pacers require the hardest, smoothest track. Heavy going frequently induces double-gaited horses to trot instead of pace and seriously interferes with pacing performance. Runners do best on the turf or on a dirt track that has had the surface loosened with a scratch harrow, thereby providing footing that has some cushion.

Cynthiana, noted gaited mare, owned at one time by Dixiana Farms, Lexington, Kentucky, and shown very successfully in ladies' classes some years ago by Miss Mary Fisher. This picture demonstrates perfectly the sequence of hoofbeats when a horse is working at the rack, a four-beat gait done at speed and in form. Photograph by Haas, courtesy Dixiana Farms.

Honey Gold 451147, one of the top walking mares of the country. This picture shows the sequence of the hoofbeats at the running walk. The gait is a diagonal, four-beat gait with a slight interval occurring between the impact of diagonal fore and rear feet. Photograph by Tom Hill, courtesy Mr. Wood.

Defects and Peculiarities in Way of Going

Forging, or striking the end of the branches or the undersurface of the shoe of a fore foot with a toe of the hind foot.

Interfering, or striking the supporting leg usually at the fetlock with the foot of the striding leg. Commonly interference occurs between a supporting front leg and a striding front leg or between a supporting hind leg and striding hind leg.

Brushing, the term used when the interference is slight, possibly just roughing up the hair.

Striking, the term used when the interference results in an open wound.

Paddling, an outward deviation in the direction of the stride of a fore leg, the result of a toe-narrow or pigeon-toed standing position.

Winging, exaggerated paddling, very noticeable in high-going horses.

Winding, a twisting of the front leg around in front of the supporting leg as each stride is taken. This defect in gait is sometimes called threading, plaiting, or walking the rope.

Scalping, or hitting the hind foot above or at the line of the hair (coronet) against the toe of a breaking over fore foot.

Speedy-cutting, which occurs when a trotter or pacer at speed hits a hind leg above the scalping mark against the shoe of a breaking over fore foot. In trotters, legs on the same side are involved. In pacers, diagonal legs are involved.

Cross-firing, essentially forging in pacers, in which they hit the inside of the near fore and off hind foot, or the reverse, in the air as the stride of the hind leg is about completed and the stride of the fore leg is just begun.

Pointing, a stride in which extension is much more marked than flexion. Pointy-strided horses break their knees very little and are low-gaited in front. Thoroughbreds in the use of their front legs at the trot are pointy-gaited.

The term "pointing" is also used to indicate the pose in standing position where a horse stands on three legs and points with the fourth; that is, he rests or saves a leg.

Dwelling, a perceptible pause in the flight of the foot, as though the stride had been completed before the foot strikes the ground. A horse may be guilty of dwelling with either his front or his rear legs. Dwelling as a defect in gait is quite common in heavy harness horses, heavy harness ponies, and some saddlers.

Trappy, a quick, high, but comparatively short stride.

Pounding, a heavy contact usually accompanying a high, laboring stride.

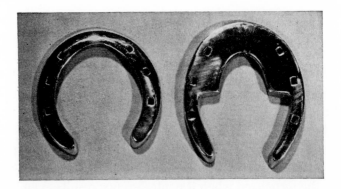

A roller-toe shoe and a heavy weighted-toe shoe, both of them front shoes that are in common use on saddlers. The roller-toe shoe aids and hastens the breakover of a front foot. The weighted toe helps the front leg to function like the pendulum of a clock, increasing the length of the stride in front. The roller-toe shoe weighs sixteen ounces; the weighted-toe shoe weighs twenty-one ounces.

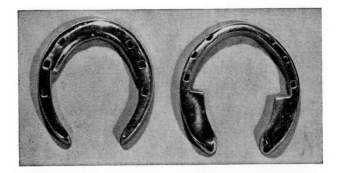

Two shoes that differ in design, each of them in common use on saddle horses, but used for altogether different purposes. The shoe at the left, with additional weight at the toe, is designed to increase the length of the stride. The shoe at right, with additional weight at the heel, is designed to make a horse break or fold his knees and go with a higher stride. The shoe on the left weighs twelve ounces; the shoe on the right weighs eleven ounces.

Harness show pony shoes, front and rear. The front shoe on the left weighs twelve ounces; the hind shoe on the right weighs ten ounces.

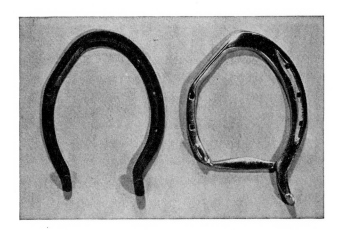

Common types of hind shoes for cross-firing pacers. The shoe on the left is an oblique toe, half-swedged shoe for use on the left hind foot of a pacer that cross-fires. The oblique toe furnishes a margin of difference which keeps the pacer from hitting the inside rear toe of a hind foot against the inside of a breaking-over diagonal fore foot. The half-swedged feature of this hind shoe, plus the use of an outside heel calk on the shoe, gives to the hind foot a retarding grip on the ground, making it possible for the diagonal fore foot to get out of the way. The shoe on the right is an oblique toe, half-swedged shoe which has a longer trailing heel calk and a light bar connecting the extremities of the shoe. This bar strengthens the shoe, thereby increasing the life of the shoe. The shoe on the left weighs 3 ounces; the shoe on the right weighs 5 ounces. Photographs courtesy Department of Photography, Ohio State University.

Rolling, a defect in gait due to excessive lateral shoulder motion, as in wide-fronted horses. Excessively wide-fronted drafters have the rolling-gaited tendency at the trot.

The Importance of Action in Judging

The value of a horse depends largely upon what he can do. Horses earn their living on the move, not by standing still. Therefore, horse judging consists in large part of a study of form in relation to function.

Good Looks vs. Performance Requirements

Good looks may enhance value. But a good-looking horse unable to meet performance requirements in a special field is never a top horse in his field. A saddle horse posed for inspection at the end of the bridle reins may be as good-looking as saddle horses ever are. But if this same saddle horse fails to give a good account of himself in motion, he will be inspected and found wanting by those who are in quest of a high-class pleasure horse or a top show horse. To satisfy the trade in any division of the industry horses must be able to do something.

The performance of a horse depends a great deal upon the way in which he is put together. There is a definite relationship between form and performance. If a horse is defective in the set or position of his legs, there will be a predisposition to defect in gait. If a horse stands toe-wide on his front feet, he cannot break his feet over at the toe and carry them straight forward. Such horses will swing their front feet inward on the move and are guilty of the defect in gait known as winging in or dishing. If a horse stands both toe-wide and base-narrow in front, the winging-in tendency may result in striking a supporting leg with a striding leg. Quite commonly, horses that stand toe-wide in front will hit their ankles when in action. If the horse in question happens to be a toe-wide trotter performing at speed, he may hit his ankles, his shins, his knees, or his elbows and have to wear ankle boots, shin boots, knee boots, and elbow boots for protection. With the exception of quarter boots, this list of boots for a toe-wide, base-narrow trotter includes all of the boots that are made for the front legs of a horse.

The Trainer's Point of View

I heard a top trainer of saddle horses say one day, when we were inspecting a toe-wide, nigger-heeled, base-narrow gaited gelding, that he would just as soon someone else owned all the gaited saddlers whose bodies, when lined up in north and south position, stood on front feet that pointed east and west. Needless to say, that trainer had been through the mill. He had learned by experience that toe-wide horses may pound a supporting front leg with a striding front leg. Splints on the inner side of the cannon bones are oftentimes seen in horses which assume a toe-wide position on their front legs.

Faulty Position on the Legs an Indicator of Faulty Action

If a horse stands pigeon-toed in front, he cannot carry his feet straight forward on the move. But instead of winging in or dishing, the pigeon-toed horse is guilty of winging out or paddling. Collected, coordinated action is desired in all types of horses.

What happens when a horse forges. Drawing courtesy Department of Photography, Ohio State University.

Any horse that wings out or paddles is defective in gait because such horses go more or less uncollectedly. Winging in and winging out are defects in gait which feature the stride of toe-wide and pigeon-toed horses. Therefore the set of the underpinning is an indicator of performance because horses have to do as they are made to do. Hence it is necessary for anyone who hopes to be a discriminating judge of horses to have an intelligent understanding concerning the parts of a horse in their relationship to the function these parts are supposed to perform. Defective set of underpinning almost inevitably means defective action.

When horses are in motion, a stride represents the distance from imprint to imprint of the same foot. A number of features of the stride contribute to a horse's efficiency on the move. Length as a feature of the stride is very important in the case of the work horse, whose job it is to work at the walk. I believe that some action enthusiasts underemphasize the importance of the walk as a draft horse gait and overemphasize the importance of the trot as a requirement. One hears such expressions as the following: "He can go as high as a fence." "He can move like a train." "He can mock a hackney or a trotter."

As a matter of fact, however, the work horse does not have to go as high as a fence nor does he have to be able to imitate a hackney. In pulling farm machinery, a drafter is not supposed to trot. He works at the walk. Years ago, when I first went to The Ohio State University, the Hoster Brewery Company in Columbus had 325 head of horses in its service. The men who drove the heavy teams on the heaviest brewery wagons had strict orders to walk their horses. Dr. Carl Henigst, the superintendent of the stable, made it a rule that any teamster caught driving one of the heavy teams at the trot could come to the office and get his money.

I cite this example as testimony of the fact that the drafter on his job does not have to move like a train. He works at the walk. His length of stride contributes to efficiency of performance in covering ground. Trueness or directness of stride reduces to a minimum the possibility of interference. Promptness or rapidity of stride ensures against loss of time in taking a single step. Height of stride is a requirement which varies a great deal with the type of horse in question.

As for the work horse swinging along at a brisk walk, the height of his stride should be such as to guarantee completion of each stride without stumbling or blundering. Spring or springiness of stride refers to the way in which the weight is settled upon the legs and feet at the completion of each stride. Regularity of stride refers to the rhythmical way in which strides are taken or repeated. Regularity should feature the stride of all kinds of horses. Lameness is an example of irregularity of stride. Balance as a feature of a horse's stride refers to his ability to coordinate his action and to go handily and collectedly and in good form.

In summary, horses earn their living on the move, and their value is based largely on what they can do. Therefore, in the judging of horses, action should be given careful consideration, because a horse's ability on the move determines in large part his usefulness on the job.

Moreover, a horse's ability to do is based largely upon the way in which he is put together. Defective set of the underpinning predisposes to defective action. Defective action predisposes to interference. Interference may result in blemish or unsoundness. Unsoundness depreciates value and is the single most important factor in appraising the worth of a horse. These are reasons why action is of real importance in judging horses.

Questions

1. Give two synonyms for the word "utility."
2. In judging horses, why should one understand the relationship between form and function?

3. Mention a half-dozen correlated features in horse make-up.

4. Mention three examples of correlated features in horse make-up which enhance action.

5. Mention three correlated features in horse make-up which predispose to defective action.

6. Cite a few examples to show how the way of going helps to determine function.

7. Define these terms: length, directness, promptness, power, height, spring, regularity, and balance as features of a horse's stride.

8. Define the term "gait."

9. Define the walk as a gait.

10. Define the trot as a gait.

11. Contrast the requirements of the trot as performed by a roadster and a heavy harness horse.

12. Define the pace as a gait of the light harness horse.

13. Define the rack as a saddle horse gait.

14. Define the canter as a saddle horse gait.

15. Define the gallop.

16. Define the run.

17. Define the running walk.

18. Define the fox trot.

19. Define the stepping pace.

20. Cite a few examples, showing how direction and set of legs and feet can influence gait.

21. Cite instances of breeding as a factor in determining gait.

22. Discuss schooling as a factor in developing gaits.

23. Cite examples showing how shoes and shoeing can affect gaits.

24. Define these terms: forging, interfering, brushing, striking, paddling, winging, winding, scalping, speedy-cutting, cross-firing, pointing, dwelling, pounding, trappy, rolling.

25. Why is action very important as a determining factor in judging horses?

26. Cite a few examples of faulty position on the legs as an indicator of faulty action.

27. Why should there be sharp discrimination against unsoundness when judging horses?

5

The Classes of Horses for

Market and Show

———

Basis of Class Distinctions

The characters upon which class distinctions are based are height, weight, form, quality, substance, condition, temperament, action, manners, and color.

Height

Stature is measured at the highest point of the withers in hands, 4 inches to the hand. Fractions of a hand are expressed in inches, as 15 hands, 2 inches, or 15–2.

A horse or pony to be measured should be stationed with his feet on level ground. A level concrete surface is quite satisfactory. When the measuring stick is applied, the head should be in normal position insofar as good judgment can determine.

The measurement should be taken from the highest point of the withers because a horse's height represents the vertical distance from the highest point of the withers to the surface upon which the horse stands. The tip of the fifth thoracic vertebra is the highest point of the withers when the skeleton is exposed. The highest point in the live horse is a matter of judgment;

This pair of pictures shows how the pigment fades out of the coat of a gray horse as he grows older. Above is the Percheron stallion Libretto 121447 (97907) as a six-year-old weighing 2,100 pounds. Below is the same horse, four years later, weighing about a ton. Note how the pigment has faded from his hair coat. Photographs courtesy Hildebrand and Photography Department, The Ohio State University.

hence the head should not be lifted so high that the crest of the neck is crowded back over the withers. Nor should the horse's head be dropped downward between his knees, out of position. If the man who does the measuring is honest, he will insist that the head of the horse be in normal position insofar as can be determined.

Weight

Height and weight combined determine scale, which is synonymous with size.

Jay Farceur 17628, one of the most noted show stallions and one of the most noted sires in the history of the Belgian breed in America. He has been champion at the Chicago International, at the American Royal, and at all the leading state fairs in the Middle West. During his stock horse career, Jay Farceur sired so many futurity winners and so many champions that he deserves the rating "a breeder of breeders." Photograph courtesy J. F. Abernathy.

Form

The general contour of outline determines whether a horse is smoothly turned or angular, massive or lithe, low-set or leggy, rangy or compact. "Form" is a term that refers to the shape of a horse or to the shape of any part of a horse.

Quality

Quality refers to texture and finish, as determined by the character of the individual units of structure. It is indicated in hide, hair, and bone. Quality is a term that refers to degree of refinement.

Substance

Substance refers to the amount of structural material, as determined by the number and size of the individual units of structure. Bone and muscle are the indicators of substance.

Condition

Condition is not so much the state of health as that which comes as the result of fitting. In the ordinary market horse it is the difference in being fat and thin. In the race horse, it also suggests the trained as against the untrained.

Temperament

A horse may be too hot, nervous, and excitable for a work horse or too cold, sluggish, and phlegmatic for a race horse.

Manners

Manners are a very important requirement because a horse's value is materially influenced by what he can do. It is essential that a horse do all that he is expected to do and do that as well as he can. Manners, therefore, really count in appraising the worth of a horse to the user.

Color

Color is an important factor in determining the value of horses, especially show horses. A good horse is said never to have a bad color; yet certain colors are preferred or even required in some classes of horses, whereas other colors are undesirable or even prohibited.

Color is the most conspicuous feature by which a horse can be described or identified, so that a uniform and comprehensive color standard is important. Colors may be generally classified as solid or broken, distinguished by the presence or absence of white spots. Solid colors are further differentiated as hard or soft. A hard color is one in which the shade is sharply pronounced, while soft colors are characterized either by a total absence of pigment, as in the case of the white horse with the pink skin, or by a washed-out or faded shade of some of the other colors.

Broken colors are either the piebald and skewbald, in which the amount of white is considerable and the distribution irregular; or the marked, when the white is limited in amount and definitely restricted in its location. There are also a number of odd colors and markings which do not conform to the above distinctions or admit of any but a group classification.

Captivation 3954, one of the greatest Hackney mares ever produced in America. A liver-colored, chestnut mare, with white markings, she was always easy to look at when posed for inspection. Few indeed are the horses that have ever been able to imitate her match-less action. She was shown very successfully by Longview Farms, Lees Summit, Missouri. David Smith driving. Photograph by Rounds, courtesy Mrs. Loula Long Combs.

CLASSIFICATION OF COLORS
Solid, hard colors are
Bay—bright or cherry bay, blood-red bay, mahogany bay, or dark bay.
Brown—bay, seal, mealy, black.
Chestnut—golden, red, burnt, black.
Black—jet, sooty.
Gray—dappled, steel, iron, black, flea-bitten.
Roan—blue, red, strawberry.
Solid, soft colors are white (pink skin), mealy bay, and washy chestnut.
Broken colors are piebald, skewbald, and marked.
Odd colors are cream, mouse, dun. The dun may be grouped into light or Isabella, and dark or buckskin.
Markings—white, baldface, blaze, strip, star, snip, splash, stocking, sock, fetlock, pastern, coronet, heel.
Black—points, lines.

Odd—tiger spots, leprous spots, wall-eyed.

The standing of different colors will often depend upon the class of the horse in question. In general, the different shades of bay may be considered as the best all-round color.

Bay has been referred to as "everyman's" color. It is a color that is easy to to keep clean.

Brown is also a staple color like bay.

Chestnut, especially the golden and red, is one of the most attractive colors and when accompanied by white markings, as chestnut is quite likely to be, presents an extremely flashy appearance. This is one of the most popular colors in high-class harness and saddle horses.

Black, although very popular in fiction, is in fact not the best color in selling. It is objected to chiefly on the ground that it is not often fast black, but fades and sunburns badly in hot weather. This criticism applies more to the sooty black than to the jet black.

Black is also objectionable on account of the flecked appearance which it acquires as the horse is warmed up. No matter how carefully the coat is groomed, every hair that is turned appears as a dirty gray fleck as soon as the sweat dries. Black harness horses in many instances in the heyday of the business were cross-matched with grays. At one time undertakers constituted the chief market for black horses.

Gray was the color most in demand at one time in the draft horse and work horse area, though frequently discriminated against in horses of any other type. When the work horse business was booming, years ago, buyers of work horses used to say that they preferred gray because there was less difficulty in matching up a team of two, four, or six grays than in the case of any other color. This may be accounted for to some extent by the fact that gray was a popular Percheron color and the number of Percherons in the draft horse area always outnumbered the other breeds in this country. It would seem at first thought that bays could be more easily matched than grays. But bays are more frequently marked with white, which necessitates a matching of markings as well as of shade.

Grays, furthermore, were popular with work horse owners because the gray seemed to harmonize better with the red, green, or yellow combinations in which most commercial vehicles were finished. It is also reasonable to claim that the gray horse was less susceptible to heat than the horse of darker color, since white has the physical property of reflecting the sun's rays, while black absorbs them. This fact is borne out by one's own experience with white and black suits of the same weight and material.

Gray horses, outside the work horse division, are generally objected to on account of the conspicuousness of their hair when shed; the degree to which they show stable stain, although this difficulty is largely overcome by the use of peat moss bedding; and the inevitable disappearance, with advancing age, of the black pigment in the hair, resulting in white color and a predisposition to melanotic tumors.

On the other hand, gray horses show dandruff and body dirt less than do horses of most other colors. The darker shades are most preferred, although in the hunting field, on the race track, or even in the show ring a beautifully dappled light gray will invariably catch the eye. History has done much to offset the prejudice against gray horses because Napoleon, General Lee, and other famous military leaders had as their favorite mounts horses which were white or gray in color.

Roan of any shade was a popular Belgian and work horse color all through the heyday of the work horse business. In harness and saddle horses, especially walking horses, roans are quite a common color today.

Piebalds and skewbalds are popular colors in ponies, in sporting fours, and in tandems where striking colors are a feature; they are also used for advertising wagons, in the circus, and wherever conspicuousness is desirable. A piebald is a black-and-white combination; any other color than black, such as bay, brown, or chestnut, combined with white constitutes a skewbald.

Cream, dun, and mouse colors are generally in disfavor except for some special purpose, although the buckskin—a darker shade of dun which is distinguished from cream by black points—has a reputation for stamina.

White markings are most desirable in horses of the show type, since such colors enhance the brilliance of a flashy performance. Even in the shows, however, too much white is not preferred in ladies' singles or pairs.

Black points are as a rule considered indicative of greater wearing qualities, and it is a fact that the blue horn of the black foot is more dense and tough than the white. White points behind are less objectionable than in front. In fact, they are generally considered to improve a horse's appearance as does some white in his countenance. White markings, wherever they may be, should be as symmetrical as possible and sharply defined. Large, irregular white patches or splashes are objectionable.

Odd markings are also undesirable. The leprous spots are the small more or less regular areas, completely denuded of pigment, that are seen about the muzzle, the eyes, and under the tail. The so-called tiger spots are the large, irregular areas of a pinkish or yellowish tint, surrounded by a zone of lighter shade, which resemble in appearance the spots on a tiger lily. They are especially common over the croup.

Invasion demonstrates the heavy harness horse trot. Mrs. Loula Long Combs driving. Photograph courtesy Mrs. Combs.

THREE CHAMPIONS IN THEIR RESPECTIVE DIVISIONS DEMONSTRATE THE TROT.

Cadet's Crystal Gazer demonstrates the heavy harness pony trot. Mrs. R. C. Flanery driving. Photograph courtesy Mr. R. C. Flanery.

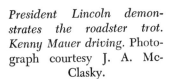

President Lincoln demonstrates the roadster trot. Kenny Mauer driving. Photograph courtesy J. A. McClasky.

Paul D 74204, 2:03¾, a grand champion road horse when posed for inspection and when in motion. His championships in 1950 included Houston, the Kentucky State Fair, and the Illinois State Fair. He is owned by Mrs. Paul Davis of Henderson, Illinois, and is shown by R. C. Flanery. Photograph courtesy J. A. McClasky.

Market and Show Classes

By classes of horses are meant the creations of the market and the show ring. Class is based upon use. The classes should not be confused with types, which are mechanical distinctions.

1. Work:
    a. The work horse classification in the heyday of the business
        (1) Drafter
        (2) Logger
        (3) Chunk
        (4) Feeder
    b. The work horse classification in recent years
        (1) Drafter
        (2) Wagon
        (3) Farm chunk

Kate Shriver 43606, champion fine harness mare, sired by Anacacho Denmark and out of Reverie's Desdemona, winner of the Junior Fine Harness Stake at Louisville in 1949. She came back as a five-year-old to win the $10,000 Fine Harness Stake at the Kentucky State Fair in 1950. She has good looks and a fine harness trot. She is owned by Mr. and Mrs. R. C. Goshorn, Jefferson City, Missouri, and has been shown by Garland Bradshaw.
Photograph by John R. Horst.

    (4) Southerners
2. Heavy harness horses—usually Hackney bred
3. Light harness horses
    a. Speed—trotters and pacers
    b. Show—roadster (a trotter, pacers barred)
4. Saddle horses
    a. Thoroughbred: race horse, runner
    b. Three-gaited: walk, trot, canter
    c. Five-gaited: walk, trot, slow gait, rack, canter
    d. Combination { three-gaited (in harness and under saddle) / five-gaited (in harness and under saddle)
    e. Fine harness: gaited horse hitched
    f. Hunters: lightweight, middleweight, heavyweight
    g. Walking horses: flat-foot walk, running walk, canter
    h. Quarter horses and stock horses: breeding and performance classes

Emerald Sweet Sue 46757, sired by American Ace, and out of Janet Sue. As a junior mare in 1949, she won the junior stakes at Dayton, Cincinnati, and the Ohio State Fair. She was reserve at Lexington, Louisville, and Harrisburg. Measured by the yardsticks of performance and good looks, Emerald Sweet Sue is one of the top mares of the country. Photograph courtesy J. A. McClasky.

    i. The Appaloosa: breeding and performance classes
    j. The Morgan
    k. The Palomino: breeding, performance, and parade classes
    l. Parade horses: miscellaneous horses in full-dress regalia that can do a
       parade trot
5. Ponies
    a. Shetland and harness show ponies
    b. Heavy harness ponies: 12–2 hands and under
       Heavy harness ponies: 12–2 to 13–2
       Heavy harness ponies: 13–2 to 14–2
    c. Polo

Drafters

    Drafters are work horses that on most markets are sixteen hands and up in height, sixteen hundred pounds and up in weight. In the heyday of the business the drafter was the highest-priced work horse on the market. In

Smoke Dreams 43905, winner of the amateur three-gaited and under 15–2 stakes at the American Royal in 1950. This mare has won the same stakes at Tulsa, Little Rock, Shreveport, and Lexington. She is owned by Pin Oak Stables, Houston, and is shown by Miss Josephine Abercrombie. Copyrighted by McClasky.

his highest estate, he was a city horse whose job it was to furnish power to the packer's van or the jobber's dray. He was employed on short-haul assignments, through the congested areas and the frequent-stop territory.

Discriminating city users of drafters wanted horses which in harness served as walking advertisements for the firm that owned them. Soundness was a prime consideration when buyers bought work horses for the city streets.

Loggers

Loggers were drafters in height and weight but lacked quality. These horses were bought for service in the woods. They were acceptable to buyers, therefore, even though they had a few touches of secondhandedness, minor blemishes, and scars. Wire cuts across the face of a hock or a sidebone or two would not stop a buyer when inspecting horses for service in the logging business. City buyers, on the other hand, would reject such horses for use on city streets.

Chunks

On most markets chunks have been work horses that were under sixteen hands in height and under sixteen hundred pounds in weight. They are what horsemen call "big little" drafters or vest-pocket editions of drafters. At the crest of the work horse era chunks were used in the quick delivery service in cities. The best-mated pairs of chunks were work horses that were balanced in conformation, smart-fronted, and full of quality—horses that could work at a brisk walk or a smart trot. Most of the work horses on the market today are nondescript chunks—many of them testimony of a vanishing work horse industry.

Feeders

When the work horse business was good, feeders were lean drafters, lean loggers, or lean chunks which a farmer could buy thin in the spring of the year for a summer's work. He would then put them in the barn and fatten them during the winter months for later sale to a shipper who bought horses to go east to users in Buffalo, Pittsburgh, Philadelphia, New York, or Boston.

Wagon Horses

Wagon horses are undersized drafters capable of working at both the walk and the trot. Usually they stand from 15–2 to 16–2 hands in height and weigh from 1,350 to 1,650 pounds, although the majority of them used on milk wagons, in large cities, weigh from 1,400 to 1,600 pounds in work condition. They have less depth of body, more length of leg, and more quality than draft horses and are able to wheel their load more easily at the trot.

Farm Chunks

Farm chunks are work horses that stand less than sixteen hands in height and weigh less than sixteen hundred pounds. As compared with the work chunks which were in demand on city streets years ago, the farm chunk offering on the present-day market is inferior in quality and of nondescript breeding.

Southerners

Southerners are small, more or less nondescript work horses in type, many of them through the years coming from Western ranges. These horses stand 14–2 to 15–2 hands in height and weigh from 1,000 to 1,100 pounds.

THREE CHAMPIONS IN THEIR RESPECTIVE DIVISIONS DEMONSTRATE THE TROT.

The Auctioneer demonstrates the three-gaited saddle pony trot. "Bob" Whitney riding. These photographs courtesy **J. A. Mc-Clasky.**

Vanity demonstrates the fine harness horse trot. Mrs. Victor Weil driving.

G. I. Joe demonstrates the harness show pony trot. Louis Robinson driving.

Heavy Harness Horses

There is an implication about the term "heavy harness horse" which is not generally understood. Harness horses are of two classes, heavy and light, the adjective in each case describing the harness and not the horse.

The heavy harness horse is one of fashion, an English creation, and it is to English sentiment that he owes his name. He conforms to the Englishmen's idea that "to drive handsomely one must drive heavily." Their vehicles are of dignified and elegant design and are of heavy construction. The harness by which the horses are hitched to the vehicles is correspondingly heavy, characterized by weight of leather, Kay collars, metal mountings, Liverpool-elbow and Buxton bits, with side rein or no bearing rein. To complete this equipage and be capable of both acting and looking the part, the horse must be close and full-made with extreme finish, style, and action.

Heavy harness horses today are used for purposes of show only. They must be able to use their legs, that is, fold their knees, flex their hocks, set their chins, display action in front and behind, work at a park gait or step on at the command of the judge—balanced in stride and collected in form. Wooden-legged heavy harness horses, unable to fold their knees or flex their hocks, fall far short of the show ring requirements. They must be able to untrack themselves. Most heavy harness horses are Hackney bred.

Light Harness Horses

These horses are as distinctly American in their origin as the heavy harness horses are English. Since maximum speed requires minimum draft, American road wagons or buggies are built of such material and in such fashion as to impose upon the horse the least weight that is consistent with the safe and comfortable conveyance of one or two people. They are therefore in striking contrast to the English carriages and require a harness that is correspondingly light.

There are two divisions of light harness horses, the racing division and the show division. In the racing division are subdivisions, one for trotters and one for pacers. In the show division are classes for roadsters in harness and roadsters under saddle. In both of these roadster divisions, the entries must trot. Pacers are barred.

Horsemen look upon the pacer as a kind of counterfeit roadster because pacers are greatly handicapped in the mud, in the sand, or on rough ground. The pacer to do his best must have smooth footing that is tolerably hard.

In competitions at the shows, roadsters must trot not only the straightaway stretches but the turns. Some roadsters on the turns will shift from the trotting gait and amble or pace or rack their way around the turns, shifting again to the trot on the straightaway. Mixy-gaited roadsters are greatly handicapped in stiff competition because the best roadsters can trot both the straightaway and the turns and discrimination against a horse that is "pacey-gaited" in his performance is sharp.

In roadster competitions the entries are worked both ways of the ring. Usually when roadsters enter the ring, the entries are worked the wrong way of the track at a jog. Then they are reversed and asked to jog the right way of the ring; finally they are asked to turn on or to trot on at speed. Following the workout at speed, the entries are called to the center of the ring for inspection in standing position. As a test of manners it is common practice to ask road horses to back.

Most good road horses are Standardbred. That is, they are registered or are eligible for registry in the books of the United States Trotting Association.

Road horses are hitched singly or in pairs, but speed horses are seldom used to a pole. The road buggy is the typical roadster hitch, while race horses are hooked to light sulkies. In roadster classes, speed only to count, the entries are hitched to a sulky.

Saddle Horses

"Saddle horse type" is a term which refers to the sum total of those features which are sought in the make-up of a commonly accepted ideal saddle stallion, saddle mare, or saddle gelding.

The saddle horse was primarily a utility horse, as a matter of necessity, in pioneer times before the construction of roads and vehicles, but he has become, in addition, a most popular source of pleasure, with circumstances attending his use so diversified as to call for a variety of types.

Some horses are ridden for the ease with which they carry one, while others are ridden for exercise and the liver stimulation which they afford. Some are ridden in dignified manner on the bridle paths in the parks or on the boulevards, while others are ridden rough in the fields and across country.

The distinction between the first two, in this country, is very largely one of schooling and trimming. The difference in the latter refers to the fact that some saddlers are shown with full mane and tail while others are shown with roached mane and shaved or clipped tail.

The race horse, the truest exponent of the speed type, is used essentially as a saddle horse whose assignment it is to gallop or to run fast; he is therefore classified in the saddle horse division. The way of going of these horses is distinctive; they have a wonderful reach and length of jump at the run and

Runancarry, one of the best types ever to appear in the hunter classes in the shows of this country. Winner one year at Devon of six blue ribbons and the green hunter champion-ship. Sired by Runantell and out of Graceful Carrie, this champion mare was owned by Bryn Du Farms, Granville, Ohio, and was shown by Mrs. Sally Jones Sexton. Study this photograph. Note the balanced conformation as well as the set and the quality of the underpinning. Photograph by Haas, courtesy Mrs. Sexton.

they gallop splendidly, but they have a low, pointing stride at the trot. They run on the flat or over a steeplechase course of jumps, according to their own natural aptitude and the schooling they have received. Running race horses are handicapped by the weight required to be carried, an impost of a few ounces making a considerable difference in the speed that is possible.

Walk, trot, canter saddlers or three-gaited horses are shown with a roached mane and clipped or shaved tail. The mane is taken off close to the crest of the neck and the upper portion of the tail is trimmed close to the bone with a plume or bush of hair at the end of the tail. Three-gaited sad-dlers, as the name implies, are asked to do three gaits: a flat-foot walk, the trot, and the canter. The best-trained walk, trot horses actually do a flat-foot walk without any prance, dance, fidget, or fuss. Such a horse should drop the bit in his mouth and walk without any duel between his mouth and the rider's hands. The chin should be set and not extended.

A three-gaited saddle horse at the trot should trot in form at moderate speed, not so fast that he appears to be racing, not so slow that he appears to be sluggish or phlegmatic. Moderate speed, with the folding of the knees and the flexing of the hocks that result in a balanced trot, that is to say, trot-ting in front, trotting behind, with chin set and going collectedly—these are some of the most important requirements of three-gaited saddlers at the trot. All saddle horses should go straight in front and work their hocks close together when viewed from the rear. Winging in or out with the front feet, sprawling in front and landing on the heels, going pointy-gaited in front, hitching or dwelling behind, trailing the hind legs, going spraddle-gaited behind—these are defects in gait which the best saddle horses do not have.

Because of the fact that five-gaited horses at the trot and the rack work at speed, they are permitted to wear quarter boots to protect the heels of the front feet. Quarter boots, however, are not permitted in classes for three-gaited saddlers.

Five-gaited saddle horses, sometimes called gaited saddlers, are distinctly an American product. They are shown with full mane and tail. Five gaits are required. These gaits, listed in the order in which they are usually requested by the judge, are the walk, the trot, the slow gait (which is usually the stepping pace), the rack, and the canter.

Gaited saddle horses at the trot are supposed to work at speed and in form. If a gaited saddler can trot fast and still go in form, so much the better. However, form should not be sacrificed to attain speed. The gaited saddler that can trot fast, fold his knees, flex his hocks, set his chin, and go collectedly is the horse that will furnish real competition for the other horses.

The slow gait or stepping pace is a slow, four-beat gait, done under restraint, in form, with animated countenance and expression. It is one of the showiest gaits when properly executed. It is right on the edge of a four-beat gait, the interim between hoof beats occurring between lateral feet.

The rack or single-foot is a four-beat gait done at speed and in form with the interval between hoof beats occurring between diagonal feet. A horse should have his chin set and should have the legs working underneath him so that the four hoof beats will be heard distinctly. Any tendency to pace at the rack is a real fault because the pace is a lateral two-beat gait done at speed and is very rough to ride. The rack, on the other hand, is a smooth, gliding gait that contributes to the comfort of the rider.

The canter is a three-beat gait done under restraint. A hind foot makes the first beat in the series, the other hind foot and diagonal fore foot make the second beat in the series together, the other fore foot makes the third beat in the series; then the body is projected clear of the ground and a hind foot makes the first beat in a new series.

Horses at the canter should support their weight largely on their haunches, their fore feet should strike the ground lightly, without any tendency to pound or labor, and the chin should be set, not extended. The horse should have a cheerful countenance and, as the Kentuckians say, should canter slowly and collectedly all day in the shade of an apple tree.

Of course, a horse at the canter should be ambidextrous, that is, able to canter on either lead. When going to the left in the ring, the left forefoot

The champion hunter Times Square *demonstrates fine jumping form, with his owner,
Mr. V. G. Cardy of Montreal, riding.* Photograph by ABC News Pictures, courtesy
Mr. Cardy.

should be leading. When going to the right, the right forefoot should be
leading.

Let me repeat, saddle horses should canter on their haunches, not on their
heads. They should not gallop on, hanging in the bridle and pulling the rider's arms out of the sockets. They should canter on their haunches, taking
as light hold of the bit as possible.

If a horse at the canter in an oval arena is leading with the front foot
that is next to the rail he is guilty of a cross-legged canter. Horses should not
canter cross-legged for two reasons. First, a cross-legged canter means a
rough ride. Second, a horse that canters cross-legged in an oval arena is off
balance and predisposed to stumble. Any horse that stumbles may fall and
any horse that falls may injure his rider. Sure-footedness is a prime requisite
in any saddle horse.

The collected, springy, weight-carrying trot of the three-gaited saddler
differs from the fast, more extended trot of the gaited saddler. The saddle
horse trot, both the trot of the three-gaited and the five-gaited saddler, differs
from the extended, ground-covering trot of a trotter pulling a sulky and try-

The grand champion hunt team, Gold Lode, Times Square, and Maple Leaf, owned by Mr. V. G. Cardy of Montreal, Canada. Photograph by ABC News Pictures, courtesy Mr. Cardy.

ing to win a race. The saddle horse trot also differs from the high-acting, sometimes pounding trot of the heavy harness horse.

Walk, trot, canter horses are sometimes shown as hacks. There is a distinction between park hacks and road hacks. The former have the finish and style characteristic of all park horses and are usually saddle-bred. Road hacks are not necessarily saddle-bred horses. They may be plainer in make-up but serviceable and tractable, with good mouths and manners and capable of taking a cross-country run if necessary.

There is also a tendency to differentiate between the saddle-bred walk, trot, canter saddle horse and the one of Thoroughbred breeding and type. The former is characterized by stylish, high carriage of head, neck, and tail, with a more imposing, peacocky look about its front and capable of more knee and hock action. Many Thoroughbred saddlers are a little erratic in disposition, with a low, pointy trot that is not conducive to either a safe or a comfortable ride; however, there are some very acceptable saddlers whose make-up shows them to be distinctly Thoroughbred in type.

Three-gaited saddle horses at the shows are commonly grouped in classes which call for horses that are under 15–2 hands in height, and 15–2 or over. The most satisfactory ladies' mounts, everything considered, are three-gaited saddlers that are under 15–2.

A show classification provides combination classes for both five-gaited and three-gaited saddlers. A five-gaited combination horse is a five-gaited saddler in harness. A three-gaited combination horse is a three-gaited saddler in harness. In either case a combination horse is a saddle horse in harness. He is not a harness horse under saddle.

In combination classes, the entries come into the arena hitched to an appropriate four-wheeled vehicle. In the back of the rig are a saddle and bridle. After a judge has worked the entries in harness both ways of the ring, all horses are lined up in the center of the ring for individual inspection. A judge usually asks all horses to back to test their manners. Then the judge orders that the horses be unhitched, unharnessed, saddled, and bridled. Rigged with saddle horse tack, all entries are worked under saddle both ways of the ring, then lined up in the center of the arena and asked to back under saddle. Then the judge makes his rating after having seen all entries work in harness and under saddle. In other words, a combination horse has two jobs to do: he must work satisfactorily in harness and must turn in a finished performance under saddle.

A fine harness horse is a five-gaited horse in harness. Three-gaited saddlers are not shown in fine harness classes. Sometimes fine harness horses have been referred to as the "gentleman's driving horse of the South." A fine harness horse is exactly what the name implies, a fine horse presented in fine harness with fine equipage. He is truly the "peacock" of the show ring and should go with a springy, balanced, high and animated trot. He should not go with a short, choppy, trappy stride. A bouncy, ground-covering stride is preferred in fine harness, for, in reality, such horses have a parade assignment in harness instead of under saddle.

A fine harness horse should not be a wooden-legged horse, helpless when in motion. He must fold his knees, flex his hocks, set his chin, go in form, and go collectedly. His countenance and his whole make-up, standing still and on the move, should be indicative of that indefinable thing we call "class" in horses. Whatever it is, no matter what you call it, a really fine harness horse has it. We call it presence in men. We call it charm in women. Perhaps these last two comparisons will be helpful in making crystal clear to you what is meant by class in horses.

Sometimes a gaited saddler that refuses to rack but has a high springy collected trot makes a very satisfactory fine harness horse, if he or she is blessed with good looks.

Hunters are ridden to hounds, cross-country and, as a rule, with con-

Peggy Grey, sired by The Second Whip, a Welsh pony stallion, and out of a Shetland pony mare. Miss Marjorie Kays is in the saddle. Photograph courtesy Cook and Gormley.

siderable weight, since adults rather than children usually participate in such sport. In order to qualify satisfactorily, all hunters, in addition to being able to carry weight, must have staying ability and be able to endure long, hard runs, jump safely, preferably in their stride, all common obstacles in the field, such as fences, walls, and ditches, and be able to gallop fast enough to keep pace with the pack. They must also be intelligent and tractable and of such temperament that they do not become too hot in company and run away through fences or into quarry holes.

In order to meet these requirements, the hunter should have all the features of the weight carrier conspicuous in his make-up. He should also have long, sloping shoulders, high withers, muscular hind quarters with thickness through the stifles, and ample bone. Quality in the make-up of hunters which actually follow the hounds may be sacrificed to substance, but at the same time a hunter should show breeding and not appear cold in pedigree. He is not good-looking in the same sense that many park horses are good-looking, but he has an impressive appearance when measured by the yardsticks of resourcefulness and serviceability. Some degree of size or scale is demanded by buyers and users of hunters and apparently for good reasons. In the first place, a five-foot jump is four inches lower for a sixteen-hand horse than for a fifteen-hand horse. Many people who ride hunters to hounds are in the sport as a form of exercise to keep down their weight, so that it takes a horse of some size to be able to carry the weight at which the owner rides. Finally, the bigger horse is claimed to give a safer ride because the momentum of his greater weight gives him a better chance of breaking through a fence in case of a blunder, instead of being tripped by it and coming down.

Hunters are classified as to the weight they are capable of carrying; light-weight, 135 to 165 pounds; middleweight, 165 to 190 pounds; and heavy-weight, 190 pounds and up. At the shows, hunters are also classified as green (suitable to become hunters), qualified, working, handicap and hunter hacks.

All hunters are jumpers in some degree, but a jumper is by no means necessarily a hunter. Hunters are as distinctive in type as a gaited saddler. A jumper, on the other hand, can be any kind of horse that can jump. Hence the jumping classes feature many horses that are nondescript in type. A jumper may clear six feet on a single trial, then blunder over an ordinary post-and-rail fence. To be a safe horse following hounds cross-country he must be a consistent jumper of fences that are between four and a half and five feet high.

The use of hunters is not restricted to the hunting field, although the number for that purpose is constantly increasing. Horses of the hunter type are preferred by many who never follow the hounds, because hunters are most useful as hacks as well as on the bridle trails.

Other Saddle Horses

For detailed discussions of the Tennessee Walking Horse, the Quarter Horse, the Appaloosa, the Morgan, the Palomino, and parade horses see Chapter Eleven, "The Light-Legged Breeds."

Ponies

Generally speaking, any horse under 14–2 is a pony, but lack of stature alone does not constitute the pony type. In ponies there is a distinct confor-mation, in miniature, to either draft horse, heavy harness, or saddle horse type. As is true of horses which lack distinctive type, a pony in stature could be a nondescript runt rather than a show pony.

THE SHETLAND PONY The native home of the Shetland pony is the Shetland Islands, located about two hundred miles north of Scotland. In topography, these islands are rocky and rough, generally barren and unpro-ductive as a grazing area and subject to unfavorable weather conditions most of the time. Temperatures are low, feed is scarce.

The origin of the Shetland pony is uncertain, but it is believed that the ancestry of the present-day pony can be traced to the small pony stock that was found in the adjacent countries of Iceland, Scandinavia, Ireland, and Wales.

In many ways, the early Shetlands resembled a draft horse in miniature. As a breed they have always been docile, gentle, and tractable, their disposition and their size being two reasons why they have made such strong appeal to children.

In the early days, the height of Shetlands varied from 9 to 11 hands and their weight ranged from three hundred to four hundred pounds. They are of many colors—bay, black, brown, chestnut, gray, roan, and spotted, both piebald and skewbald. Their hair coat, particularly in winter, is long and shaggy.

Hardiness and longevity are well-marked characteristics of the Shetland. They have been used in America chiefly as children's pets, both for riding and for driving. Many a potential horseman has had his first horse experience with a Shetland pony. In the British Isles and in their native homeland, they have been used for pack and draft purposes and in the coal mines of Great Britain. In England, the height limit determining eligibility for registry has been 10–2. In Canada, the height limit has been 11 hands and in the United States the height limit for years has been 11–2.

In recent years, pony breeders and exhibitors have gone in quest of a pony that excelled the so-called "old-time" Shetland. Breeder goals have called for a nicer looking pony, more nicely balanced in conformation and one that could do more when in motion at both the walk and the trot. Many Shetlands have been too plain in their heads and necks, and uneven in top line from withers to tail. Too many of them have been coarse and thick at the withers, short and steep in the croup, with too much set to their hocks as viewed from the side. On the move they have lacked in length and height of stride and, measured by show standards, have put on a rather phlegmatic, unanimated performance.

As a consequence, breeders started to cross Shetland mares with good Welsh pony stallions and with good Hackney pony stallions. The result has been a pony with a more stylish front, a longer neck, a more attractive head, a pony that is much more symmetrical in body lines, that stands more correctly on his legs, and that makes much more appeal when in motion.

In 1938 the executive committee of the American Shetland Pony Club sponsored a register for crossbred ponies so that those breeders who wanted to show the high-going, animated ponies could honestly record them and still show them in the shows, but not under the name of registered Shetlands. This register, which was later changed from that of crossbred pony to that of harness show pony, required that both sire and dam be registered and that one

Fame 132 and Fortune 134, one of the greatest pairs of harness show ponies that have ever appeared together. They are models of beauty and motion. Owned by Miss Josephine Abercrombie, of Houston. Photograph by Trapp, courtesy Miss Abercrombie.

Popularity 133, a harness show pony extraordinary. A model in standing position, and a pony whose action very few ponies are able to imitate. Owned by Miss Josephine Abercrombie, of Houston. Photograph by Trapp, courtesy Miss Abercrombie.

of them be a Shetland. The height limit, set at 11–3, still holds if such ponies are exhibited in accordance with the rules of the American Shetland Pony Club.

Harness show pony rules of The American Horse Shows Association suggest that member shows do not offer pony classes under the name of a breed, such as "Shetland," unless it is specifically intended that the judge shall rule out every pony which does not definitely belong to such breed. It is recommended that classes include all types of ponies.

The rules of The American Horse Shows Association also state that a harness show pony may be any breed or combination of breeds. The height of the harness show pony eligible to compete in such classes is fixed at 12 hands. Thus, the American Shetland Pony Club and The American Horse Shows Association are not in agreement with reference to height requirements for harness show ponies.

The best harness show ponies are vest-pocket editions of the best fine harness horses. Balanced in conformation, attractive in countenance because of clean-cut head features, a fine throat, a long neck, and smart ears, and

Mascot Swing 4977 and Mascot Sway 4978, a pair of Hackney ponies that have been shown very successfully as a ladies' pair at all of the leading shows. Mrs. R. C. Flanery driving. Copyrighted by McClasky.

standing squarely on their legs as viewed from the front, side, and rear, these ponies make strong appeal when posed for inspection and when in motion.

On the move, the best harness show ponies can work their knees and hocks, set their chins, and go in form with balance and rhythm as features of their stride. They should not wear shoes of excessive weight, they should be able to go at a park gait, stepping on at moderate speed, and they should always be in form. The bridles they wear usually feature Liverpool or elbow bits and side bearing reins.

Worked in a tandem, the wheeler should be a little taller than the leader, and the lead pony should be a happy combination of form, quality, style, and action. In other words, the leader should be flashy, with knee folding and hock flexing as outstanding features of the stride. The traces of the wheeler should be tight. The traces of the leader should sag slightly, furnishing proof that the wheeler's job is to pull the vehicle, giving the leader a chance to perform brilliantly and wholly unimpeded by the weight of the vehicle.

In 1950, the American Shetland Pony Club registered 1,121 ponies. The last decade has brought a great increase in the volume of business, for the registration figures in 1941 totaled only 212 head. Headquarters for the American Shetland Pony Club are located at South Bend, Indiana. Mr. Wayne C. Kirk is the secretary.

THE WELSH PONY   In its native habitat, this breed of ponies is the most numerous of the various pony types. It is a very old breed, having been in existence for many centuries, probably since Saxon times in England, where it became localized in Wales and adjacent counties, whence it derives its name, the Welsh pony.

It has been reported that about the year 1825 a Thoroughbred stallion was turned loose among the bands of Welsh pony mares that ran wild in the more remote areas of the Welsh countryside and that the Thoroughbred influence is traceable in the individuality of the present-day Welsh pony. In their native country, these ponies were 12 to 12–2 hands in height. Their ruggedness and their agility made them useful for riding and driving purposes as well as for light agricultural assignments in the field.

There are but few Welsh ponies in America. Welsh pony stallions have been crossed on Shetland pony mares and the resulting progeny have displayed an improvement in both conformation and action.

The Welsh Pony Society of America maintains registration headquarters at Ann Arbor, Michigan. Mr. Frank H. Smith is the secretary. Only 75 ponies were registered in 1950.

HEAVY HARNESS PONIES   Usually these ponies are of Hackney breeding and in reality are miniature heavy harness horses. Commonly, the shows provide classes for heavy harness ponies whose height varies from 11 to 14 hands. The bridles which they wear usually feature Liverpool or elbow bits with a side bearing rein.

Hackney ponies should be at least serviceably sound, balanced in conformation, refined about their fronts, lean and clean in quality of bone and joint. Of course they must be able to work their legs. Folding of knees and flexing of hocks are very important features in the stride of the best Hackney ponies.

Stiff-kneed or lazy-hocked ponies cannot furnish much competition for ponies that have high all-around action, that can set their chins, go straight in front, work their hocks close together, and go collectedly. Ponies that sprawl and paddle, that spraddle and point and labor in front, that hitch and dwell and hop behind, that leave their hocks behind them—such ponies will have a tough time on show day if the competition is keen.

The top heavy harness ponies are a happy combination of shape, quality, and action. Dressy fronts that result from long, lithe necks, clean-cut head features, and smartly carried ears are requisites of the best ponies. Sharp withers, long sloping shoulders, short backs and couplings, level croups and heavily muscled thighs, width of rib and depth of rib both in front and behind—such features should be well-marked characteristics as a judge searches a pony posed for inspection.

In motion, no matter whether at a park gait or stepping on at moderate speed, height, length, and trueness should be features of the stride contributing to a coordinated and finished performance. The length of the toes and the weight of the shoes should not be so great that action is artificialized. The trot of the Hackney pony should be a God-given trot rather than a man-made one. A Hackney pony that is artificialized in every move he makes is not a show pony.

The American Horse Shows Association recommends the following divisions for Hackney ponies upon a basis of height: first, 12–2 hands and under; second, 12–2 up to and including 13–2 hands; third, 13–2 up to and including 14–2 hands.

POLO PONIES   Polo ponies are miniature race horses or hunters in scale, many of them showing Thoroughbred features. They are used primarily to play polo, although those which are mallet-shy, or for any other reason cannot play the game, make very nice little hacks. Cutting cattle and playing polo make similar demands on ponies; therefore in many instances polo ponies and cutting ponies look much alike in general type.

The American Horse Shows Association recommends two classes for polo ponies: lightweight, up to 175 pounds; middle- and heavyweight class over 175 pounds.

At the shows, polo ponies should enter the ring and be shown as a group at the walk, trot, and canter; then individually, with special emphasis on handiness, way of going, mouth, manners, and balance while cutting a figure eight, first slowly, then at a rapid pace. The judge may ask that the pony gallop forward a given distance, stop straight, reverse in tracks, gallop back, stop straight, and back readily. The judge may ask for further tests, such as riding off, racing another contestant to a given mark and return. The judge should emphasize those features of conformation which contribute to handiness and playing performance. The conditions for polo classes, according to The American Horse Shows Association rules are as follows:

Conformation—25%
Mouth-manners, way of going, hacking—25%
Slow work including handiness—20%
Test work including handiness—30%

Questions

1. The height of a horse is expressed in hands. What is a hand?
2. Give a synonym for the term "scale."
3. Define the term "conformation."

4. Define the term "quality."

5. Define the term "substance."

6. Define the term "condition."

7. What do you understand by the term "temperament"?

8. Briefly discuss manners as a factor in appraising the worth of a horse.

9. What is meant by the term "solid color"? "broken color"?

10. Define the term "piebald."

11. Define the term "skewbald."

12. Define the term "star" as a color marking.

13. Distinguish between a blaze and bald face.

14. Discuss black as a utility color in horses.

15. Define the term "snip."

16. As color markings where do leprous spots occur in horses?

17. Name four general classes for horses on the open market.

18. What are the height and weight requirements for drafters on most markets?

19. Name the chief difference between loggers and drafters.

20. What are the height and weight requirements for chunks on most markets?

21. What is the meaning of the term "feeder" as a market work horse term?

22. Name two subclasses of light harness horses.

23. Name five subclasses of saddle horses.

24. Give a synonym for the term "three-gaited saddler."

25. Give a synonym for the "five-gaited saddler."

26. In terms of weight and stature describe a farm work chunk.

27. What is the chief use for heavy harness horses?

28. Why are pacers barred from roadster classes at the shows?

29. Contrast the manes and tails of a three-gaited and a five-gaited saddle horse for show.

30. What gaits are required of three-gaited saddle horses in competition?

31. What gaits are required of five-gaited saddle horses in competition?

32. What are the gait requirements for a roadster at the shows?

33. Contrast the trot of the three-gaited and the five-gaited saddler.

34. What are the requirements at the walk in the case of three-gaited saddlers?

35. Define the rack and discuss the show ring requirements for this gait.

36. Define the canter and discuss the show ring requirements for this gait.

37. Define the slow gait and discuss the show ring requirements for this gait.

38. What is a cross-legged canter and why is it objectionable?

39. Why is a saddle horse that is under 15–2 hands, rather than over 15–2 hands in height, preferred for a lady's mount?

40. Distinguish between a three-gaited and a five-gaited combination saddle horse.

41. What is a fine harness horse?

42. Name the three general classes for hunters.

43. Distinguish between a hunter and a jumper.

6

Judging Livestock

Livestock judging consists of making a careful analysis of animals, measuring them against a standard commonly accepted as the ideal.

Judging is selection, the means by which the breeder molds forms by mating the approved and culling out the undesirable. It should not be understood as the placing of awards in the show ring only, although that is a most important function of the judge because it imposes upon him the responsibility of establishing ideals and standards which are to lead or mislead the rank and file of breeders.

The successful buyer or breeder must be a competent judge, whether he has ever placed a ribbon in a show ring or not.

Steps in Judging

For purposes of discussion, livestock judging may be said to consist of the following steps:

Information

Information is the basis for all intelligent procedure in the business of judging livestock. For example, without the needed information concerning gaited saddle horses, it is impossible for anyone to reach a sound conclusion in placing such horses in competition.

Hesitation Leon 216511 was the grand champion Percheron stallion at the Chicago International in 1938 and at the Ohio State Fair in 1939. Notice the feet, the pasterns, and the ankles of this horse. Also notice the set of his underpinning, the style and character about his front, and his symmetrical body lines. This horse was shown by The Ohio State University and sold to Mr. Frank B. Foster, Phoenixville, Pennsylvania, for $3,000. Photograph courtesy Strohmeyer & Carpenter.

Observation

In placing all kinds of livestock, it is necessary that one's observation be both accurate and complete. Inaccurate observation is the reason for errors of commission in judging. Incomplete observation is the reason for errors of omission. Thus the final judgment may be in error because it is based upon inaccuracy or incompleteness of observation.

Comparison

This third step in judging gets many students and many adults into trouble. This is the step in judging which calls for judging soundly, balancing situations, and knowing where to place the emphasis. Students are confused when they see such faults as narrow feet and calf knees in the make-up of one horse and crooked hind legs in the make-up of another horse. They wonder what to do. They need some signpost to direct them.

Conclusion

The fourth step in judging is based largely upon the data which a student gathers in taking the first three steps. It is this information, carefully

Beau Gallant 15782, a model saddle stallion when posed for inspection and a horse whose trot on a loose lead rein has made him difficult to defeat in breeding classes. He topped the halter stallion class at the Kentucky State Fair in 1948. Photograph by John R. Horst.

Bombs Away 76253, 2:04½, record made as a two-year-old, a son of Volomite 2:03¼, the stallion that has twenty-three sons and daughters in the 2:00 minute list. Bombs Away is one of the best type studies among the leading Standardbred sires of the present day. He is owned at Castleton Farm, Lexington, Kentucky. Photograph by John R. Horst.

weighed, which tells him where to place the emphasis. After having made a careful examination from the nose to the heels of the horse which has the narrow feet and calf knees, and after having made a similar examination of the horse with the crooked hind legs, the student is in a position to reach a conclusion, thinking in terms of the number of the best of the features he seeks and which should be included in the make-up of an ideal saddle horse.

The horse is the unit of placement and the most of the best of the features sought should constitute the type. If the horse having the most of the best features is not entitled to win in competition, then a student has a right to ask what should constitute the pattern in the class.

What Judging Means

Judging is more than measuring against a standard or the analysis of the individuals under consideration; the element of comparison must figure in the observations from which definite conclusions can be drawn. It is the balancing of the sum total of merit and deficiency of one individual against that of another in much the same fashion that a judge on the bench weighs all the evidence before returning a verdict.

There have been many capable buyers of market horses, who, in carload after carload, will not have a poor one, yet they would not tackle the task of designating the first, second, third, and fourth choice in any one carload lot.

These buyers have a definite standard in mind by which they can accept or reject horses with unerring accuracy. But they fail when it becomes necessary to weigh the importance of a good head and neck and the defective hocks of one horse, against a good back and coupling and the poor feet of another.

Yet selection, both in the breeding and in the buying of horses, most frequently involves the choice of one from among several, just as does the ranking of entries at the shows.

Accuracy and Rapidity

The quickness with which decisions are arrived at is second only to the accuracy of the decisions themselves. The man who stands at the sales ringside and buys at the rate of a horse a minute must make rapid, accurate decisions. So must he who picks his short leet and ultimate winners from a class of forty stallions at a show.

The expert is able to place an entire class of show horses or to pick out a carload in the time required by the novice to score one individual. The former has a fixed standard as well as a trained eye which enables him to discern instantly any deviations from that standard.

Furthermore, he recognizes the law of correlation and goes by indices, largely, without delaying to consider each detail minutely. One feature or part is correlated with another, whereas it may be extremely opposed to a third. Dimensions of the same class are correlated, for instance, while those of opposite classes are related as extreme. A long-legged horse is also long in neck, body, and stride, but is proportionately narrow and shallow-bodied; a horse in which width is marked will be short and deep-bodied with a short, thick, neck, will be low-set on his legs, and will have a short, perhaps trappy, stride.

A systematic method of making observations contributes both to accuracy and to dispatch in judging. By this means each look is made to count, repetitions or omissions are avoided, the proportions and relations of the part are kept in mind, and a more comprehensive conception of the whole is obtained.

System of Examination

The most logical system of examination begins with a view of the horse from in front, rating the temperament and disposition as indicated by the expression of the countenance, all the features of the head, the width and depth of chest, the station, the direction and conformation of the fore legs and the fore feet.

Then passing to the side (the near side usually), the observer should consider the stature and scale, the length or compactness, the station, the depth (especially in the flanks), the carriage and shape of head and neck, the shortness of back and coupling, the levelness of the top line, the length and straightness of the under line, the height and shape of withers, the length and slope of shoulders, the direction and conformation of fore legs and fore feet, the back, the rib, the loin, the flank, the coupling, the croup, the tail, the stifle, the thigh, the direction and conformation of hind legs and hind feet.

From the rear, the symmetry, the levelness, the width and rotundity of hips, the fullness of thighs and quarters, the direction and conformation of hind legs, and the set of the rear feet may be determined. A view from the opposite side to confirm or check the original side view would complete the examination of the horse while he stands.

The horse should then be moved away from the observer in order that the length, directness, and rapidity or promptness of stride may be seen. Then as the horse returns to the observer he should recheck the features of the stride displayed as well as the height, spring, and regularity of stride, all of which contribute to a balanced, coordinated way of going. An expert judge may seem careless of and apparently indifferent to any system; yet this very manner may have been acquired from long practice in a systematic way.

A show ring judge should not act without good and sufficient reasons. He should have the courage of his convictions and be able to give a full account of the whys and wherefores of his work. Often the wisdom of an award appears very different to onlookers at the ringside when the judge's reasons have been explained.

Judges should keep in mind constantly that the sum total of the features sought in the make-up of a horse constitutes the type or pattern. This is another way of saying that the most of the best of the things sought and found in one individual should constitute the pattern in the class.

Value of First Impressions

If the first impression in judging is the result of a careful analysis that is accurate and complete, a student or an adult will seldom reach a sounder conclusion. Many a student in the classroom and many a judge at the shows have changed their minds at the last minute, have re-marked their cards, and have spoiled most acceptable ratings based on first impressions.

Methods of Presenting Livestock before the Judge

A good horse often loses a class because he is poorly shown. In large breeding classes, for example, an entry may be poorly posed for inspection, or when in motion on a lead rein may be in the hands of a leader who is actually a hindrance instead of a help. The judge observes that the horse is trying to tell the leader what to do, both in standing position and on the move. For example, many an inexperienced leader at the shows, when posing his horse for inspection in standing position before the judge, selects ground where the horse's front feet are placed in a hole, with the hind feet on high ground, and with the horse standing six inches higher at his croup than he is at his withers.

A head and neck character study in a Belgian stallion. Photograph courtesy Earl Brown.

A study in Percheron stallion character. Photograph courtesy Cook and Gormley.

A study in Percheron brood mare character. Photograph courtesy Cook and Gormley.

Score Card

In large classes of horses, in both breeding and performance classes, the judge should follow a system which permits him to analyze all entries accurately and completely before attempting a conclusion. The score card consists of a word picture of an ideal horse in which a numerical value is attached to each part for the purpose of indicating its relative importance.

The hock is as essential a part of the horse's anatomy as the forearm; yet the defects to which the hock is subject are so much more numerous and their effect on the serviceability of the horse is of so much more importance that it is deserving of more careful consideration. On this basis the score card allots to the hock six points and to the forearm two points.

Scoring

Scoring is the application of the score card as a standard of merit to the individual for the purpose of determining and expressing numerically his degree of perfection. Applied successively to a number of individuals, it affords a means of determining their relative merits. However, this system is not applicable to show ring judging or to sales ring selection.

The chief use of the score card is in the classroom, where continued practice in scoring affords the best means of training the eye in making accurate observations; at the same time a fixed picture of the ideal is being developed. Once the ideal expressed on the score card is indelibly fixed in the mind, the card may be given up, for the mental picture has taken its place as a standard of judgment.

In the development of good judgment, the score card is indispensable, but for the practice of judging, as noted above, it is of little use. Condensed or summarized score cards have been arranged which facilitate scoring for such purposes as the advanced registry of dairy cattle and other livestock. But for students' use, the full, detailed accounting of every part is essential.

A Score Card Comparison of the Action Requirements in Horses

Horses on the open market are classified according to their jobs. All horses earn their living on the move (if they earn it at all), not standing still. Hence a horse's value depends largely upon what he can do when he is in motion. Draft horses, heavy harness horses, light harness horses, saddle horses —all have moving assignments or action requirements on their respective jobs. These action requirements differ, depending upon the type of horse, because the job differs for each type of horse. Hence the points on the score card differ according to the type of horse:

SCORE CARD QUOTA OF POINTS FOR ACTION

	Draft Horses	Heavy Harness Horses	Light Harness Horses	Saddle Horses
Walk	6	6	6	5
Trot	4	10	10	5
Slow gait	—	—	—	5
Rack	—	—	—	5
Canter	—	—	—	5

SCORE CARD QUOTA OF POINTS FOR FEET AND LEGS

	Draft Horses	Heavy Harness Horses	Light Harness Horses	Saddle Horses
Front feet	6	6	6	5
Front legs	4	4	4	4
Hind feet	4	4	4	4
Hind legs	4	4	4	4

This allocation of points raises several questions indicating that the emphasis of the score card in several instances is questionable. For example, why should only five points be allotted to the front feet of saddlers, when in addition to their own weight, they have to bear the weight of the rider? Six points are allotted to the front feet of draft horses, heavy harness horses, and light harness horses. In neither of these instances does the horse have to carry weight on his back.

A second question that might be asked is with reference to the points allotted to the hind legs. The front legs are known as the supporters, the hind legs as the propellers. The hock joint of the hind leg, the pivot of action in horses, is sometimes called the hardest-worked joint in a horse's body. It is susceptible to more unsoundnesses than any joint in a horses' underpinning. Here is a partial list of hock unsoundnesses: bone spavins, curbs, bog spavins, thoroughpins, jack spavins, Pennsylvania jacks or Michigan pads, stringiness or crampiness, capped hocks. It is upon the hock joint that maximum strain is brought to bear in making a maximum pull or when the legs have to bear the weight as a horse rears from the ground. Why, then, should the score card allot the same number of points to the hind legs that are allotted to the front legs? Perhaps some of our college score cards need revision.

Let us make a brief, comparative study of the general headings which appear on score cards for draft horses, heavy harness horses, light harness horses, and saddle horses, all of these score cards being typical of those that have been used in college classrooms for years. Note the number of points allotted to the various headings.

SCORE CARD QUOTA OF POINTS FOR CONFORMATION

	Draft Horse	Heavy Harness Horse	Light Harness Horse	Saddle Horse
General appearance	16	12	12	12
Head and neck	7	7	7	8
Forehand	24	22	23	22
Body	11	11	11	12
Hindquarters	32	32	31	31
Way of going	10	16	16	15

A score card such as this immediately raises several questions.

1. Is there any real reason why the item General appearance should have 16 points allotted to draft horses, while only 12 points are allotted to heavy harness horses, to light harness horses, and to saddle horses, respectively? Heavy harness horses and saddle horses in a show should be as balanced in conformation and have as much quality as any other type of horse.

2. Why should the item Head and neck be allotted 7 points for drafters and only 7 points for heavy harness horses and for light harness horses? Drafters do most of their work at the walk, a gait in which a short bulky neck would be of least disadvantage.

Heavy harness horses and light harness horses, on the other hand, should have long, thin, mobile necks, with long, sloping shoulders and long elevator muscles in their shoulders, a combination of characteristics which enhances both looks and action. Therefore, should the allotment of points for head and neck be the same for drafters, heavy harness horses, and light harness horses?

3. In the case of the hindquarters as a score card item, why should the allotment of points to the hindquarters of saddle horses be less than to drafters, or heavy harness horses. Quarter Horses, whose job it is to rustle and rope cattle, and hunters, whose job it is to take fences, walls, and ditches in their stride, should feature hindquarters as a requirement second to no other kind of horse. Yet the score card allocates only 31 points to the hindquarters of saddle horses, with 32 points each for the hindquarters of drafters and heavy harness horses.

A head and neck likeness of the celebrated Man o' War 67. An unusual study in both sex and breed character, two most important requirements in breed building stallions. Etching by Palenske.

4. Finally, why does the heading, Way of going, allocate only 15 points to saddle horses, when gaited saddlers have to do five gaits, one of the most difficult action assignments that any type of horse has?

Score Card Revision

A score card for saddle horses recently published under the auspices of the Iowa Horse and Mule Breeders' Association is a constructive approach to this problem because it evaluates unsoundnesses and tells students something about how to deal with unsoundnesses as a problem in judging horses.

Soundness

A horse is sound, provided there is not a partial or total loss of function, preventing or likely to prevent him from performing the ordinary duties of his class.

SCORE CARD—SADDLE HORSES TO HALTER

	1	2	3	4
WEIGHT, 900 TO 1,200 POUNDS				
Height, 14–3 to 16–1 10				
Extremes undesirable				
FORM 25				
Saddle horses should possess beauty, refinement, symmetry, and style				
Body: round, full-ribbed, heavily muscled with well-sprung ribs				
Back and loin: short, wide, and well muscled				
Croup: long, level, and muscular				
Quarters: deep and muscular				
Gaskins: heavily muscled				
Withers: prominent, showing good saddle base				
Shoulders: deep, well laid-in (sloping 45 degrees)				
Chest: fairly wide, deep, and full				
Arm and forearm: strongly muscled				
FEET AND LEGS 20				
Feet: proportionate to size of horse, good shape, wide and deep at heel, dense texture of hoof				
Legs: correct position, front, side, and rear view				
Pasterns: long, sloping, 45 degrees				
Cannons: clean, flat, with tendons well defined				
Knees: broad, tapering gradually into cannon				
Hocks: deep, clean-cut, and well supported				
HEAD AND NECK 15				
Head and neck: alertly carried, showing style, character, and good breeding				
Neck: long, nicely arched, clean-cut, gracefully carried, throat latch clean				
Head: proportionate in size to body, with clean-cut, lean features, straight face-line, and large, prominent eyes				
Ears: medium in size, pointed alertly, and well carried				
QUALITY 10				
Bone: flat with tendons well defined; joints clean and sharply defined				
ACTION (front or rear view) 20				
Walk: straight with a long, springy, free, easy stride				
Trot: prompt, free, straight, true and balanced, with hocks carried closely; high flexion of knees and hocks				
Total 100				
Final Placing				

Reprinted by permission of the Iowa Horse and Mule Breeders' Association.

EVALUATION OF UNSOUNDNESS AND DEFECTS (*opposite*)

Blindness—disqualification	Bog spavin—serious discrimination
Bone spavin—disqualification	Broken wind—disqualification
Capped hock—discrimination	Cocked ankles—serious discrimination
Cracked feet—discrimination	Curb—discrimination
Filled hocks—discrimination	Hip down—discrimination
Lameness—disqualification	Parrot mouth—serious discrimination
Stifled—disqualification	Monkey mouth—serious discrimination
Bowed tendon—serious discrimination	Stringhalt or crampiness—disqualification

The real significance of soundness is quite generally misunderstood by the users of horses, much to their own disadvantage and to the misfortune of many an unsound horse. The importance of an existing unsoundness is directly proportionate to the extent to which it incapacitates a horse for the service to which he is otherwise best adapted. If it causes him little or no inconvenience, and is not likely to, it is of little or no consequence. The technically sound horse is an exceptional individual but he has less actual additional value over the serviceably sound horse than is generally credited to him.

On the other hand, the nature or extent of an unsoundness may be such as to cause the total disability of a horse either at present or in the future. Serviceable soundness is all that it is practical to seek or require; just what constitutes serviceable soundness is arbitrarily determined by the nature of the work which the horse is intended to do. If more thought were given to the real causes of unsoundness, present and prospective, and less to its technical existence, it would probably give less annoyance.

The Equine Machine

The durability of any machine is a matter of construction, and includes the grade or quality of the materials used, the assembling of all parts, the alignment and adjustment of all bearing and wearing parts in order to minimize friction, distribute wear, and facilitate operation in general. Allow any little cog to slip or make a wrong adjustment, and either the whole machine is rendered useless or its operation is greatly impaired.

It is so with the equine mechanism. Most unsoundnesses have their origin in structural defects or imperfections. The spavin and the curb make their appearance on a crooked or badly shaped hind leg as a result of the cuneiform bone and curb ligament being called upon to do more than their normal share of the work of the leg and on account of the deflection in the line in which weight is borne and power applied.

Sidebones are most common on the outer quarters of wide-fronted draft horses because such horses are inclined to be "toe-narrow," which brings the outer quarter nearer to the center of weight bearing, thereby imposing

A show mare that became a brood mare. America Beautiful was one of the most success-ful three-gaited show mares in the history of the show ring.

This photograph shows America Beautiful with her first foal by Nawbeek's Highland King. The cameraman caught this famous mare with her foal in a rather unusual pose.
Photographs by John P. Horst, courtesy Carolanne Farms.

Cadet Commander 2487, one of the very top Hackney ponies in the history of the breed in this country. A model of good looks when posed for inspection, he also has scintillating action when in motion. He has been one of the best ponies before the show-going public in recent years at leading state and national shows. R. C. Flanery driving. Copyrighted by McClasky.

King's Commando 2697, a harness show pony that has set the pace many times in competition with the best harness show ponies of the present day. He is owned by Mrs. Alfred G. Wilson of Rochester, Michigan. Copyrighted by McClasky.

weight and wear which should be borne by the other quarter. As a result, the cartilage ossifies or changes to bone.

If an unsoundness has apparently developed, independent of predisposing causes of conformation, and does not impair the horse's usefulness, it is of less account than when the causative defect in conformation is apparent but, as yet, no actual unsoundness exists. In the first case, a repetition of the unusual condition to which the unsoundness is due is not likely; in the second case, the predisposing cause is continually operative, and the ultimate development of actual unsoundness is well-nigh inevitable. Once developed, its condition is repeatedly aggravated by the same cause which originally induced it.

Rejecting for Unsoundness

It is not consistent to reject a horse, in all other respects suitable for one's purpose, because he cannot be certified absolutely sound, only to accept on the strength of a certificate of soundness a horse woefully deficient in regard to most other requirements. The advice of the veterinarian should be sought regarding the true importance of the unsoundness, if it exists, rather than for the sake of mere detection of unsoundness.

Soundness is but one of the attributes which render a horse of service. Horses unsound in some degree are giving perfectly satisfactory service in all fields in which horses are engaged, and so long as that is the case it is unjust to the horses and detrimental to the owners to discard them for a mere technicality. Provided a horse goes sound in spite of some unsoundness to which he is subject, and promises to continue so to go, the unsoundness should not outweigh in importance the other essentials of a good horse, such as type, conformation, and performance.

Age

The Importance of Age

Age plays an important part in determining a horse's market value. In the heyday of the business, statistics showed the best selling age to be from five to eight years, although experience with city horses has demonstrated that the best wearing and most serviceable age is from eight to twelve. After a horse passed eight and had had some city wear, the market classed him as secondhanded and discounted his value accordingly. This was done more in response to demands of buyers than to any real depreciation in the serviceability of the horse.

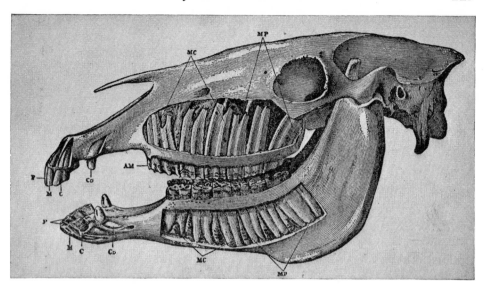

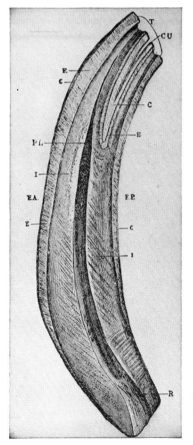

Above: *The whole dentition of the horse.* P, *pincers;* M, *intermediates;* C, *corners;* CA, *canines;* AM, *supplementary premolars;* MC, *deciduous molars or premolars;* MP, *permanent molars. The bars of the mouth in this specimen are the interdental spaces between the canine teeth and the premolars. Note that the lower jaw is hinged and hence is mobile. The upper jaw is fixed or immobile. If the lower jaw extends beyond the lower limits of the upper jaw, a horse is called monkey mouthed. If the lower jaw recedes, a horse is called parrot mouthed.* From Sisson, *The Anatomy of the Domestic Animals,* courtesy W. B. Saunders Company.

Left:*Longitudinal and median section of a permanent inferior pincer (enlarged)*. Fa, *anterior face;* FP, *posterior face;* C, *cement;* E, *enamel;* I, *ivory;* PL, *pulp cavity;* CU, *cup;* T, *table;* R, *root.* From Gabaux and Barrier, *The Exterior of the Horse.*

The average horseman reckons the probable period of usefulness as the difference between the present age and the age to which the average horse lives; but there are too many other influences which may impair a horse's usefulness or terminate his existence altogether to make this a sound line of reasoning.

A horse that has withstood ordinary wear so well that he is comparatively fresh and sound at twelve years of age gives promise of having more years of usefulness ahead of him than the average four- to six-year-old fresh from the country.

Both city stables and the farm furnish numerous instances of horses that have been from sixteen to twenty years on the job and still give little evidence of the infirmities that are supposed to come with advancing years. The mechanical excellence of conformation is a much more important factor in determining the period of usefulness of a horse than his age.

Disposition, temperament, and intelligence have much to do with determining a horse's value and usefulness. Together they determine the kind and character of his performance, within the limits of his possibilities as fixed by type, conformation, and soundness. A good, honest, game horse will oftentimes give more satisfactory service in spite of some physical infirmity than a sound horse that is sour, crabbed, or sulky, and deficient in horse sense. Whether one rides or drives for profit or pleasure, the cheerful responsiveness with which horses do their work is an important factor.

Intelligence, temperament, and disposition are all reflected in the horse's countenance, the expression of the eye, the set and carriage of the ear, and his general behavior.

The Determination of Age

There is nothing mysterious or empirical about the determination of the age by the teeth. Up to five years it is simply a matter of the eruption of the teeth, which in the normal individual follows the same regular course that characterizes all other physiological processes. After the permanent teeth are all in, the indications are the result of wear, which is uniformly accomplished in the normal mouth on account of the extreme durability of the individual teeth and their arrangement.

Certain general features must be understood before any attempt is made to differentiate the appearance of the mouth at various years. After their eruption the permanent teeth may be distinguished from the milk teeth, which are shed as the permanent teeth come through, by greater size, by a broader neck showing no constriction, by perpendicular, parallel grooves and ridges on their face, and by a darker color.

The incisor teeth, which are the ones depended upon because they are the most easily exposed to view, are originally oval-shaped at the table or wearing end, gradually becoming triangular toward the root. The longitudinal dimensions of the teeth are curved, with the convexity forward toward the lips and the concavity toward the mouth. The table itself is cupped out in the center by a depression, into which the enamel of the tooth dips.

As wear commences, the surface enamel is worn off, leaving two distinct enamel rings, one around the margin of the table and the other around the cup.

The cup itself becomes gradually more shallow until it is finally worn almost completely away. As wear on the table removes more and more of the end of the tooth, the level of the pulp cavity in the center of the tooth is finally reached, and the exposed tip of this canal appears between what is left of the cup and the front of the tooth.

Other sequences of the continued wearing away of the tooth are the changes in outward outline of its transverse diameter, becoming, first, more oval from side to side, then more distinctly triangular as wear continues toward the root. Also, as the mouth end of the tooth is worn away, the levels of the tables and their contact are maintained by the tissues which close in behind the root and force the tooth forward. This gives the angle of the incisors less curve and more slant, at the same time rendering the margin and the outline of the jaw sharper and flatter. As the arch becomes more slanting, the surfaces of the teeth meet at a different angle. In the case of the corners, the lower teeth do not wear clear to the back margin of the uppers, so that a hook or notch is gradually formed, worn away, and formed again at different years. These, with the eruption of the canines which occurs in males at five or six years, are the principal changes upon which the age is reckoned.

It remains now to indicate just what changes are characteristic of the different yearly periods. Charts and actual inspection of mouths are helpful visual aids in making such determinations.

Helpful Information in Making Age Determinations

The teeth of the horse function as organs of prehension and mastication. They also serve as weapons of combat. Horses have two sets of teeth. The first set of teeth is referred to by the names "baby," "milk," "temporary," or "deciduous." These are replaced during the period of growth by the second set known as the permanent teeth.

Classification of teeth is based upon their form and position. The front teeth are called incisors. The central incisors or nippers are the first pair of incisors to erupt. The next pair lateral to the central incisors are called the intermediates. The third and outside pair are called the corner incisors. Permanent incisors may be distinguished from the milk incisors as follows:

1. They do not have a well-defined neck joining root and crown as do the milk teeth.

2. They are larger, longer, and more nearly rectangular.

3. They are not so white in color.

4. They are more flat in curvature.

THE INCISORS AS SIGNPOSTS OF AGE

1. The milk teeth are shed at regular intervals and replaced by permanent teeth. The dates at which these changes occur are helpful in age determination.

2. The angle formed by the incisor teeth of the two jaws is called the angle of incidence. This angle decreases as the horse gets older.

3. As a horse ages there is a distinct difference in the length of the teeth, the gums appearing to recede.

4. With age, permanent teeth lose their oval shape, becoming much more cylindrical.

5. The disappearance of the cups indicates age. The cups in the tables of the upper incisors are deeper than in the lower. Therefore the lower cups disappear before the upper.

The canine teeth, also referred to as tushes or tusks, are located in the interdental space between the incisors and molars. In mares the canine teeth rarely erupt, as is shown by an examination of the mouths of eight thousand mares. Of these, only 2 to 3 per cent had canine teeth erupted in both jaws; only 6 to 7 per cent in the upper jaw; and only 20 to 30 per cent in the lower jaw.

Sisson gives four to five years as the date of eruption for the canine teeth.

The molars or the large back teeth are sometimes called the grinders.

TABLE SHOWING NUMBER OF DECIDUOUS TEETH—INCISORS, CANINES, AND PREMOLARS

$$2\left\{ \text{Di}\frac{3}{3}\ \text{Dc}\frac{0}{0}\ \text{DP}\frac{3}{3} \right\} = 24$$

TABLE SHOWING NUMBER OF PERMANENT TEETH—INCISORS, CANINES, MOLARS, AND PREMOLARS

$$2\left\{ \text{I}\frac{3}{3}\ \text{C}\frac{1}{1}\ \text{P}\frac{3\text{--}4}{3}\ \text{M}\frac{3}{3} \right\} = 40\text{--}42$$

Note on above tables: In the mare the canines usually do not erupt, thereby reducing the number of teeth to 36.

The number of teeth in the upper jaw may be increased by the presence of so-called "wolf" teeth. Such teeth are much-reduced vestiges of teeth, situated just in front of the first well-developed premolar. There is one on each side of the upper jaw. Often these teeth are not more than half or three quarters of an inch in length. They may erupt during the first six months and be shed about the same time as the milk teeth behind them. They may remain, however, indefinitely. The occurrence of similar teeth in the lower jaw, which rarely erupt, increases the number of teeth to 44.

TABLE SHOWING ERUPTION OF THE TEETH

Deciduous Incisors:

Middle incisors: Erupt at birth or from first week to 10 days.
Intermediate incisors: Erupt between 4 and 8 weeks.
Corner incisors: Erupt between 6 and 9 months.

Permanent Incisors:

Middle incisors: Erupt at $2\frac{1}{2}$ years.
Intermediate incisors: Erupt at $3\frac{1}{2}$ years.
Corner incisors: Erupt at $4\frac{1}{2}$ years.

Horsemen often say that the milk incisors erupt in pairs at 8 days, at 8 weeks, and at 8 months. This easy rule should help one to remember the dates of eruption for the milk incisors. The permanent incisors will be full grown six months after eruption; hence at five years of age a horse should have a full mouth. In other words, at five years of age all permanent incisor teeth should be down, squared off, and in wear.

A green mouth is any mouth which features all or some deciduous incisors.

A full mouth is one which features all permanent incisors.

A smooth mouth is the term applied when horses are ten years old or older.

In a typical six-year-old mouth, the corner incisors are up and in wear at both the anterior and the posterior borders of the teeth, and the grinding edges are on a level with the intermediate and central incisors. Usually the cups of the lower central incisors show considerable wear or are completely gone.

In a seven-year-old mouth, the upper corner incisors are commonly characterized by a hook on the posterior borders. The cups of the lower intermediate incisors show considerable wear or are completely gone.

For information concerning eight-year-old mouths, nine-year-old mouths, ten-year-old mouths and older, see the cuts in this chapter and the accompanying legends.

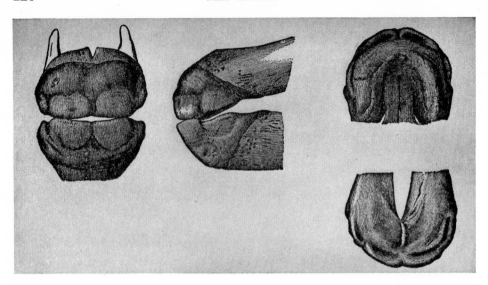

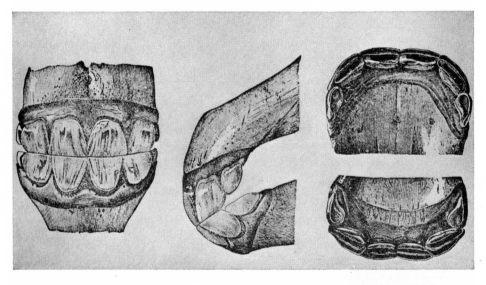

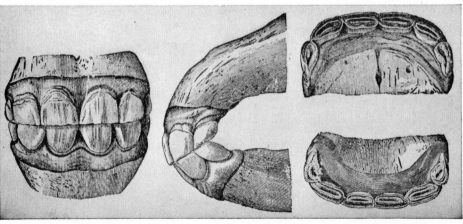

BIRTH: Top Left. *None of the incisor teeth has penetrated the gums. The buccal mucous membrane still covers those which were to appear first. In front, under the gums, the two pincers are perceived above and below. In profile, we distinguish the intermediates, less developed than the pincers. The jaws are very round at their extremity and but little separated from each other. On each side of the median line the dental tables show the prominence formed by the anterior border of the pincers and, external to these, but less developed, the borders of the intermediates. The internal side of these teeth is the more prominent, and it is this side which would have first pierced the mucous membrane.* From Gabaux and Barrier, *The Exterior of the Horse.*

ONE YEAR: Middle Left. *Viewed in front, all the milk incisors are visible; the pincers and the intermediates are well penetrated through the gums. In profile, the superior corners are not yet in contact with the inferior. The tables show that the posterior border of the pincers and the intermediates is worn more. Nevertheless, this character is liable to vary, according to the mouths which are examined, because of the unequal height of this border. However, it will be easy to avoid too great an error by recognizing the degree of wear of the anterior border. Ordinarily, at this period, the latter presents a yellow line, elongated transversely, which is surrounded by the remainder of the dentin; this is the dental star. We must also compare the degree of wear of the pincers and the intermediates. If the latter are the more worn off, it will tend to make the young animal older rather than younger. The corners are still virgin. The incisive arcades are wider transversely and less round in their middle.* From Gabaux and Barrier, *The Exterior of the Horse.*

TWO YEARS: Bottom Left. *Contrary to the preceding illustration, these jaws belonged to a colt of a lymphatic type, since the period of his weaning, having been fed almost entirely on forage. Also, to judge of the age from the state of the dental tables alone would be to make this animal only about twenty months old. The subject, nevertheless, was two years and twenty-six days old. The mouth, however, presents some special characters which tend to modify the inferences that would be formed at first sight. Viewed in front, the pincers and the intermediates are quite free from the gums at their base, the superior pincers especially. This fact indicates that the permanent teeth should have accomplished their eruption in seven or eight months. In profile, the neck of the corners is visible. The tables of the latter show decided wear; the dental star is distinctly visible in these teeth, and the wear slightly involves their external border. The central enamel of the superior intermediates forms a complete circle. Finally, the incisive arcades, much elongated transversely, are greatly depressed in the region of the pincers and the intermediates. If to these signs be added the information obtained from the nature of the ailment, the period of the year, the general development, and so on, one will easily be able to arrive at an accurate determination.* From Gabaux and Barrier, *The Exterior of the Horse.*

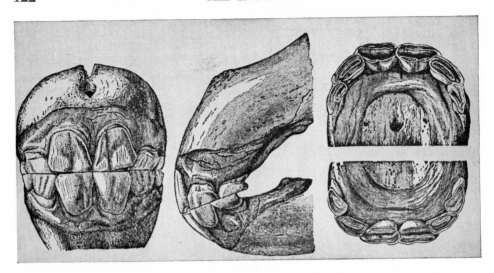

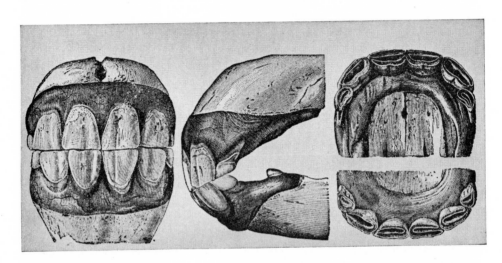

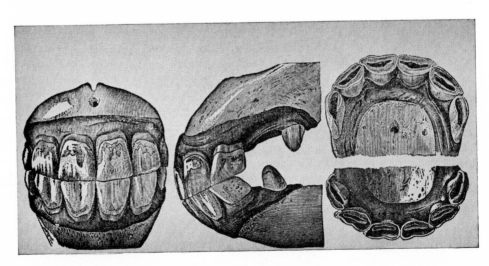

THREE YEARS: Top Left. *Viewed in front, the four permanent pincers are seen to be much wider and larger than the neighboring teeth. The anterior border of the superior pincers is slightly oblique; as a result, its external part is not in contact with the corresponding border of the inferior. In profile, the milk intermediates are much pushed out and very short; the corners are constricted at their base and shortened; their table is worn off squarely. Between the corner and the intermediate, on the left, is found a prominence due to the protrusion, under the gums, of the permanent intermediate, whose eruption was about to take place. The dental tables of the inferior intermediates are very much worn; above they are somewhat less so. The inferior corners are almost destitute of the central enamel. As to the permanent teeth, the wear is not the same in both jaws; the inferior are the more worn, because they come out before the superior.* From Gabaux and Barrier, *The Exterior of the Horse.*

FOUR YEARS: Middle Left. *Viewed in front, all the permanent superior teeth are in contact with the inferior; the jaws, in the part which corresponds to the pincers and the intermediates, have acquired so much width, from one side to the other, that the deciduous corners can scarcely be seen. In profile, the latter appear very small; the superior had commenced to be pushed from their sockets; behind the inferior is seen the extremity of the canine tooth. The tables of the intermediates are much worn, especially those of the superior, which come out first. The central enamel in the pincers forms a distinct oval only in the superior incisors; if this character is absent in the others, the absence is due to the fact that the external dental cavity is more or less fissured in the vicinity of its external border. The inferior corners are almost leveled, and the superior are more so. Moreover, they are stripped around their base and a portion of their root is seen.* From Gabaux and Barrier, *The Exterior of the Horse.*

FIVE YEARS: Bottom Left. *The mouth is entirely made. All the permanent teeth are on the same level in their respective jaws. Viewed in front, the jaws appear very convex in both directions. In profile, they have a similar disposition; the canines are completely out. Upon the tables it is seen that the corners were already commencing to wear at their anterior border. The pincers are almost leveled, but the infundibulum, or cup, is still very much elongated transversely, and narrow from before to behind; it is closer to their posterior border. This form of the infundibulum indicates that the external dental cavity was not very deep in consequence of the abundance of the central cement; these teeth are also soon leveled. Almost the same disposition, as regards the external dental cavity, exists in the inferior intermediates. In order, therefore, not to misinterpret the significance of the leveling, it is necessary to consider the form and dimensions of the central enamel. In this way alone can the degree of wear of the tooth be inferred. The incisive arcades form an almost regular semicircle in each jaw.* From Gabaux and Barrier, *The Exterior of the Horse.*

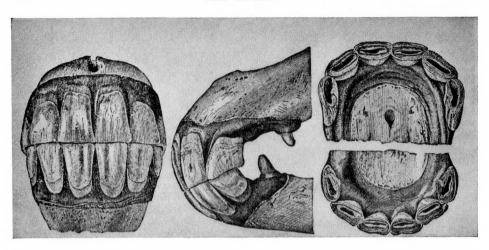

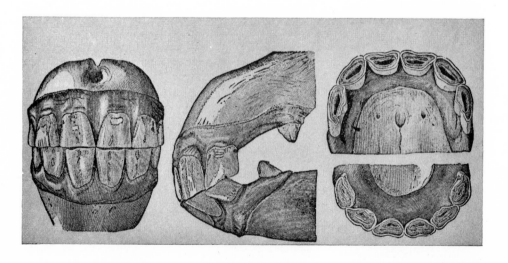

SIX YEARS: Top Left. *Viewed in front, the jaws present almost the same characters as at five years. In profile, we see here a retarded eruption of the canines; these teeth had not yet reached their full length; they are therefore incapable of giving any exact infor·mation as to the age. The tables furnish by far the best indications. The posterior border of the inferior and superior corners is notably worn. The pincers are ordinarily leveled, and the table tends to take an oval form. In the figure, the leveling of the inferior pincers is not altogether complete. Nevertheless, the central enamel is wider from before to behind, and narrower from one side to the other, than at five years; it is also closer to the posterior border of the table. The same remarks apply to the intermediates. It will be noticed that the external dental cavity is fissured upon its posterior face in the two superior corners. This irregularity of form, somewhat common, amounts to little in the determination of the age.* From Gabaux and Barrier, *The Exterior of the Horse.*

SEVEN YEARS: Middle Left. *No marked change is shown by the jaws viewed in front except that the teeth appear whiter because the layer of cement, which at first covered their anterior face, is worn off. In profile, it is found that the table of the inferior corners is narrower from side to side than that of the superior; this results in the formation of a notch upon the latter. The incidence of the incisive arcades is always less perpendicular than at six years. As to the tables, they are leveled upon the pincers and upon the intermediates; the ring of central enamel is wider anteroposteriorly and shorter from side to side. The surface of friction in the corners is larger; sometimes the central enamel forms a complete ring, and sometimes it is incomplete. These differences often result from an irregular form of these teeth. In some subjects, their posterior border is almost absent. It then requires a longer time for the table to be completed behind. The pincers are oval; the intermediates tend to become so. The superior corners are fissured at their posterior border.* From Gabaux and Barrier, *The Exterior of the Horse.*

EIGHT YEARS: Bottom Left. *The direction of the incisors is noticeably changed; the superior and inferior teeth are opposed obliquely. Hence, viewed in front, the jaws project at the level of their line of meeting. In profile, this fact is more apparent, for the anterior face of the incisive arcades has no longer the form of a regular semicircle, as at five years. Their arc appears broken at the place where the tables of the superior and inferior incisors meet, and it acquires more and more the curve of an ogive. The base of the corner is cut squarely by the gum. The incisive arcades are still regular, but narrower than at five years; the surfaces of friction represent, in fact, sections closer to the summit of the cones constituted by the teeth. All the inferior teeth are leveled. The pincers and intermediates are oval; the corners were becoming so. Finally, the dental star appears upon the pincers and intermediates, between the anterior border of the table and the corresponding border of the central enamel.* From Gabaux and Barrier, *The Exterior of the Horse.*

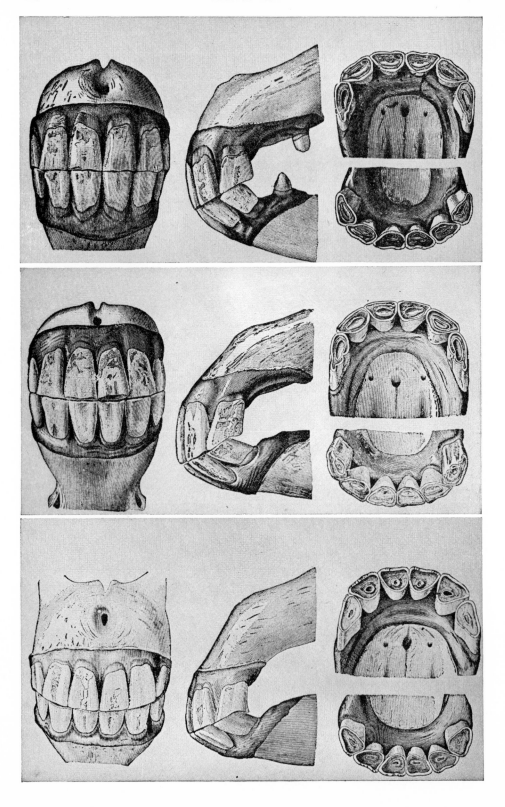

NINE YEARS: Top Left. *No marked change is to be seen upon the jaws viewed in front or in profile. The teeth are ordinarily more oblique and less fresh looking than at eight years of age. The notch on the superior corner has often disappeared. The characters furnished by the tables are more positive. The pincers are round; their central enamel has a triangular form; their dental star is narrower but more distinct, and occupies almost the middle of the dental table. The intermediate teeth are becoming round, and the corner teeth are oval. At this age, the superior pincer teeth are leveled in most jaws. The inferior incisive arcade is narrower transversely and depressed in the center.* From Gabaux and Barrier, *The Exterior of the Horse.*

TEN YEARS: Middle Left. *In consequence of the more marked obliquity of the teeth, the jaws become prominent in front when they are examined from this point, and it is necessary to raise the head of the horse higher in order to have a good view of the inferior incisors. In profile, this character is still more apparent. The ogive formed by the contact of the two arcades is smaller, the inclination of the corners augments, and the interspace which separates them from the intermediates is larger. Upon the tables, the inferior pincers are still more round; their central enamel is smaller, distinctly triangular, and closer to their posterior border. Finally, their dental star, more visible, encroaches upon the middle of their surface of friction. The intermediates are round, and the corners tend to assume this form. In the illustration the latter have an irregular table because they as well as the superior corners are fissured on their posterior border; this border has been checked in its development and hence is but slightly prominent. The inferior incisive arc is more depressed in its middle.* From Gabaux and Barrier, *The Exterior of the Horse.*

FIFTEEN YEARS: Bottom Left. *Viewed in front, the inferior teeth appear shorter than the superior because the jaws are viewed without being elevated. In profile, the incisors are found to be of almost the same length. The notch in the superior corner always exists. The inferior tables all present in their center a rounded and very distinct dental star. The pincers are almost triangular; the intermediates were becoming so. The central enamel, in the superior pincers, is much smaller than at thirteen years. The incisive arcade is greatly depressed in front and narrow transversely.* From Gabaux and Barrier, *The Exterior of the Horse.*

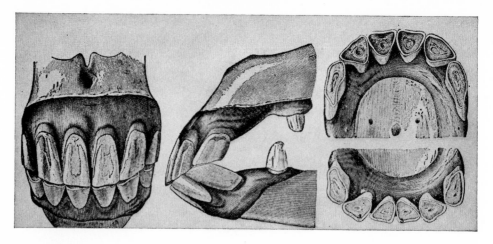

TWENTY-ONE YEARS: The teeth have become so horizontal that, when viewed in front, it is difficult to see their anterior face, unless the head of the horse be raised. The triangular interstices, situated at the base of the superior incisors, augment more and more; this shows the convergence of the intermediates and the corners at their free extremity. In profile, the jaws are thin. The inferior corner, almost horizontal, has caused the disappearance of the notch on the superior corner. This disposition causes the formation, in these two teeth, of a surface of friction which is elongated from before to behind or, rather, from the external to the internal side, instead of remaining triangular. The superior tables, in the pincers and the intermediates, are wide from their anterior to their posterior borders, they are regularly triangular, and the central enamel, in most instances, is absent. The inferior tables tend to become flattened from one side to the other and more and more divergent in front. From Gabaux and Barrier, *The Exterior of the Horse.*

Questions

1. Define the term "livestock judging."

2. List and discuss briefly the four steps in livestock judging.

3. Comment upon accuracy and rapidity as important qualifications of a good livestock judge.

4. Why is it very important that a judge be systematic?

5. Discuss the value of first impressions.

6. What are the chief purposes served by the use of the score card?

7. Make a score card comparison of the action requirements for draft horses, heavy harness horses, light harness horses, and saddle horses.

8. Compare the score card quota of points for feet and legs in the case of draft horses, heavy harness horses, light harness horses, and saddle horses.

9. List a half-dozen unsoundnesses which constitute disqualifications when judging horses.

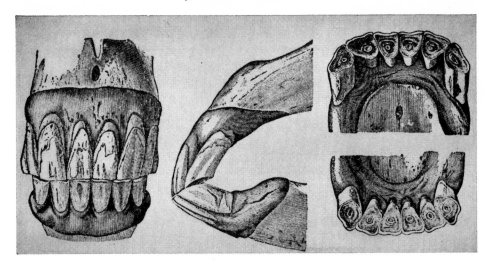

THIRTY YEARS: The characters of this period are those of extreme old age. In front, the superior arcade overlaps the inferior, which is considerably narrowed; the convergence of the corners and the intermediates becomes more and more distinct. In profile, the inferior incisors are very horizontal, especially the corners; the jaws are thin and separated from each other at the level of the bars. The inferior tables are flattened from side to side, or biangular; the peripheral enamel having tended to disappear from their posterior border. The superior tables are flattened in the same sense, and their peripheral enamel has a similar disposition. Sometimes in one of the incisive arcades, and at times in both, the teeth have acquired an excessive length; then the central enamel has not yet disappeared. At other times, on the contrary, they are worn down almost to the gums and surrounded by a thick layer of radical cement, directly applied upon the dentine, which is deprived of its peripheral enamel. Finally, the incisive arcs are very narrow and rectilinear from one side to the other. From Gabaux and Barrier, *The Exterior of the Horse.*

10. Should unsound horses always be disqualified, irrespective of the class in which they are showing?

11. Discuss age as a factor in determining a horse's value.

12. List three or four functions of a horse's teeth.

13. Give three synonyms for the term "deciduous teeth."

14. How many incisor teeth does a horse have?

15. Name the pairs of incisor teeth.

16. How are the permanent incisors distinguished from the baby incisors?

17. In what ways do the incisors serve as signposts of age?

18. Give a synonym for the term "canine teeth."

19. What are "wolf" teeth?

20. Formulate a rule covering eruption dates in the case of baby teeth.

21. Formulate a rule covering eruption dates in the case of permanent teeth.

22. Following eruption, how long does it take permanent incisors to get down and in wear?

23. What is meant by a green mouth? a full mouth? a smooth mouth?

24. Describe a typical three-year-old mouth.

25. Describe a typical seven-year-old mouth.

26. Compare the incisor teeth in a typical five-year-old and a typical ten-year-old mouth.

7

Horse Judging

Important Considerations in Judging Draft Horses

Commercial Classes—Draft Geldings

Draft type
Soundness
Size
Conformation
Quality
Constitution and feeding capacity

Substance (muscle and bone)
Condition
Action
Color
Age

Breeding Classes—Draft Mares or Stallions

Draft type, breed type, sex type
Soundness
Size
Conformation
Quality
Constitution, breeding, and feeding

capacity
Substance (muscle and bone)
Condition
Action
Color
Age

Important Considerations in Judging Saddle Horses

Commercial, Pleasure, or Using Classes

Saddle horse type	Substance (muscle and bone)
Soundness	Condition
Size	Action
Conformation	Color
Quality	Age
Constitution and feeding capacity	

Breeding Classes

Saddle horse type	Constitution, breeding, and feeding capacity
Breed type	
Sex type	Substance (muscle and bone)
Soundness	Condition
Size	Action
Conformation	Color
Quality	Age

Terms for Use in Giving Reasons

Terms of Commendation

Bigger	Thicker
More massive	More substance (muscle and bone)
More rugged	Lower set
More size	Shorter-legged
More scale	Heavier muscled
More drafty	More uniform in body lines
More compact	More even in body lines
Wider	More balanced in conformation
Deeper	

Terms of Criticism

Leggy	Light-muscled
Long-legged	Too fine in the bone
Upstanding	Too light in the bone
Rangy	Too coachy in the bone (draft horses)
Shallow	Rough
Off the ground	Plain

Jay Farceur 2nd 28147, grand champion Belgian stallion, Chicago International, 1948. Balanced in conformation, standing on legs that are correctly placed, with lean ankles, springy pasterns and big shapely feet, this stallion includes in his make-up the features sought in modern-day Belgians. Photograph courtesy J. F. Abernathy.

Muriel Ann Degas 244381, grand champion Percheron mare, the Ohio State Fair, 1947. Note her muscle and her bone. Also study her ankles, her pasterns, her feet, and the set of her legs. This mare was owned at The Ohio State University for a number of years and made a great classroom mare in training students. She was shown to her championship by The Ohio State University. Photograph courtesy J. F. Abernathy.

Front End

Terms of Commendation

More upheaded
More stylish about the front
More dressy about the front
Cleaner cut about head and throat
Finer featured
Longer necked
More slope of shoulder
More definition at the withers
Finer at the withers

Sharper at the withers
Higher at the withers
A more masculine front
A more studdy front
A nicer mare front
A more feminine front
More broody about the front
More refinement about the head and
     neck

Terms of Criticism

Coarse-headed
Plain-headed
Plain-fronted
Heavy-eared
Coarse-eared
Mule-eared
Short-necked
Thick-throated
Throaty
Thick at the throttle
Thick-withered
Flat-withered

Coarse at the withers
Rounding at the withers
Low at the withers
Too straight in the shoulder
Rough-shouldered
Ewe-necked
Too straight on top of the neck
Too straight from poll to withers
Low-headed
Low-fronted
Plain about the front
Pony-headed (draft horses)

The Body

Terms of Commendation

Shorter topped
Wider topped
Stronger back
Wider ribbed
More arch of rib
Stronger ribbed
Stronger loined
Stronger coupled

Closer coupled
Deeper flanked
More muscle on the arms
Longer, wider croup
A nicer turn of croup
More drafty in the thighs
Stronger in the stifles
Thicker in the breeching

Sparkling Waters 14438 is sired by Sparkling Firefly, and out of Dorothy Lloyd by Bourbon King. A very attractive type study in gaited saddle stallions, he is a proven stock horse. He is the sire of the mare Show Boat, undefeated as junior gaited mare and winner of the mare division of the $10,000 stake at the Kentucky State Fair in 1950. Photograph by John R. Horst, courtesy Dodge Stables.

Terms of Criticism

Too long in the back
Low in the back
Weak in the back
Sags in the top
Narrow at the loin
Slack in the coupling
Low in the coupling
Long in the coupling
High-hipped
Plain-hipped
Steep-rumped
Steep in the croup

Too short and steep in the croup
Shallow-middled
Slim-middled
Light-middled
Racy-middled
Short-ribbed
Needs back rib
Too short in the back rib
Light-waisted
Wasp-waisted
Hound-gutted

Underpinning—Feet and Legs

Terms of Commendation

Takes a nicer position on legs and feet
Has legs more squarely placed beneath him
Stands more squarely on the feet
Cleaner in the legs
Cleaner in the underpinning
Has more quality in bone and joints
Has harder bone
Has sharper bone
Has cleaner bone

Has flatter bone
Has longer pasterns
Has more sloping pasterns
Has bigger more shapely feet
Bigger, more nicely proportioned feet
Bigger feet, wider and deeper at the heel
Has tougher feet
Cleaner in the hocks
Leaner and cleaner about the ankles

Terms of Criticism

Stands too close in front
Pinched between front legs
Too close in front legs
Too close at the knees
Knock-kneed
Calf-kneed
Back at the knees
Buck-kneed
Easy on the knees
Over on the knees
Sprung in the knees
Knee-sprung
Stocked in the legs
Coarse in the ankles
Thick in the ankles
Coarse in the pasterns
Short in the pasterns
Too straight in the pasterns
Stubby in the pasterns
Toe-wide
Pigeon-toed
Toe-narrow
Base-narrow
Too light in the gaskins

Too much set to the hocks
Sickle-hocked
Rounding in the hocks
Knuckles on ankles and pasterns
Buckles on ankles and pasterns
Over on the ankles
Too straight on the ankles
Cocked ankles
Up on the ankles
Shallow-footed
Flat-footed
Nigger-heeled
Shallow-heeled
Splay-footed
Short, stubby feet
Small, narrow feet
Boxy feet (small, steep, and narrow)
Pinched at the heels
Narrow at the heels
Soft, shelly feet
Contracted in the feet
Rough at the hoof heads
Coarse at the hoof heads
Hard at the hoof heads

Crooked in the hind legs
Crooked in the hocks
Too straight in the hocks

Secondhanded at the hoof heads
Has sidebones

Action

Features of the Stride to Consider

Length
Directness or trueness
Height
Rapidity (snap, promptness)

Power
Spring
Regularity
Balance

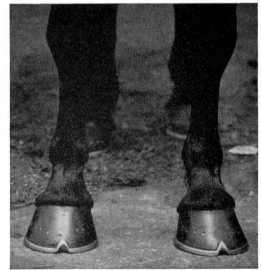

A splendid study in lean ankles, springy pasterns, and big, tough shapely feet. This picture also features Scotch-bottom show shoes, a winning entry in the Blacksmiths' Contest at the Ohio State Fair. Note the drawn toe clips and the even spacing of the nails. Photograph courtesy Cook and Gormley.

Terms Describing Action

Terms of Commendation

Longer stride
Truer stride
More direct stride
A prompter stride
An easier, freer stride
Folds his knees and works his hocks
Lifts his knees and pulls his hocks

Has more knee and hock action
Is more stylish on the move
Has more style at walk and trot
Is more upheaded on the move
Goes closer in the hocks
Works his hocks closer together
Goes more collectedly

Terms of Criticism

A short, choppy stride
A short, stilty stride
Goes short in front
Goes sore in front
Paddles
Wings out
Spraddles in front
Goes open in the knees
Goes too close in front

Walks the rope
Crosses over in front
Goes wide at the hocks
Goes open in the hocks
Goes spraddle-gaited behind
Drags the hocks
Rotates the hocks
Goes stringy behind

Methods of Introducing Action as a Topic for Reason Discussion

In action
On the move
At the walk and trot

he moves
he goes
he gets away
he tramps away
he tramps off
he swings off

Some Directions for Judging Horses

In making a rating on a class of horses shown at the halter, it is a good plan to pose each one for individual analysis and inspection and then move each one at the walk and the trot.

1. Look at the eyes. Be sure to do this. Blindness or impaired eyesight

Three champions in their respective divisions demonstrate the trot. From the top down:

Jay Farceur demonstrates the draft horse trot. Earl Allen at the halter.

The Replica 21758 demonstrates the five-gaited saddle horse trot. Lee Robey riding.

Fiery Crags demonstrates the three-gaited saddle horse trot. Charles Dunn, riding. Photographs by Abernathy, Horst, and Rounds.

disqualifies. If the foretop is draped over an eye, lift the foretop and look at the eye.

2. Note the position of the front legs and the front feet. Open knees, knock knees, pigeon toes, toe-wide position, splints, width or fullness of feet at toes and quarters are observations to make from the front.

3. Look between the front legs at the base of the hocks for jack spavins. Normal hock joints should be smooth at the base on the inside.

4. View the horse from the side position. Note the position of the legs, front and rear. Calf knees, buck knees, hocks that are too straight, and sickle hocks are observations to make from the side.

Thinking in terms of balanced conformation, note the symmetry of body lines. Observe the length of neck, the length and the slope of shoulder, the definition at the withers, the turn of the top from withers to tail, the length of the back and the coupling, the turn of the croup, the fullness of heart and the depth at fore and rear flanks, the bulge of the hind quarters, and the strength of the stifle.

Study the underpinning carefully. Note the amount and quality of bone, especially the strength of bone beneath knees and hocks, the cleanness of the hocks, the leanness and set of the ankles, the length and the slope of the pasterns, the fullness of the hoof heads, the size and the shape of the feet, and the texture of the hoof walls.

5. View the horse from the rear. Note width through the breeching, width and depth of the heels in front and behind, and the crest of the neck to see if it is broken or straight. All horses should have sufficient muscle in their thighs to make them at least as wide through the breeching as they are at the points of their hips. After having looked at the horse from the front, the side, and the rear, complete the trip to the front end, where the inspection began.

6. In examining draft horses three years old or over, palpate the hoof heads for sidebones. In examining two-year-old drafters, palpate the hoof heads that look suspicious. Do not touch the hoof heads of yearlings. Light-leg horses are rarely afflicted with sidebones.

7. Move the horse at the walk. Move him at the trot. Watch for lameness. On the turns watch for signs of crampiness or stringiness. If lameness is questionable, have the horse trot slowly. If stringiness is questionable, back the horse or pivot him on his front feet, turning the rear end in each direction.

8. When the horse comes back to you at the trot, listen to detect wind unsoundness.

9. On the move, at the walk and the trot, note the style displayed and study knee and hock action, length of stride, and trueness and promptness of stride. Note whether the action is collected or sprawling and uncollected. The front feet should break over straight. The hocks should be carried close

Meadow Princess 40823, a fine harness champion that became a three-gaited champion. She is sired by Blue Meadow King, by Captain King, by Bourbon King, and is out of the mare Thrill Girl by Oklahoma Peavine. She won the three-gaited championship at the Kentucky State Fair in 1950, and also the three-gaited championship at the Junior League Show at Lexington 1951. Arthur Simmons driving. Earl Teater riding. Photographs by J. A. McClasky and John R. Horst.

together. Prompt, true action with length of stride is desired at the walk and the trot in all kinds of horses.

Reaching Decisions and Explaining Them

Horse judging consists of making a careful analysis of animals, measuring them against a standard commonly accepted as the ideal. Actual practice in the placing of livestock helps to familiarize students with the types of animals most in demand.

Practice sessions in placing livestock constitute a very important phase of a student's training in animal husbandry. But the reasons for the placings that are made constitute a much more important part of a student's training because the obligation to explain decisions imposes upon the student the task of making a careful study of the relationship between form and function, and its importance in all phases of livestock production.

The following system of note taking is suggested as a method which may help students to prepare their reasons for presentation in classroom and laboratory. It has been used for years by students who have represented the Ohio State University in intercollegiate judging contests at the American Royal Live Stock Show at Kansas City and at the International Live Stock Show at Chicago.

Judging Saddle Mares Shown to Halter

(A sample set of notes for use in giving reasons):

INTRODUCTORY STATEMENT　　I placed this class of saddle mares 1–2–3–4. In case of the first pair 1 and 2.

ADMISSION COLUMN 1–2	CONTENT COLUMN 1–2	CRITICISM COLUMN 1–2
I admit that 2 is a more rugged mare (bone and muscle).	But I placed 1 over 2 because she has a more stylish front—a longer neck—is more nicely balanced in conformation—has cleaner hocks and leaner ankles—stands on longer pasterns—has tougher feet—goes with a longer, truer stride.	I fault 2 because she lacks the style and quality of the top mare—she is a trifle long in her coupling—she has too much set to her hocks as viewed from the side.

Show Boat 36264, an unusual type study in gaited saddle mares, both when posed for inspection and when in motion. In 1950 she won the gaited mare championship at the Junior League Show at Lexington, at the Ohio State Fair, at the Kentucky State Fair, and at Harrisburg, Pennsylvania. She is owned by Mr. and Mrs. Frederick L. Van Lennep, Castleton Farm, Lexington, Kentucky. Earl Teater up. Photograph by John R. Horst, courtesy Dodge Stables.

ADMISSION COLUMN	CONTENT COLUMN	CRITICISM COLUMN
2–3	2–3	2–3
Regarding my second pair 2 and 3, I admit that 3 stands on wider feet.	But I placed 2 over 3 because of more substance— she has sharper withers— a deeper, roomier middle— stands more correctly on her front legs as viewed from the side—has wider stifles and more rugged bone—she works her hocks closer together.	I fault 3 because she is plain in her head and neck—is a little calf-kneed—goes too wide at the hocks.

ADMISSION COLUMN	CONTENT COLUMN	CRITICISM COLUMN
3–4	3–4	3–4
Referring to the last pair 3 and 4, I admit that 4 stands on more bone— she works her hocks closer together.	But I placed 3 over 4 because she is more feminine and stylish about the front —she is more nearly level from withers to tail—she is deeper in her middle—has springier pasterns—goes with a longer stride.	I criticize 4 because of thick withers—she is coarse in her underpinning—she is low in her back and goes wide at the hocks.

CONCLUSION   For these reasons I placed this class of saddle mares 1–2–3–4.

Practice in Reason Giving as an Aid in Student Training

As a result of practice in giving reasons students learn that there are two indispensable requisites of speaking: have something to say, say it as though you mean it. Moreover, practice in giving reasons helps students to think more clearly and to state their thoughts more expertly. It also sets a student up on his feet, gives him speaking poise, teaches him to concentrate, and develops his memory.

Continued practice in giving reasons will conquer the problem of fear in speaking and will teach a student to speak correctly without making grammatical errors, to enunciate plainly, and to choose his words carefully.

The student learns that directness of delivery aids in effective speaking. He uses his eyes as effective agents of expression because he learns in practice that the eye helps to control and discipline an audience and is in no small way responsible for the attitude of his listeners.

Students in practice sessions with each other will have a chance to compare the recitative method of reason giving with the argumentative, conversational method. They learn that the recitative method is objectionable because a speaker who writes out his reasons and memorizes them is likely to forget what he intended to say. Furthermore, the student learns that this method results in a performance that sounds artificial and "singsongy."

The argumentative, conversational method of giving reasons, on the other hand, has two advantages. First, students who use this method give the impression that they are actually thinking about their animals; hence they are less likely to forget what they intended to say. Second, the argumentative method sounds much more convincing.

Measuring the Worth of Reasons

Several criteria may be used in appraising the worth of a set of reasons:

1. The content of a student's reasons. What did he say?

2. Accuracy of statement. In grading reasons heavy penalties always accompany inaccuracy of statement.

3. Completeness as proof that a student analyzed each animal carefully.

4. Terminology. The use of stockmanlike terms always strengthens reasons.

5. Fluency of utterance, a pleasing voice, systematic organization of material and a good speaking presence.

6. Emphasis. Explanations that hinge upon the important differences in animals make the strongest appeal to practical stockmen who spend their lives studying the relationship of form to function as they attempt to maintain or improve the levels of excellence in their herds and flocks.

Questions

1. Itemize the important considerations in judging saddle classes, both commercial and purebred classes.

2. Define these terms: scale, conformation, quality, condition, substance.

3. Give synonyms for these terms: sex character, upstanding, lower set, heavy-eared, finer at the withers, a more studdy front, wider-ribbed, thick withered, slack in the coupling, sickle-hocked, too short in the back rib, calf-kneed.

4. Give ten terms indicative of defective underpinning and opposite each term list a synonym.

5. Define the following features of the stride: length, directness, height, rapidity, power, spring, regularity, balance.

6. List ten expressions indicative of defective action.

7. If you were judging horses in halter classes, discuss in detail the system you would follow when inspecting horses in standing position.

8. If you were judging horses in halter classes, discuss in detail the system you would follow when inspecting horses on the move.

9. Comment upon the importance of reasons.

10. Why and how does practice in reason giving aid in student training?

11. Compare the recitative method with the argumentative, conversational method of giving reasons.

12. What yardsticks of judgment are important in measuring the worth of a set of reasons?

8

Common Horse Unsoundnesses

and Ailments

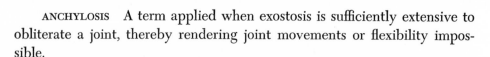

ANCHYLOSIS   A term applied when exostosis is sufficiently extensive to obliterate a joint, thereby rendering joint movements or flexibility impossible.

AZOTURIA OR MONDAY MORNING DISEASE   A term applied when the legs of a horse suddenly become afflicted with a semiparalysis due, it is thought, to a toxic condition caused by overfeeding on idle days. The hind legs become stiff and useless, the croup muscles stiffen and harden, and horses oftentimes knuckle over in front.

BOG SPAVIN   A soft, fluctuating enlargement located at the upper, inner aspect of the hock and due to a distention of the joint capsule.

BOWED TENDON   Any one or all of a group of tendons and ligaments, usually the superflexor tendon, the deep flexor tendon, and the suspensory ligament, may be involved when a horse bows a tendon. The bowed tendon, as a result of severe strain and wear and tear, shows up as a thickened enlargement of the tendons which occupy the posterior space in the cannon regions between knee and ankle joint or between hock and ankle joint. Bowed tendons are more commonly seen on front legs than on rear legs. Bowed tendon is the name horsemen apply to ruptured tendon tissue. Sprains which result in bowed tendons are not at all uncommon in the case of light-leg

146

horses which work at speed. Their occurrence calls for the service of a skilled veterinarian.

CAPPED HOCKS, KNEES, AND ELBOWS   Swellings located, respectively, on the point of the hock, the front of the knee and the tip of the elbow, caused by injuries which result in excess secretion of the synovial fluid. Capped elbows are also referred to as *shoe boils*.

COLIC   Often called *gripes* or *bellyache*. The term "colic" is commonly misused. It is simply a symptom of some difficulty and not a disease in itself. Colic is the outward sign or evidence of some abdominal pain. The pain might be due to indigestion, an impacted caecum, poisons, intestinal worms, a loop in the intestine, and so on. Correct diagnosis requires a veterinarian.

CORNS   Bruised and discolored areas of the sole of the foot, usually located in the angles between the bars of the foot and the hoof wall.

CURB   An enlargement located on the back, side base of the hock joint and oftentimes due to strain or injury which may result in a thickening of ligament, tendon sheath, and skin at this point.

EXOSTOSIS   A bony growth, the result of an inflammation in the bone, which causes a throwing out of bone cells similar to the formation of proud flesh in the soft tissue.

FISTULA   An ulcerous sore or lesion found at the withers. A fistula is usually the result of an abscess, bruise, or injury.

HEAVES   Sometimes called *asthma* or *broken wind,* an ailment of the lungs resulting in a permanent overexpansion of the air cells. When a healthy horse exhales, there is always some air left in the lungs. In cases of heaves, the amount of air left in the lungs at each breath is greatly increased. The lungs contract in an attempt to force this air out, but in their weakened condition are unable to do it. The horse therefore brings his abdominal muscles into play trying to assist the lungs at each expiration. This accounts for the double lift in the flank of "heavey" horses. Healthy horses exhale in one continuous motion. Horses with heaves use two jerky movements because the air cells of the lungs have lost the power to contract sufficiently.

HIP DOWN   The os coxa or hipbone is the largest of the flat bones of the skeleton. The tuber coxa forms the basis of the point of the hip. It is a large quadrangular portion of the hipbone, narrow in its middle, enlarged at either end, where it bears a pair of tuberosities. When these tuberosities are broken loose, because of severe injuries, the point of the hip drops down; hence the horseman's term "hip down." Lameness usually lasts until the inflammation due to the injury subsides; then the horse with a "hip down" may work sound. The blemish, however, as an imperfection in the conformation of the horse's hip remains.

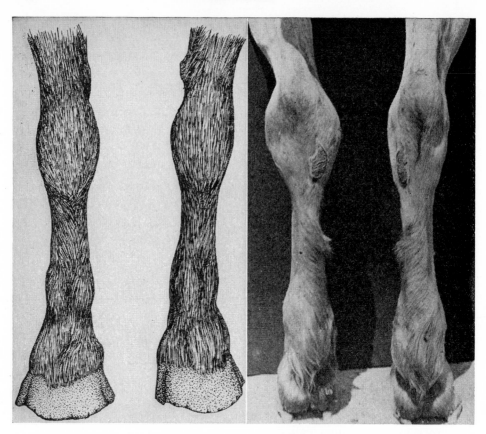

Chipped or split hoofs.

Anchylosis of the hock joint. This horse swung his left hind leg from the stifle because the hock joint was immobile.

Left: A normal pedal bone. Right: A pedal bone with ossified lateral cartilage.

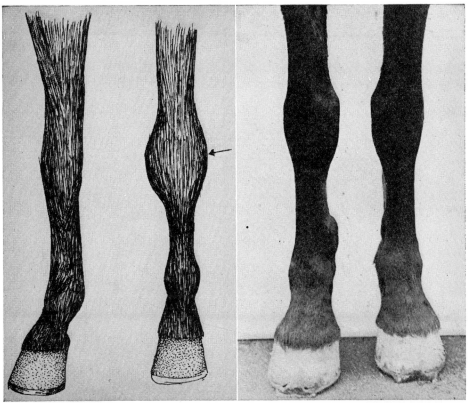

Above Left: *Knee spavin.* Above Right: *Splints, low down.*
Photograph courtesy the Veterinary Clinic, The Ohio State
University.

Above: *Sidebone unexposed. Sidebone exposed.* This
drawing and that shown on the right were adapted from
Holmes, *Principles and Practices of Horse Shoeing.*

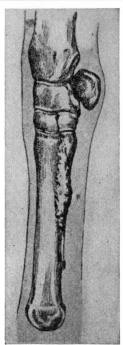

Right: *Splint, high up.*

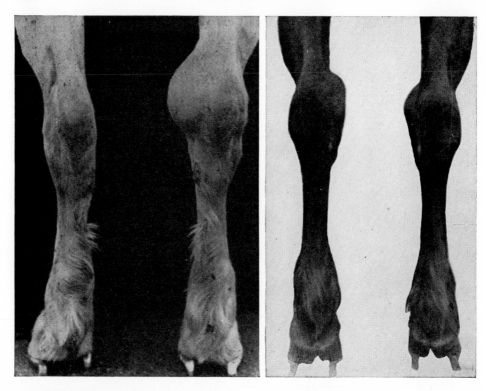

Thoroughpin and bog spavin combined.   *Thoroughpins.*

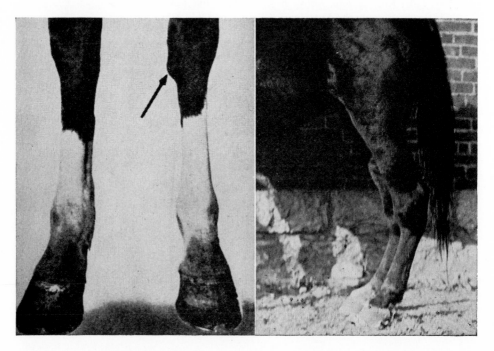

A large jack spavin.   *Sickle hocks with curbs.*

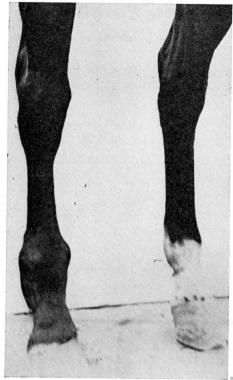

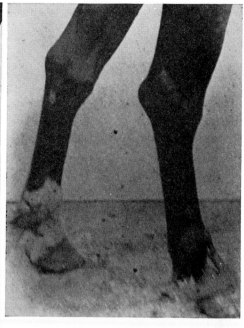

A capped hock.

Road puffs or wind puffs.

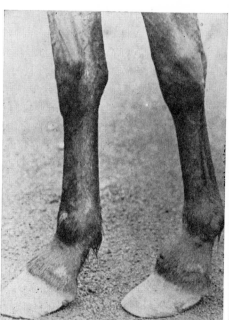

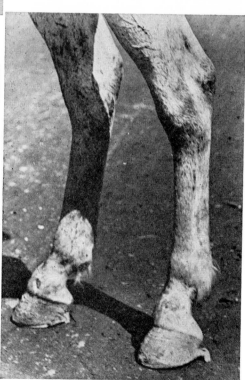

Long, low, weak pasterns, shallow heels with ringbone formation on front pasterns.   *Crooked hind legs, ringbone formation on rear pasterns.*

A typical pose in a case of laminitis or founder.

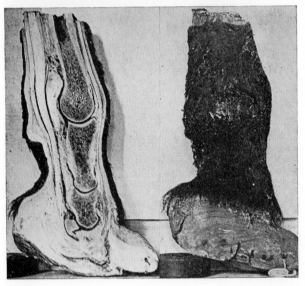

A sagittal section of the lower limb, showing the effects of acute founder, or laminitis.

A typical pose in a case of navicular disease.

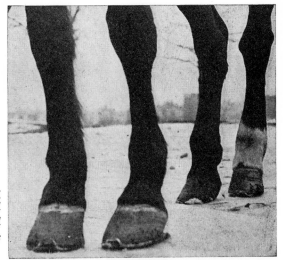

Pigeon toes, a cocked ankle, a bog spavin, a thoroughpin, a stocked hind leg, a thick rear ankle and coarse pasterns are all visible in this picture.

Crampy or stringhalt.

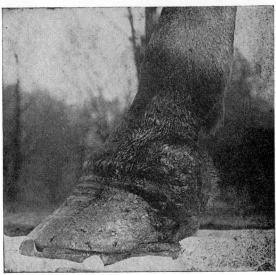

A quittor.

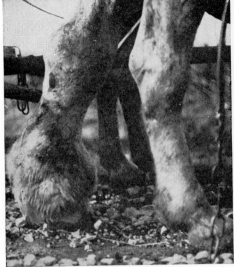

Milk leg or elephantiasis.

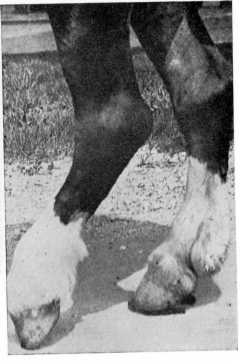

Contracted tendons.

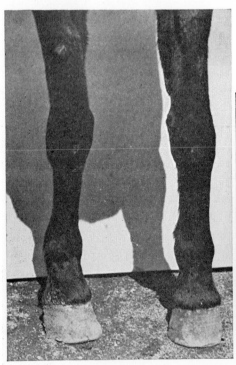

Pigeon-toed and forward on the knees.

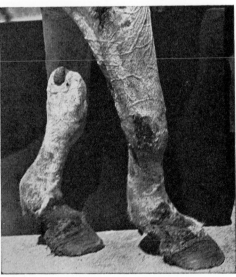

Buck knees and dermatitis.

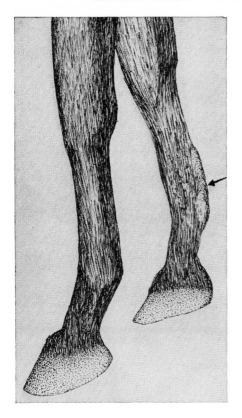
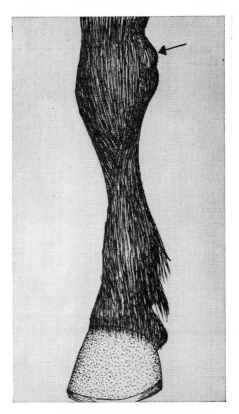

A *bowed tendon.*   A *knee joint enlargement.*
                          A *distended tendon sheath.*

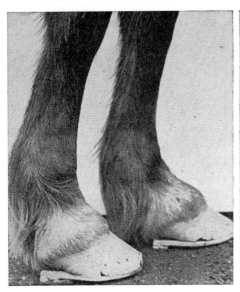
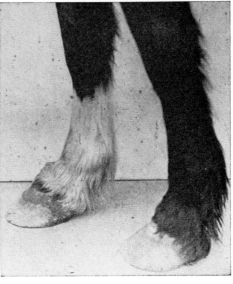

*Long, low, weak pasterns and very shal-
low heels. Coon-footed.*   *Long, weak pasterns, thin or flat front feet,
with ringbone on pastern of off fore foot.*

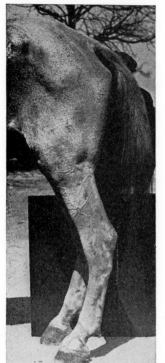

Above, *Location and the extent of a lateral cartilage. When a lateral cartilage ossifies, a sidebone is the result.* From Dollar, *Horse Shoeing.*

Left, *Sickle hocks which reveal a curb at the base of the hock on the left leg. Sickle hocks predispose to curbiness.*

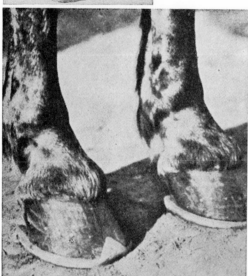

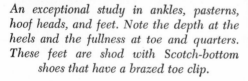

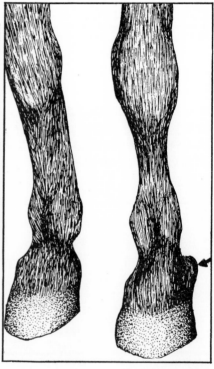

An exceptional study in ankles, pasterns, hoof heads, and feet. Note the depth at the heels and the fullness at toe and quarters. These feet are shod with Scotch-bottom shoes that have a brazed toe clip.

A large sidebone on the left fore foot.

JACK SPAVIN   A bony enlargement located at the inner, lower aspect of the hock joint.

LAMINITIS   Commonly called *founder,* an inflammation of the laminae of a horse's feet.

LYMPHANGITIS   A severe inflammation of the lymphatic vessels of the leg, resulting in a pronounced swelling, from which the term *big leg* is derived. Usually occurs in one or the other of the hind legs.

NAIL PUNCTURES AND WIRE CUTS   Nails and barbed wire are common sources of injury to horses. When a horse's foot is punctured by a nail there is always the danger of tetanus or lockjaw. A shot of antitoxin by a veterinarian to prevent lockjaw is always good management in the case of nail punctures.

There are several reasons why wire cuts should be given prompt attention. Tetanus or lockjaw infection may result from a wire cut. Wire cuts, when neglected, may fail to heal because of an invasion of proud flesh and, when healed, will ultimately leave a bigger scar than if the wound had been cared for promptly.

Clean stable practice and the application of some standard antiseptic solution may be helpful in treating minor scratches and cuts. The assistance of a skilled veterinarian is called for in treating deep, ugly wounds.

NAVICULAR DISEASE   A chronic inflammation which may affect the navicular bone, the navicular sac or bursa, and the flexor tendon of the foot.

PERIODIC OPHTHALMIA OR MOON BLINDNESS   An inflammation of the interior of the eye. The tendency of this difficulty to disappear and then reappear, until it impairs or destroys sight, accounts for use of the word "periodic." Eyes squint in the light, tears flow freely, the eye becomes discolored, regains normal appearance for a time, then becomes discolored once more. The treatment used has had little or no success.

POLL EVIL   A fistula of the poll of the head, commonly due to bruises or injuries. Cases of fistulous withers and poll evil call for the services of a veterinarian.

QUITTOR   A festering of the foot anywhere along the border of the coronet or the top of the hoof wall. A quittor may result from a calk wound, a neglected corn which festers and works up through the foot, a gravel which works from the bottom of the foot to the top of the coronet, and so on. Such cases call for treatment by a veterinarian and should not be neglected.

RINGBONE   An exostosis or bony enlargement on the pastern bones. May occur on both front and rear pasterns.

ROARING   A noise in breathing made upon inspiration and due to the paralysis of one of the cartilages of the larynx.

SCRATCHES OR GREASE HEEL   A low-grade infection or form of eczema, affecting the hair follicles and skin at the posterior base of the fetlock joint, the posterior region of the pasterns, and the base of the heels. The hairy-legged breeds are more susceptible to scratches than are the short-haired breeds.

An infection in the blood stream may cause scratches, but more common causes are filthy stables and muddy paddocks, which may result in chapped skin and breaks in the skin which lead to low-grade infection.

Oftentimes scratches are seen in horses that are undernourished and are victims of poor stable management. Good feeding, clean stable management, and application of standard antiseptic solutions to arrest infection will clean up most cases of scratches.

SIDEBONE   An ossified lateral cartilage. Sidebones may occur on front or rear feet but are more commonly found in front. Sidebones occur with much greater frequency in draft horses than in any of the light-leg types.

SPLINT   A bony enlargement which appears, usually, on the inner aspect of the cannon bone; commonly on the front legs, sometimes on the rear legs.

STRINGHALT   Stringiness or crampiness is an ill-defined disease of the nervous system. It is indicated by a sudden lifting or jerking upward of one or both of the hind legs. This defect of action in the hind legs is most obvious when a horse takes the first few steps after standing, when he is asked to back, or when he is asked to make a pivot turn in either direction.

SWEENY   The term applied usually to the atrophy of the shoulder muscles which overlie the scapula of the horse. Sweeny may be due to injury or strain. The superscapular nerve may be affected. Sometimes sweeny occurs in the croup muscles of mares at foaling time.

THOROUGHPIN   A soft, fluctuating enlargement located in the hollows of the hock and due to a distention of a synovial bursa.

THRUSH   An inflammation of the fleshy frog of the foot, accompanied by a characteristic, blackish, purulent, foul-smelling discharge.

WINDGALLS OR ROAD PUFFS   Soft enlargements located at the ankle joints and due to the distention of synovial sacs.

Questions

Review this chapter and be able to define all the unsoundnesses listed.

A note to students: A working knowledge of horse unsoundnesses is very important because soundness is the single most important factor in appraising the worth of a horse. A judge who does not know normal structure and is, therefore, an incompetent diagnostician of unsoundness will find himself constantly in hot water on any horse judging assignment.

9

Miscellaneous Problems
in Judging Horses

In this chapter are gathered together and expanded some of the earlier discussions of the most common problems which arise in connection with the judging of horses or, indeed, in connection with any phase of horse production.

Lameness

As noted before, horses earn their living on the move, not standing still. The worth of any horse is enhanced because of his ability to do the job that he is supposed to be able to do. This statement is true of work horses, heavy harness horses, light harness horses, saddle horses, or ponies. Inability to do the job depreciates value. Lameness is one of the most common reasons why a horse's value may be suddenly impaired. A work horse that is lame is greatly handicapped, although he may be asked to work only at the walk.

Any show horse or show pony that is lame on show day is doomed if in competition with good sound horses because lameness is not one of the requirements sought in a good show horse. To the contrary, it is a disqualification. Not only is it proof of the pain to which a horse is subjected at each stride; it introduces into the stride the feature of irregularity, which destroys rhythmical precision of stride and makes impossible a balanced, coordinated performance.

Before spending their money, all prospective buyers of horses for work, for pleasure, or for show should make it a point to inspect these animals on the move as well as in standing position. If horses move out lame, the best plan is leave them in the hands of their owner—at least until they move sound. Buyers who ride the country in quest of horses are not looking for lame horses. They are in search of sound horses which they hope will not go lame after they are purchased.

The common method of handling the lame-horse problem at the shows is therefore to excuse lame horses from the ring.

Blindness or Impaired Eyesight

Good vision is a primary requirement in horses and ponies of all types. Blindness or impaired vision handicaps horses in all areas of horse production. A blind horse is a special management problem, whether the horse is in stable, paddock, or pasture. Of course there have been instances where blind brood mares have been the dams of good, sound foals and where blind stallions have proved to be satisfactory sires. But blind stallions and blind mares are not commonly sought as seed stock because they are a special problem for anyone who owns them.

In the breeding classes at the shows, blind stallions and blind mares are commonly disqualified. Show managements do not provide classes for blind horses. Therefore, disqualification of horses because of blindness is the common practice and is considered sound judgment.

Glass Eyes

"Glass eye" is the term applied to a horse's eye, the iris of which is devoid of pigment. Such an eye is just as functional as the dark, hazel-colored eye, which is the kind of eye that is sought in all horses and ponies.

Glass eye, watch eye, walleye, and Clydesdale eye are synonymous. The term "Clydesdale eye" is used because glass-eyed horses appear with so much frequency in that breed.

Glass eyes are objectionable, chiefly on the basis of looks. Since they are just as functional as dark, hazel-colored eyes, there have been many instances at leading shows where glass-eyed horses, both mares and stallions, not only topped their class but have been made grand champions of their divisions.

WHY IS THE SPLAY-FOOTED POSITION OBJECTIONABLE IN HORSES?

All horses at the walk and trot should be able to rock their front feet upward from the heel, break them over squarely at the toe, carry them forward in a straight line and set them down again. It is impossible for a splay-footed horse to carry his front feet straight forward. Study the adjacent diagram and learn why the splay-footed or nigger-heeled position in horses is objectionable. The following statements supply the answer.

1. The splay-footed position on the front feet predisposes to faulty action and results in a defect in gait known as dishing or winging in.

2. Winging in is a defect in gait that predisposes to interference. Toe wide horses quite commonly hit their ankles, their shins or their knees.

3. Interference predisposes to blemish or unsoundness.

4. Blemishes and unsoundnesses depreciate the value of a horse, thereby affecting the economics of the horse business. Hence the reason why there should be sharp discrimination against splay-footed horses.

←Diagram showing course taken by a front foot in case of toe-wide or splay-footed horses.

Nigger Heels

"Nigger-heeled" or "splay-footed" is the term applied when a horse stands on his front feet with his toes turned outward. With such a defect a horse cannot rock his front foot upward from the heel, break it over at the toe, and carry it straight forward. Splay-footed horses on the move will swing the striding foot inward toward the supporting leg and be guilty of a defect in gait known as winging in or dishing.

In such cases interference is almost inevitable. Even a work horse, doing most of his work at the walk, if he stands nigger-heeled on his front feet, will wing in sufficiently to brush or strike the fetlock of a supporting leg with the striding foot.

If the splay-footed horse be a trotter at speed or any other type of horse whose gaits call for speed, he may strike not only his ankles, but his shins, his knees, and his elbows. A bold, high-going, splay-footed trotter might have to wear quarter boots, ankle boots, shin boots, knee boots, and elbow boots. That is, he might have to be rigged with all of the boots that are made for the front legs of a light harness horse.

The most intelligent horsemen discriminate sharply against splay-footed horses. In such cases, faulty position on the legs predisposes to a defect in gait known as dishing, which in turn predisposes to interference. Interference results in blemish or unsoundness; in turn, blemishes and unsoundnesses depreciate value. Experienced buyers of horses for use in areas where the competition is keen will therefore not spend their money for horses whose splay-footed position in front is almost a sure guarantee that they will pound a supporting front leg with a striding front foot.

Pigeon Toes

Horses that stand pigeon-toed in front are predisposed to swing their front feet outward when on the move. This defect in gait is known as paddling. Exaggerated paddling is sometimes referred to as "winging out."

There is definite correlation between the pigeon-toed position on the front feet and the defect in gait known as paddling, just as there is a correlation between the splay-footed position in front and the defect in gait known as dishing.

The horse that paddles, however, cannot pound a striding front leg against a supporting front leg, as does a splay-footed horse that wings in. The objection to the pigeon-toed horse that wings out arises from the fact that his spraddling, winging tendency in front results in uncollected action.

A straight line is the shortest distance between two points. Therefore, the best-going horses are those which can fold their knees and carry their front feet straight forward without any tendency to wing in or out.

Calf Knees

If a horse's knees as viewed from the side break backward, the horse is said to be calf-kneed. "Breaks back at the knees," "stands back at the knees," "calf-kneed" are synonymous. Calf knees in all horses are objectionable, because a calf-kneed horse stands and goes up hill all the time. Also, in horses whose calf-kneed position constitutes a glaring defect, there is a predisposition to whip the front feet to the ground at the completion of the stride, thereby increasing concussion to a maximum.

Buck Knees

"Over on the knees" and "easy on the knees" are synonymous expressions for "buck-kneed." Buck-kneed horses are less stable on their front legs than are horses whose knees as viewed from the side are perfectly straight and squarely placed beneath the body for purposes of support. If buck knees are accompanied by long toes, the predisposition in such horses is to stumble, particularly if the going is a little soft.

Knock Knees and Bow Knees

Knock-kneed horses are sometimes referred to as horses that stand "in at the knees" or are "too close at the knees." "Bow-kneed" and "bow-legged" are synonymous terms. Knock-kneed horses, especially if worked at speed, are predisposed to interfere. Bow-kneed horses quite often stand over on the outside of their front feet. This faulty position brings undue weight upon the outside portions of the front feet, especially upon the outside lateral cartilages of the feet, with a predisposition to the early formation of sidebones.

A primary function of the front legs of a horse is to support weight. If the front legs are straight as viewed from the front and from the side, the chances for an early breakdown of these legs in service are reduced to a minimum. The way in which a horse sets on his legs determines in large part the kind of service of which he is capable, as well the length of that service.

Sickle-hocks

"Sickle-hocked" and "too much set to the hocks" are expressions that are applicable when a horse's hind legs as viewed from the side are altogether too crooked. The hind legs of a horse are referred to as the propellers because the efforts of propulsion which are necessary to move the body forward are centered primarily in the hindquarters. Of course the hind legs of a horse also function as pillars of support for the body.

Balanced conformation is a goal sought in the make-up of all types of horses. Sickle hocks do not contribute to balanced conformation; on the other hand, they help to destroy symmetrical form. There is a well-marked correlation between steep croups and sickle hocks as features in horse make-up. Steep croups destroy trueness of top line from withers to tail and thereby destroy the symmetry of form which is always a well-marked feature of the best horses. Since there is a correlation between sickle hocks and steep croups, sickle hocks help to destroy balanced conformation.

But there is a second and much more important reason why sickle hocks are objectionable features in horses. When the hocks of any horse or pony, as viewed from the side, have too much set to them, the hind feet are displaced too far forward beneath the body, and the hock joint has to bear a disproportionate share of the body weight.

Spavins and curbs, especially curbs, may be the result of sickle hocks because the cuneiform bone of the hock and the curb ligament are called upon to bear more than their normal share of the work assigned to the hind legs of a horse. On account of the deflection of the line of the leg upon which weight is borne and power applied, a curb may result. Hence sickle hocks are objectionable features in all kinds of horses and ponies because they predispose to curbiness.

Bandy Legs

When a horse stands pigeon-toed on his hind feet, with the points of his hocks turned outward, he is said to stand bandy-legged behind. There are several objections to this faulty position on the hind legs.

First, such horses are predisposed to go wide at the hocks, thereby making the most collected performance impossible. Horses and ponies of all types should work their hocks fairly close together instead of wide apart, because the goal of performance in the case of all horses is collected, coordinated action. Fairly close hock action with the hind legs working beneath the body makes collected action possible, whereas spraddle-gaited hock action makes it impossible.

A second objection to the bandy-legged horse is that it is impossible for a horse so stationed on his hind legs to rock his hind feet upward, break them over at the toe, and carry the hind legs forward with the hocks working fairly close together. On the contrary, the bandy-legged horse rocks his heel upward, and as the foot breaks over at the toe, he gives a lateral twist to his hock, a defect in gait known among horsemen as "rotating hocks." Some horsemen in describing the hock action of a bandy-legged horse refer to such horses as limber-hocked horses.

Since the action of a horse depends upon the way in which he is made, any bandy-legged horse is predisposed to rotate his hocks. This limber-hocked tendency is objectionable because rotating hocks cannot withstand maximum strain; hence early unsoundness of the hock joint is to be expected. Even a bandy-legged work horse, working at the walk, will rotate his hocks when he lifts with his hind legs and exerts the effort necessary to move a load.

Flat Feet vs. Contracted Feet

In the best days of the horse business the feet of draft horses on city streets commonly went wrong in one way, while the feet of light-leg horses in their various areas of service quite commonly went wrong in a distinctly different way. Flatness has always been the prevailing ailment of the draft horse's foot in service, whereas contraction and navicular disease have been prevailing foot ailments of light-leg horses.

Mr. James Johnstone, who for years wrote a draft horse column for the *Breeders' Gazette*, describes the ideal foot for the drafter as follows: "The ideal foot for a drafter should be big in proportion to body bulk, wide and deep at the heel, full and rounding at toe and quarters with enough arch of sole and strength of hoof wall to oppose flatness."

A horse's weight is borne chiefly upon the hoof walls of his feet. When the hoof wall draws inward and sinks downward, and when the sole of the foot drops, then to the latter, which is not primarily a weight-bearing surface, is assigned the task of supporting body weight. This, of course, results in sole bruises and lameness. By experience horsemen have learned that the flat-footed work horse needs shoes all of the time and that his feet are the most difficult to shoe and shoe properly.

Because the feet of light-leg horses are much smaller and much more narrow at the heels than are the feet of draft horses and because many light-leg horses are used at speeds at which the feet are subjected to maximum concussion, the prevailing ailments of light-leg feet are contraction and navicular disease.

Navicular disease is an inflammation of the sesamoid sheath, induced by repeated bruising or laceration and complicated in many cases by inflammation, ulceration, and partial disintegration or chipping of the navicular bone itself. Of course, this navicular condition results in lameness and if it is accompanied by contraction of the heels, the navicular difficulty becomes even more aggravated.

The old saying that "an ounce of prevention is worth a pound of cure" is most applicable in the case of navicular trouble because such cases rarely recover, although they may show temporary improvement.

When the feet become dry and hard, the tissues contract. Therefore, any management procedure that helps to retain the moisture in the foot tissues will aid in preventing contraction. Packing the feet with puddled clay helps to retain the moisture in the tissues of the feet. In the case of a saddle horse whose feet have been packed with clay to retain the moisture, a foot pick is used to remove the clay when the horse is worked. The feet are then repacked when the horse goes back to his stall.

Leather pads or rubber pads beneath the wings of the shoe oftentimes help to prevent contraction. Usually, some oakum with tar or with Corona wool fat is smeared on the bottom surface of the foot before the pad and the shoe are nailed into position.

Flat feet and contracted feet in horses are a source of great annoyance to both horses and owners. Horses with flat or contracted feet should therefore be sharply discriminated against by prospective purchasers and by judges whose assignment it is to make a rating on them at the shows.

Sidebones as a Problem in Judging Horses

Sidebones, common features of the hoof heads of draft horses, occur very infrequently on the hoof heads of light-leg horses. A sidebone is an ossified lateral cartilage. That is to say, when the cartilaginous tissue of a normal lateral cartilage becomes completely invaded with osseous tissue, we have what is commonly known as a sidebone.

The lateral cartilages, two in number on each foot, are located on the dorsal aspect of the wings of the pedal bone. In extent each cartilage embraces about two thirds of the lateral circumference of a horse's foot. They are semilunar, or bean-shaped, and their convex surface extends upward slightly above the coronet of a horse's foot.

Lateral cartilages constitute a part of the expansive mechanism of a horse's foot and help to absorb concussion and jar. Moreover, oscillating, expansive movements of the cartilages aid the circulation of the blood through the foot.

There are several causes of sidebones:

1. Dropping the shafts or the pole of a vehicle upon the hoof heads.

2. Treading upon the hoof heads, either by other horses or by the horse himself.

3. Concussions. Sidebones are common accompaniments of straight shoulders, short pasterns, and narrow, upright feet—a combination of characteristics which increases concussion to a maximum.

4. Improper shoeing. The feet may not be allowed to spread and expand at the heels normally because a shoe that is too small or one in which the nail holes are punched too far back holds the heels too rigidly in position.

Are Sidebones Inherited?

Literally, sidebones are not inherited. That is to say, no one ever put his hand on the hoof head of a newborn foal and found a sidebone. It has never been the practice of judges to palpate the hoof heads of draft foals and draft yearlings for sidebones. Judges rarely touch the hoof heads of two-year-old drafters unless the hoof heads look questionable. However, it is common practice to handle the hoof heads of all drafters three years old and up to determine the presence of sidebones.

Someone asks, If sidebones as such are not inherited, what is inherited? Why should we exercise caution, thinking of sidebones as an unsoundness and as a problem in judging? Why should we guard against them if sidebones, as such, are not inherited?

Certain inheritable features in horse make-up may lead to the early formation of sidebones. Short, straight shoulders, short, stilty pasterns, and narrow heels are a trio of characteristics which, operating together, mean hard concussions and maximum abuse of the supporting structures of the foot and which lead to the early formation of sidebones. Hence it is the predisposition to sidebones which is inherited rather than the unsoundness itself.

Sidebones as a problem in judging do not constitute a disqualification in the same sense that blindness disqualifies a horse for service. Many a work horse with sidebones, because of other features he possesses that are most essential in the make-up of good horses, is a better work horse than some which are absolutely sound at the hoof heads but are wholly lacking in other essentials.

Soundness is, of course, one of the most important yardsticks in measuring the worth of a horse. Therefore, it is best, as a usual thing, to keep the horses with sidebones out of the blue ribbon and grand champion positions at the shows because unsoundness is not a feature that is sought in the make-up of the commonly accepted ideal draft gelding, mare, or stallion at the show.

At the same time, it would be unwise to let one or more sidebones constitute a reason for eliminating horses from show competition altogether because such a practice would result in sending to the barn better work horses than were kept in the ring and permitted to win prizes. In summary, let it be said that sidebones, as a problem in judging, have to be considered in terms of the specific circumstances under which they are found. In other words, such cases call for common-sense judgment and the rating on a horse with sidebones will depend upon the competition lined up against him on show day.

The Underpinning as a Factor in Judging Horses

Too much stress cannot be placed upon the importance of underpinning as a determining factor in appraising the worth of a horse. Like the chassis of an automobile, the supporting structures are subject to constant wear and tear.

The many unsoundnesses which may affect a horse's underpinning and impair his value justify the statement that much of the grief in the horse business occurs from the elbows and the stifles down, that the minimum worries occur above the elbows and the stifles.

Scottish breeders, in developing the Clydesdale, have believed so thoroughly in the importance of good underpinning that their slogan, which accentuates the need of good underpinning beneath a real draft horse, has been passed on from generation to generation:

> Feet, ankles, pasterns, feather,
> Tops may come, but bottoms never.

Scottish horsemen learned a long time ago that the body of a horse may be improved a great deal by feeding and that the underpinning of a horse is largely a matter of breeding.

In coaching livestock judging teams over a period of twenty-eight years, I used to say to the students when horses were paraded in front of them: "Boys, remember, always, to do three things as you inspect a class of horses. First, study the set of the underpinning, front, side and rear. Second, study the quality of the underpinning. Third, determine the soundness of the underpinning. If you can do these three jobs intelligently, you will be well on your way toward a sound placing on any class of horses."

Chico Chief, one of the greatest parade horses to appear before the show-going public in recent years. Study the set of his legs. He stands back on all of his ankles; and he has ample length of pastern and feet that are shapely in their proportions. Owned by Mr. John Costello of Bentwood, Missouri. Photograph courtesy Mr. Costello.

Questions

1. What is the general rule at the shows for handling the problem of lameness?
2. What is the general rule, when judging horses, for handling the problem of blindness or impaired eyesight?
3. How would you handle the problem of glass eyes in judging horses?
4. Why should nigger-heeled horses receive sharp discrimination at the shows?
5. Why is the pigeon-toed position on the front feet objectionable?
6. Why discriminate against calf-kneed horses?
7. Why penalize buck-kneed horses?
8. What are the objections to knock-kneed and bow-kneed horses?
9. Itemize the objections to sickle hocks as features in horse make-up.
10. What are the objections to horses that stand bandy-legged on their rear legs as viewed from the rear?
11. Discuss flat feet versus contracted feet as features of horse make-up, making plain why there should be discrimination against both.
12. Define sidebone.
13. Are sidebones inherited? Cite specific data in support of your answer.
14. What are the functions of lateral cartilages?
15. Name three or four causes of sidebones.
16. How would you handle the sidebone problem in judging horses?

10

The Draft Breeds*

During the years that work horses fitted into a sound program of agricultural economy in this country, Percherons, Belgians, Shires, Clydesdales, and Suffolks were the five draft breeds that furnished the vast majority of stallions whose services on grade draft mares supplied the bulk of the work horses that were used on city streets and on the farms of our leading agricultural states.

On most commercial horse markets at the peak of the work horse business, work horses were classed as drafters if they stood 16 hands and up and if they weighed 1,600 pounds or more.

The Best Breed

In arriving at a fair conclusion of what constitutes the best breed, it is necessary to specify the conditions to be met and the characters required, for the same breed may not be best for each specific case.

Too much importance should not be attached to the partisan favor in which different breeds are held. The average buyer of market horses in the old days had very little consideration for the particular breeds which might be represented in his purchases, yet striking uniformity of work horse character or type was plainly evident in the lot of horses he selected.

* This comment on the draft breeds has been included in this text chiefly for its historical importance.

What the commercial buyer sought was a work horse in type and character rather than a representative of a particular breed, except insofar as one breed might be furnishing more of the right kind than did another breed.

Horses with middle, muscle, and bone, work horses that stood correctly on their legs and feet, horses that were prompt, clever, and handy on their job—such horses, irrespective of breed, were sought by discriminating buyers who represented discriminating users of horses in the various work horse areas.

Percherons and Belgians, a Comparison

With reference to size the Percheron is fully up to the requirements set by the drafter standard.

In size and weight the Percheron ranks third among the leading draft breeds. The Shire and the Belgian are more drafty in their proportions and are heavier. The Clydesdales are less drafty and as a breed are smaller.

In conformation, Percherons as a breed have more length of neck and more range of body than the Belgians. Percherons as a breed are not so square-ended, compact, low-set, and deep-ribbed; nor are they so uniformly drafty as the Belgians. However, the most typical Percherons cannot be said to lack draftiness because they are too leggy, too light-waisted, and too light-quartered. As a breed, the Percheron shows cleaner-cut features in head and neck, has more finish, and is more stylish than many of the Belgians.

The Percheron and the Belgian are known as the clean-legged draft breeds, while the Shire and the Clyde are known as the feather-legged or hairy-legged breeds. The most popular colors for Percheron stallions and mares are gray or black. Chestnuts, bays, and roans appear, but these colors are undesirable.

The most popular Belgian colors are sorrel, chestnut, and roan. Bay and black are discriminated against, black more than bay.

Factors Explaining Percheron Popularity

1. Endurance.
2. Docility.
3. Prompt and energetic in temperament.
4. Feeding and doing ability.
5. Demonstrated ability of Percheron stallions to sire good work horses from the common run of mares. When the work horse business was at its peak, many of the best geldings that appeared on the open market were sired by Percheron stallions.

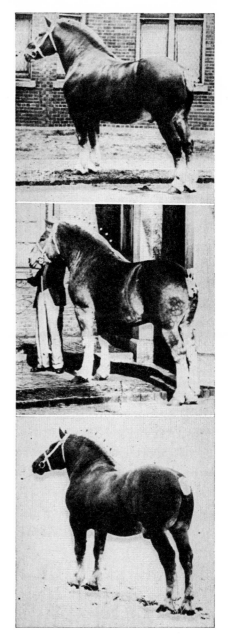

Left: *Three generations of breed-building Percheron sires.* From the top down: *Laet 133886, grand champion Chicago International, 1921. Hesitation 162152, grand champion, Chicago International, 1923. Hesitation Leon 216511, grand champion, Chicago International, 1939.* Photographs courtesy J. F. Abernathy.

Right: *Three generations of breed-building Belgian sires.* From the top down: *Jay Farceur 17628, grand champion Belgian stallion, Chicago International, 1938, 1939, 1940.* Photograph courtesy Cook and Gormley. *Kenfleurs Jay Farceur 25199, grand champion, Chicago International, 1941.* Photograph courtesy J. F. Abernathy. *Modern Trend 28238, grand champion, Chicago International, 1950.* Photograph by Durand Studio.

Criticisms of Percherons

1. In too many instances a lack of draftiness due to light bone, long couplings, and shallow middles.
2. Small, narrow feet.
3. Short, stubby pasterns.
4. Crooked hocks.
5. Low couplings, high hips, steep croups.

Factors Explaining Belgian Popularity

1. Tractable and easy to handle.
2. Good feeders, good doers, good shippers.
3. Breeding record of Belgian stallions, who, bred to all kinds of mares, sire foals that are uniformly drafty. When mature, very few Belgians classify as "cherry pickers," a market term for horses that are leggy, rangy, and slim-bodied.

Criticisms of Belgians

1. As a breed, some of the Belgians are a little sluggish and phlegmatic in temperament as compared to Percherons.
2. As a breed, they lack the quality of the Percheron and the Clyde.
3. Short necks, small feet, short pasterns, high hips, and steep croups are still too common as features of the breed.

The above criticisms to the contrary, the Belgians have made more improvement in the last thirty years than any of the draft breeds. Belgian geldings as work horses in the hands of all kinds of hired help, competent and incompetent, can come as near taking care of themselves as can any draft gelding.

A Trio of Breed-Building Percheron Sires

Although the motor trucks and the tractors have driven most work horses from the city streets and replaced them on the majority of farms, a brief comment will be made here concerning a few of the leading sires of the Percheron breed, a breed whose representatives once led all other draft breeds in the number of registrations and were in the lead also as a breed, whose grades and crossbreds sold in the greatest number at work horse auctions in the leading horse-producing states of this country.

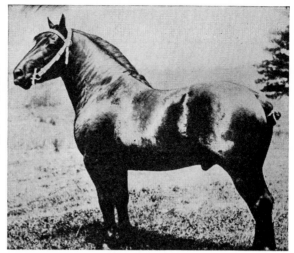

Dragon 52155, a stallion whose get did much to establish the identity of Selma Farms, owned by Colonel E. B. White of Leesburg, Virginia. Daughters of Dragon have nicked especially well with Laet 133886. Photograph by Hildebrand.

As a matter of historical interest, students of the present generation should know something about these three famous Percheron sires whose contributions were of so much importance during the many years before the tractor replaced the horse in the leading agricultural states of America. For obvious reasons, in a text of this kind, the historical sketches of these three famous stallions must be brief.

Dragon 52155 (63516)

The grand champion Percheron stallion at the Chicago International in 1907, Dragon was exhibited at the International by McLaughlin Brothers of Columbus, Ohio. He made his reputation as a stock horse, however, in the hands of Colonel E. B. White, owner of Selma Farms, Leesburg, Virginia.

Colonel White began to breed Percherons in 1903. He wanted the best seed stock available, either in France or in the United States, and this determination to have the best led him to import from France, as his prospective stock horse at Selma Farms, the famous Etudiant 70802 (59291).

At the time of importation in 1909, Etudiant was considered one of the very best Percheron stallions in France and had established a reputation as a sire. He stood about 17–1 in height, had an attractive masculine front, was balanced in conformation, and was of great substance, with an abundance of muscle and bone. Although a trifle straight on his rear pasterns, he was a horse that could make it tough for all competitors on show day.

At Nogent in 1909, at the show held under the auspices of the Percheron Society of France, Etudiant had whipped the celebrated Carnot 66666 (66666). This victory caused a great deal of talk among French breeders and among American importers.

Following the importation of Etudiant to America, plans were being made to show him at the Chicago International in 1909 when the horse contracted a case of influenza which settled in his testicles and made it impossible to show him. This sickness practically ruined Etudiant as a stock horse for several years, since he sired only seven purebred foals while in use at Selma Farms.

Dragon, grand champion at the Chicago International in 1907, was purchased by Colonel White to succeed Etudiant. The purchase of Dragon proved to be good judgment, for the get of this famous stallion did much to establish the reputation of Selma Farms as one of the leading Percheron nurseries in the history of the business in America.

Dragon was bred to breed on. He was sired by the famous Cronstadt 34112 (44910), the same horse that sired Etudiant. The dam of Dragon was the brood mare Resida (49456), a mare that is also the dam of Etradegant, a horse that became a grand champion at the Chicago International. Resida, therefore, is one of the few mares in history that has produced two grand champion sons at Chicago.

Dragon proved to be a good sire of both stallions and mares, although his daughters, mated with Laet, are the chief source of his greatness as a sire.

Dragon is the sire of Dreballegon 148719, a stallion that won the futurity at the Ohio State Fair in 1919, then returned to Columbus in 1920 to win the two-year-old class, as well as the junior and grand champion honors of the show. In performing this feat, he defeated the famous Laet 133886, a horse with which Colonel White had won the Ohio State Fair championship in 1919.

Dreballegon was out of the celebrated mare La Belle 34982, one of the greatest mares the breed ever produced as a competitor in model classes.

Dreballegon, winner of the stallion futurity at Columbus in 1919, is the sire of Louise 182177, the filly futurity winner at Columbus in 1924.

But, as mentioned above, the daughters of Dragon, rather than his sons, have made an immeasurable contribution to the progress of the Percheron breed in America. Let us call the roll of some of them:

Belle Dragon 131823 was the dam of Dralaet 166983, stallion futurity winner at Ohio in 1922.

Syncopation 113966 is the dam of Hesitation 162152, Ohio futurity winner in 1921 and Synet 185539, filly futurity winner at Ohio in 1925. Syncopation was a combination show mare and brood mare. Twice she was grand champion mare at the Ohio State Fair and twice her son Hesitation whipped all the Percheron stallions at the Chicago show, the first time as a three-year-old in 1923 and the second time as a five-year-old in 1925.

Perfection 123001, a third daughter of Dragon, was foaled in March,

Syncopation 113966, an un-usual type study among the mares of the Percheron breed. Note her thickness and low-setness. She is full in her heart, deep in her rear flank, and thick through the stifles. Lean in her ankles, with ample length of pastern and big, shapely feet, she stands on legs that are a study in correct-ness. She has been grand champion at both the Ohio State Fair and the Chicago In-ternational. Photograph cour-tesy Live Stock Photo Co.

1915. She died in 1932. She was bred to no other stallion than Laet 133886 and was the dam of the first colt recorded by Laet. She had fourteen foals, six of them figuring in championships at leading shows. She cost $800 when pur-chased by Mr. W. H. Butler, owner of Woodside Farms, Columbus, Ohio. He sold $8,000 worth of her colts. She was the dam of three futurity winners at Columbus: Perfect 162151 (1921); Perlaet 172446 (1923); and Premier Laet 200521 (1930).

Rozelle 123963, a fourth daughter of Dragon, was mated with Laet and produced a number of outstanding progeny. For three years in succession, 1927–1929, Rozelle was the dam of the stallion futurity winners at Columbus. Sir Laet 190277 was the futurity winner in 1927, Rolaet 194085 in 1928, and Prince Laet 197313 in 1929. Rozelle was not the dam of any filly futurity winners at Columbus.

In terms of grand championships, Jerome 160754 was the greatest prize-winning son of Rozelle. He was the first of her sons to win a grand champion-ship at Chicago in the year 1924.

Sir Laet is one of two Percheron stallions ever to win three grand championships at the Ohio State Fair. He did it three years in succession, as a yearling, as a two-year-old, and as a three-year-old in 1927, 1928, and 1929.

In 1937, Sir Laet's foals won the champion get-of-sire class at the National Percheron Breeders' Show in Columbus, furnishing testimony that Rozelle was another daughter of Dragon whose sons proved to be stock horses.

Sir Laet was foaled in 1926 at Highland Farms of Greensburg, Pennsylvania. He was sold to Michigan State College, East Lansing, Michigan, whence he was shown to some of his greatest triumphs. He is one of the very few Percheron stallions to win two grand championships at the Chicago International, the first one as a two-year-old in 1928 and the second one as a three-year-old in 1929.

The foregoing data concerning Dragon is proof that he was a combination show horse and sire. The mating of his daughters with the renowned Laet resulted in some of the best Percherons that have ever been produced in this country. After reading of their show ring prowess, and of their accomplishments in the stud, one can see why Laet, when used on daughters of Dragon, was known as "The Golden Cross" in Percheron breeding.

Carnot 66666 (66666)

A discussion of the noted stallions Dragon, Carnot, and Laet is impossible without including some mention of the men who owned them. Otherwise it is almost impossible to answer questions like these: Did Colonel E. B. White, owner of Selma Farms, Leesburg, Virginia make the celebrated Dragon, or did Dragon make Colonel White and Selma Farms? Did Mr. W. S. Corsa of Gregory Farm at Whitehall, Illinois, make Carnot, or did this famous stallion establish the reputation of Gregory Farm as a great Percheron nursery? Did Mr. W. H. Butler of Woodside Farms at Columbus, Ohio, make the breed-building sire Laet or did Laet establish the identity of Mr. Butler and Woodside Farms?

People may differ in their answers to the above questions but it is well to remember that each of these establishments had several other stallions which stood for service at their farms, but whose names have long since been forgotten and whose influence upon the breed was negligible. The names of Dragon, Carnot, and Laet, however, and what they did as Percheron breed-building sires will have a place in any Percheron history if the author of such a book knows Percherons, and if he presents his data without prejudice.

In operating Gregory Farm at Whitehall, Illinois, Mr. Corsa had for years used a number of grade draft mares for farm work. He had also used many grade draft mares on a farm he operated in Nebraska.

In the fall of 1902, Mr. Corsa purchased the stallion Radziwill 27328 (44228) to use on the mares at Gregory Farm. Radziwill had been imported by Dunham-Fletcher and Coleman at Wayne, Illinois. This firm had shown Radziwill at the Chicago International in 1901, where the horse had attracted much attention among the farmer visitors at the International that year.

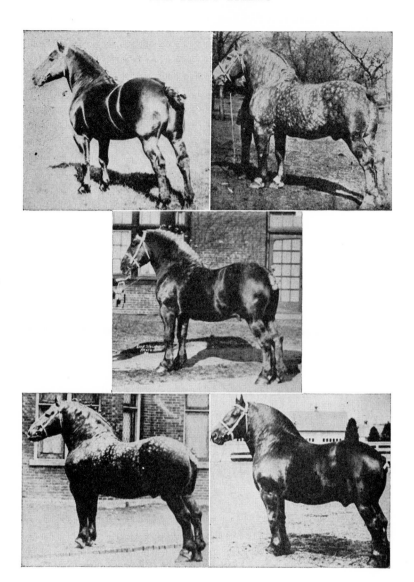

Five generations of breed-building Percheron sires. Top Left, *Carnot 66666 (66666), grand champion Percheron stallion, Chicago International, 1909.* Photograph by Hildebrand. Top Right, *Jehovah 79300 (85489), grand champion Percheron stallion, Ohio State Fair, 1918, and grand champion Percheron stallion, Indiana State Fair 1919.* Photograph by Hildebrand. Center, *Don Degas 186172, grand champion Percheron stallion, Chicago International, 1926 and 1927.* Bottom Left, *Dow Again 206636, grand champion Percheron stallion, Illinois and Indiana State Fair, 1936.* Photograph courtesy J. F. Abernathy. Bottom Right, *Lynnwood Don 231169, grand champion Percheron stallion, American Royal Live Stock Show, Kansas City, Missouri, 1941, and grand champion National Percheron Show, Minneapolis, Minnesota, 1941.* Photograph courtesy Live Stock Photo Co.
A quintet of champions whose show ring and stock horse prowess has few parallels in the whole realm of horse production.

The get which resulted from the use of Radziwill on the grade mares at Gregory Farm impressed Mr. Corsa very favorably, and having noticed a rapidly increasing demand for Percherons, he determined to purchase a few purebred mares.

The foals from these purebred mares sired by Radziwill were so satisfactory that Mr. Corsa decided to purchase the best stallion obtainable to succeed Radziwill in the stud and for use on the purebred fillies sired by him.

Carnot, a winner of the first prize at Paris in 1909 and with an almost unbroken string of victories to his credit in the United States, had been made the grand champion Percheron stallion at Chicago in 1909.

Mr. Corsa decided that Carnot was the horse he needed at Gregory Farm and he paid J. Crouch and Son of Lafayette, Indiana, $10,000 for this black champion, an unheard-of price for a draft horse in this country at that time.

Following his purchase Carnot was taken to Gregory Farm to work out his destiny as a sire. Actual breeding operations at Gregory Farm during the first decade of the present century had been pretty carefully planned, but no showing or advertising of any consequence was done until after the purchase of Carnot in 1909.

The mares that had been purchased and those that had been bred at Gregory Farm had given Mr. Corsa a good lot of seed stock, worthy of the high-priced sire selected. Subsequent breeding operations, combined with unusually skillful advertising in the show ring and in the agricultural press, soon placed Gregory Farm among the leading Percheron establishments in this country.

The Get of Carnot in the Show Ring and in the Stud

Foals sired by Carnot, both stallions and mares, soon became the pacemakers in their class at leading state fairs and national shows all over America. There was a great deal of talk about the progeny resulting from the Carnot cross on Radziwill mares, for the colts from this cross were especially promising.

SOME STALLIONS BY CARNOT Jehovah 79330 (85489) was an imported son of Carnot that for years headed the stud of Mr. George A. Dix, Delaware, Ohio. He was one of Carnot's most famous sons, both as a show horse and as a stock horse. He was out of the mare Manie 90265 (54817), a daughter of Radziwill.

During his career Jehovah was the winner of thirteen championships and first-prize awards at leading shows in France and the United States. His get have made a fine contribution to the Percheron industry in Ohio. His most famous son was Don Degas 186172, grand champion Percheron stallion at Chicago in 1926 and 1927. Don Degas was the sire of four futurity winners at the Ohio State Fair: Don's Linda Ann 202210 in 1930; Sir Don 205481 and Dona Perfection 204560 in 1931 (both futurity winners were sired by Don Degas in 1931); and Patricia Don 211153 in 1934. Hence the Jehovah branch of the Carnot family bred on.

Carvictor 136718, another noted son of Carnot, was first-prize stallion as a three-year-old and as a four-year-old at the Chicago International in 1919 and 1920. Carvictor was sold to a company of Delaware County, Ohio, horsemen in 1922 for $9,000. He proved to be a good sire.

Carbonn 172453, another son of Carnot, was grand champion at the Royal Winter Fair at Toronto and at the Eastern States Exposition, Springfield, Massachusetts, in 1923. He was also reserve grand champion at the Chicago International in 1923. During the years between 1923 and 1925, Carbonn was the highest winning son of Carnot, with eighteen first prizes and championships at the leading Percheron shows in America.

Wolfington 147858, a son of Carnot, was American-bred champion stallion at the Chicago International in 1919 and 1920.

Carnival 182478, a son of Carnot, was grand champion Percheron stallion at the Indiana State Fair in 1925 and reserve grand champion Percheron stallion at the Illinois State Fair in 1925.

SOME DAUGHTERS OF CARNOT   Carnell 172699, one of the best show mares and brood mares ever owned at The Ohio State University, was a daughter of Carnot, out of Radbie, a daughter of Radziwill. Carnell was sold March 18, 1929, to Mr. K. K. Culver, Columbus, Ohio, for $1,000.

Carnona V 158258, a daughter of Carnot, was twice grand champion mare at the Chicago International, the first time as a three-year-old in 1922 and the second time as a four-year-old in 1923. Carnona V won the first Ideal Type Study class ever held at the Chicago International. Not only a great type study when standing posed for inspection, she was also most impressive when in motion. There have been very few Percherons, mares or stallions, that could move more satisfactorily at the walk and the trot than this good, black daughter of Carnot. She had the motion that typified the best of the progeny sired by Carnot. They were noted as a family that could move.

Carfait 174912, a gray daughter of Carnot, was shown very successfully by the Tom Corwin Farm, Coalton, Ohio. She was grand champion Percheron mare at the Illinois and the Ohio State fairs in 1925. She repeated her championship at the Ohio State Fair 1926. She was a daughter of Carnot that always furnished competition for all the mares in her class.

Carveuse 180860, Carthel 183132, and Carene 177599 were other out-

Carnona V 158258, grand champion as a three- and a four-year-old, Chicago International, 1922 and 1923. Note her balanced conformation and the way she stands on her ankles, pasterns, and feet. Photograph Courtesy Live Stock Photo Co.

Couceorous 94852 (deceased), one of the greatest brood mares in the history of the Percheron breed. She is the dam of Laet 133886, Treviso 144394, and Giroust II, each of them sired by a different stallion and all of them grand champion stallions at the Ohio State Fair. This brood mare's record is without parallel. Photograph by Hildebrand.

Carthela 205924, first prize two-year-old and grand champion Percheron mare, at the Illinois, Ohio, and Indiana state fairs and at the Chicago International, 1933. She repeated these championships in 1934 and was sold for $3,000 to Lamb Brothers of Hillsdale, Michigan. This mare was bred and exhibited by Mr. William B. Murray of Wellington, Ohio. Photograph courtesy Cook and Gormley.

standing daughters of Carnot. Carveuse was first in class and reserve senior champion mare at Ohio in 1925. Carthel was grand champion mare at the Indiana State Fair in 1925. Carthel is the dam of Carthela 205924, filly futurity winner at Columbus in 1932, also grand champion Percheron mare at Chicago in 1933 and 1934.

After Carnot had established his reputation at Gregory Farm as a proved stock horse, Mr. Corsa sold a half interest in him to Mr. R. G. Leeds of Indianapolis, for which Mr. Leeds paid $20,000. Following this sale, the famous Carnot became known as the "$40,000 sire."

Colts by this noted stallion won the get-of-sire championship at Chicago for a period of ten years. Their stylish, impressive fronts, their shine, and their bloom when posed for inspection, plus their ability to move, were some of the reasons why so many judges liked the get of Carnot on show day.

Laet 133886

In the opinion of many good horsemen, the record of this famous stallion is without parallel in the annals of the breed. Because some may challenge this statement, a summary of his show ring record and his stock horse record follows.

Laet was bred by Colonel E. B. White of Leesburg, Virginia. He was sired by Seducteur 26252, a horse whose extended pedigree lists the names of many of the most famous Percherons of the breed.

The dam of Laet was the famous brood mare Couceorous 94852, whom many authorities list as one of the greatest brood mares of the breed. Couceorous was the dam of three grand champion stallions at the Ohio State Fair, all of them sired by different stallions.

To a service by Seducteur 26252 Couceorous foaled the famous Laet, a black foal that as a three-year-old was grand champion Percheron stallion at the Ohio State Fair in 1919.

Bred to Dragon, Couceorous had the black stallion foal Treviso 144394, grand champion stallion at the Ohio State Fair in 1921.

Mated to Giroust 78504 (69369), Couceorous dropped the stallion foal Giroust II 166985, grand champion stallion at the Ohio State Fair in 1923.

In addition to this trio of grand champion sons, Couceorous also had other noted progeny. Bred to the stallion Aveline 103496, she dropped the stallion foal Aveline II 154402, winner of the futurity at Columbus in 1920. This colt was sold into the state of California.

Mated to Dragon, Couceorous had the filly foal Iona 123962, winner of the two-year-old mare class at Ohio in 1917 and winner of the four-year-old mare class at the Ohio State Fair in 1919, the latter the year in which Laet was made grand champion Percheron stallion at the Ohio State Fair. Of course, Iona and her half brother Laet, both of them out of Couceorous, won the produce-of-dam class at Ohio in 1919. During her brood mare career Couceorous became the dam of ten recorded foals.

Couceorous was bred by Mr. John A. Buswell of Bradford, Illinois. She was sired by Harponneur 59010 (73927), a stallion whose get won the get-of-sire class at the Iowa State Fair in 1913. Couceorous, a yearling at that time, was a member of this winning get-of-sire group by Harponneur.

Colonel White was judge of the Percherons at the Iowa State Fair in 1913. He made Couceorous the winner of the yearling futurity class, then made her junior and grand champion mare of the show. To prove that he really liked this young mare, he decided to buy her, writing Mr. Buswell a check for $2,000 and giving him instructions for shipping Couceorous to Selma Farms.

Since that eventful transaction at Des Moines in 1913, I have heard Colonel White say that although he gave more money for Couceorous than for any mare he ever bought for Selma Farms, he considered her the cheapest mare he ever owned. Of course, on the day of her purchase, he did not know that he was buying a brood mare, three of whose stallion foals, all of them by different sires, would develop into grand champions at the Ohio State Fair.

Both the paternal and the maternal side of Laet's pedigree will bear inspection. He is out of Couceorous, one of the greatest brood mares of the breed, as her record proves. But do not forget that Chorus 52606, the dam of Couceorous and Laet's maternal granddam, was also a great brood mare. She had nine filly foals in nine years and her progeny alone made generous contribution to the success of Mr. Buswell, as a breeder of Percherons.

After Couceorous was placed in the stud at Selma Farms, she was mated the first time to Dragon. The result was a filly foal whose name was Iona. As a two-year-old Iona won her class at the Ohio State Fair. She was a nice mare, growthy, rugged, broody, and she topped her class as a four-year-old at the same fair.

But shortly after Dragon was mated to Couceorous the second time, calamity struck at Selma Farms. Dragon died of a case of impaction and Colonel White did not know where to replace him.

Mr. Wayne Dinsmore, then secretary of the Percheron Society, knew that Mr. White was in quest of a successor to Dragon. In extending some Percheron pedigrees one day in the office, Mr. Dinsmore was greatly impressed with the pedigree of the horse Seducteur 26252, a stallion that was owned near Logan, Ohio, where he stood for service.

Colonel White was so impressed with Mr. Dinsmore's comment about the pedigree of Seducteur that he asked Mr. David M. Fyffe of Ohio State University to inspect the stallion for him. As a result of the report Colonel White asked Mr. O. H. Pollock of Delaware, Ohio, to go to Logan to make a microscopical examination of Seducteur's semen. On receiving a satisfactory message Colonel White closed the transaction and gave instructions for the horse's shipment to Selma Farms.

On the very day that Seducteur arrived Couceorous happened to be in heat. She was bred to Seducteur that evening. The black stallion foal that resulted from this mating was Laet, who was destined to be a grand champion at Ohio and the Chicago International, and to sire more futurity winners and grand champions at these two shows than any stallion that ever lived.

In 1919, when Laet was a three-year-old, Colonel White brought an exhibit of Percherons from Selma Farms to the Ohio State Fair at Columbus. Laet won the three-year-old stallion class and was made the grand champion stallion of the show.

It was during the show at the Ohio State Fair in 1919 that Mr. W. H. Butler of Woodside Farms, Columbus, Ohio, purchased from Colonel White the champion Laet and seven Percheron mares—La Belle, Couceorous, Syncopation, Perfection, Iona, Intrepid 131826, and Belle Dragon. Rozelle was purchased a few months later. This transaction caused a great deal of comment among breeders, and the livestock magazines, such as *Breeders' Gazette* and *The Field and Country Life,* referred to Mr. Butler's purchase

Mr. Watson H. Butler, owner, and Mr. David P. Haxton, manager, of Woodside Farms, Columbus, Ohio, one of the greatest Percheron nurseries in the history of the breed. This is a good likeness of these men when activities at Woodside were at their peak. Photograph courtesy Cook and Gormley.

as one of the greatest transactions in the history of Percheron production in Ohio.

Subsequent events suggest that on that historic day in 1919, Mr. Butler may have builded better than he really knew. The record is impressive.

Laet first established his identity with Percheron breeders when he was made champion as a three-year-old at the Ohio State Fair in 1919 and followed with a grand championship as a five-year-old at Chicago in 1921.

Laet sired the grand champion stallions at the Ohio State Fair in 1922, 1924, 1925, 1927, 1928, 1929, 1931, 1932, 1933, 1936, 1937, as well as the grand champion mare in 1933—a total of eleven grand champion stallions and one grand champion mare at that fair.

Laet sired the grand champion stallions at the International in 1923, 1924, 1925, 1928, 1929, 1931, 1932, 1933, 1936, and the grand champion mares at the International in 1928, 1931, 1933, 1934—a total of nine grand champion stallions and four grand champion mares at the Chicago International.

Laet sired twenty-three first-prize futurity winners at the Ohio State Fair and the Chicago International. He sired thirteen futurity winners at Ohio and ten futurity winners at Chicago.

Laet sired the reserve grand champion stallions at the International

Mr. Jock Carter and Mr. Robert Watson, two of the very best fitters and caretakers in the history of the draft horse business in this country. Jock Carter spent many years of his life at Michigan State College, East Lansing, Michigan; Robert Watson is still on the job at The Ohio State University. Photograph courtesy Cook and Gormley.

in 1921, 1922, 1925, and 1932. He was grandsire of the reserve grand champions at the International in 1927, 1930, 1934, and 1937. He sired the reserve grand champion stallion and the reserve grand champion mare at the Ohio State Fair in 1921. He sired the reserve grand champion stallions at the Ohio State Fair in 1922, 1923, 1924, 1929, 1930, and 1936. He was grandsire of the reserve grand champion stallions at the Ohio State Fair in 1937 and 1938.

Laet sired both the grand champion stallion and the grand champion mare at the Chicago International in 1928, 1931, and 1933, a record never equaled.

Laet sired all of the champion Percheron stallions at the Ohio State Fair in 1929 except one, who was sired by his son. Laet or his offspring were grand champions at Chicago fourteen times in fifteen years and they were reserve grand champions five times.

Laet won champion get-of-sire classes at Ohio from 1921 to 1925 and from 1927 to 1934. At the Chicago International the get of Laet won the champion get-of-sire classes in 1922, 1925, 1928, 1929, 1931–1934, and 1936.

Laet has sired more grand champion Percheron stallions at the International than any other sire, living or dead, in the history of the breed.

Blythwood Conqueror, a Shire stallion. Photograph courtesy Professor C. S. Plumb, formerly Ohio State University.

Laet won the premier sire-of-breed award for the years 1928, 1929, 1932, 1933, 1934, and 1936.

In a period of eighteen years, Laet sired all of the progeny that won the awards listed above. There were two separate periods of three years each when the progeny of Laet won the get-of-sire class at Chicago. Colts by Laet won the get-of-sire group the first time for three successive years in 1923, 1924, and 1925. They won the get-of-sire group the second time for three successive years in 1931, 1932, and 1933. There were three years at Chicago—1928, 1931, and 1933—when the progeny of Laet won both the Percheron stallion and the mare championships.

No other Percheron stallion has equaled Laet's record, which in itself is enough to place Laet among the immortal stock horses. The character of his progeny rather than mere numbers determines Laet's rating as a stock horse. There are 212 foals sired by Laet which have been recorded—119 stallions and 93 mares. Several of his daughters made outstanding records. Five of them attained championship rank and of these, two were outstanding as premier winners.

Carthela, a daughter of Laet out of Carthel, started by winning the filly division of the futurity at the Ohio State Fair 1932. She developed into a very attractive mare and won two grand championships at Chicago, the first one as a two-year-old in 1933 and her second as a three-year-old in 1934.

Laet's Magic Queen 190170 was his second grand champion daughter. A black, she was foaled in 1921 out of Magic Queen 148068, a daughter of imported Magic 105931 (105686). In 1928, she was champion Percheron mare at the Eastern States Exposition, the Royal Winter Fair at Toronto, and the Chicago International. In 1931, as a ten-year-old, Laet's Magic Queen won her second championship at Chicago.

But it was through his sons out of Dragon mares that the progeny of Laet dominated American show rings for more than a decade. After examining his record as a sire of champions that have bred on, one can understand why historians rate Laet as a breed-building sire.

THE CONTRIBUTION OF THE CARETAKER TO THE LAET STORY   Laet made a great record as a show horse and as a stock horse. Hesitation, one of Laet's most noted sons, was twice grand champion at Chicago and made a fine record as a stock horse at The Ohio State University. Sir Laet, another famous son of Laet, was three times grand champion at the Ohio State Fair— as a yearling in 1927, as a two-year-old in 1928, and as a three-year-old in 1929. As a two-year-old and as a three-year-old, he was also grand champion at Chicago.

The show and stock horse records of Laet, Hesitation, and Sir Laet identify these horses as a trio of pacemaking sires. I wonder what kind of story there would be to tell, however, if David Haxton had not been at Woodside Farms, in charge of Laet; if Bob Watson had not been at The Ohio State University, in charge of Hesitation; and if Jock Carter had not been at Michigan State College, in charge of Sir Laet. Throughout their careers these stallions were the charges of three of the most noted caretakers in the history of the draft horse business. Horses everywhere reflect the skill of the men who are in charge of them.

The Feather-Legged Breeds

Characteristics of Shires and Clydes, a Comparison

The Shire is stronger-ribbed, deeper-flanked, thicker at both ends, and more drafty in general build than the Clyde. The Shire middle is more capacious and roomy; he is considered a better feeder than the Clyde.

The quarters of the Shire have more muscle, somewhat like the Belgian. The Clyde, on the other hand, is muscled in his thighs more like the Percheron, although the Percheron as a breed is heavier-quartered than the Clyde.

The hocks of the Shire are set and carried farther apart than the hocks of the Clyde, in which breed they typically set closer together than do those of other breeds. The inward deviation of the Clydesdale hock sets him out a little in his toes at the ground. This typical conformation is desirable because it permits the Clyde to carry his hocks close together at the walk and to trot and go collectedly.

The Shire, coarser in his bone and joints, is sometimes criticized for coarseness of underpinning. The Clyde, on the other hand, is extremely clean and cordy in his legs. The Shire stands on much shorter pasterns than does the Clyde, which has the longest and springiest pasterns of the draft breeds.

The Shire has a smaller foot than the Clyde. Stubbiness, boxiness, and narrowness are criticisms of Shire feet. The Clydesdale's foot is big, full at toe and quarters, wide and deep at the heel, and well developed at the hoof heads.

The Shire, known as the English cart horse, is more sluggish in action than the Clyde. In fact, in action the Clyde is without a peer among the draft breeds, for these horses are the only drafters that are shown without a man, whip in hand, trailing them at the walk and trot.

The Shire carries more feather on his legs than does the Clyde. It is coarser and shaggier in appearance. The color markings of the two breeds are similar. The Clyde, however, is usually splashed with more white than is the Shire. A strip or blaze in the face and white legs from hocks to the ground are common in both breeds. Body colors are commonly bay or black, with an occasional sorrel in the Shires and an occasional roan in the Clydes.

The Baron's Pride Family of Clydesdales

The Baron's Pride strain of Clydesdales was one of the most famous.

Fairholm Footprint 17587, grand champion Clydesdale stallion at Chicago in 1916, was a line-bred Baron Pride Clydesdale stallion. He was sired by the celebrated Dunure Footprint (15203), grandson of Baron's Pride (9122), and he was out of the mare Harviestoun Baroness, a champion daughter of Baron's Pride.

Listed below are the stallions that appear on the top side of the pedigree of Fairholm Footprint. I list them with their pedigree numbers and foaling dates because this line of Clydesdale sires includes the stallions that from beginning to end made contribution to the Clydesdale breed. Pacemakers or breed builders—whatever you wish to call them—each was a link in a Clydesdale inheritance chain which very few breeds of livestock can parallel because the Scottish breeders of Clydesdale horses were discriminating students of individuality and pedigree.

Four generations of Clydesdales. Upper Left: *Sir Everhard 5353.* Upper Right: *Baron's Pride 9122.* Lower Left: *Baron O'Buchlyvie 11263.* Lower Right: *Dunure Footprint 15203. A quartet of stallions whose stock horse records identify them as breed building sires. All of them were "breeders of breeders."*

Lochfergus Champion, foaled in 1861 (a foundational sire of the breed)

Conqueror (199), foaled in 1868

Darnley (222), foaled in 1872

Top Gallant (1850), foaled May 12, 1877

Sir Everhard (5353), foaled in 1885

Baron's Pride (9122), foaled May 7, 1890

Baron O'Buchlyvie (11263), foaled May 16, 1900

Dunure Footprint 15203, foaled April 19, 1908

Fairholm Footprint 17587, foaled May 30, 1913, and shown to a grand championship at the Chicago International in 1916 by Fairholm Farm, New Market, New Jersey

SOME RANDOM NOTES ON THE PEDIGREE   Dunure Footprint, the sire of Fairholm Footprint, was bred by Mr. William Dunlop, Dunure Mains, Ayr, Scotland. This famous horse, foaled April 19, 1908, was twenty-two years old when he died. His unusual pedigree, his marked individuality, his show-yard laurels, his long tenure of service as a sire, his prepotency when it came to stamping his own superior qualities as marked features of his get—these are a few of the reasons for the pre-eminence of this great Clydesdale stallion.

The records show that there were several years when more than one hundred colts by Dunure Footprint were entered in the Scotch Clydesdale Stud Book.

Dunure Footprint was bred to be a stock horse. Both his sire and dam were of great distinction and merit, for they led in the stiffest show-yard competitions in Scotland.

Baron O'Buchlyvie, the sire of Dunure Footprint, was the highest-priced draft horse ever sold when Mr. Dunlop paid $47,500 for him at public auction. At the age of fourteen Baron O'Buchlyvie was kicked by a mare at time of service and a front leg was broken, so that it was necessary to dispose of him. However, this famous stallion, through service fees and options on his colts, had paid for himself before that time. Baron O'Buchlyvie stood at a fee of $250, half of the money due at time of service, the other half due when the mare was declared in foal.

Dunure Ideal (21283), the dam of Dunure Footprint, was sired by Auchenflower 12007, who was sired by Montrave Mac (9958). Dunure Footprint was the first foal that Dunure Ideal had by Baron O'Buchlyvie, but afterward she had in succession four foals by Baron O'Buchlyvie, all of which secured the highest show-yard distinction. These foals were Dunure Index 15809, Dunure Black Silk 41976, Dunure Chosen 37306, and Dunure Keynote 17869.

Dunure Footprint himself was first as a yearling in 1909 at the stallion show at Glasgow. As a two-year-old he was first at the Glasgow stallion show at Ayr and first at the Glasgow summer show. In that year, 1910, he won the Cawdor Cup, the Junior Jubilee Cup, and the championship at Ayr. He made his last appearance in the show yard as a five-year-old in 1913, when he won the aged stallion class at the Glasgow stallion show and whipped all the aged stallions at the H. and A.S. Show at Paisley.

The first crop of foals by Dunure Footprint appeared in Aberdeenshire in 1912. In 1913, when these foals became yearlings, Dunure Footprint, through his get, jumped into third place among the winning sires of Scotland, first place that year being occupied by his sire, Baron O'Buchlyvie.

In the following year, 1914, Dunure Footprint was second among the winning sires of Scotland and his sire, was still first, but in 1915 the positions of father and son were reversed.

The leading position of Dunure Footprint's get among the winning sires of Scotland, gained for the first time in 1915, was held without a break until 1928, when he was displaced by Benefactor (20867) and ranked second.

Dunure Footprint's fame as a sire was at its zenith in 1922. At the nine principal shows he was represented by 82 of his get, who among them won

A tandem hitch of Clydesdales owned by Anheuser Busch, St. Louis, Missouri. These horses are stylish about their fronts, are balanced in conformation, have ample bone and muscle, and stand on underpinning that is a study in correctness. Photograph courtesy J. F. Abernathy.

at these shows 131 prizes, of which 7 were championships and 27 were first, 23 were second, and 21 were third prizes. At one time, at the height of his fame the service fee for Dunure Footprint reached a total of 120 guineas, half at the time the mare was presented for service, and the remainder when the mare was declared safe in foal. The service fee of Dunure Footprint, at the crest of his stock horse career, thus approximated $600 in American money. There are some who may argue that such a service fee for Dunure Footprint when he was at his peak as a stock horse would have decreased greatly the number of mares presented for service to this famous stallion, that standing at a smaller fee he would have serviced more mares than he did. However that may be, Dunure Footprint had more mares and better mares brought to his court when the stud fee was $600 than at any other time in his stock horse career.

It is stated authentically that at the height of his best stud season Dunure Footprint was breeding two mares an hour and that it required two cows to furnish him with the milk that he consumed as a part of his ration. One authority recalls that he once saw eighteen mares off the train and on the way to Dunure Mains to be bred to Dunure Footprint.

In view of all this it is probably true that Dunure Footprint was one of the most virile and prolific draft stallions that ever lived. In Volume 39 of the Scotch Clydesdale Stud Book 146 foals by Dunure Footprint are entered. In Volume 42 are found 129 foals by Dunure Footprint. If one takes into consideration the dead foals and the unentered foals sired by Dunure Footprint, it is safe to conclude that at the peak of his stock horse career he must have served between 200 and 300 mares in a single year.

Dunure Footprint sired noted sons and daughters, but his permanent influence upon the breed is more effectively traced through his daughters than through his sons.

Winners of the Cawdor Cup among his sons have been Dunure Refiner 17872 in 1913, Kismet 18417 in 1917, Flashdale 20576 in 1923, and Brunstane Again 20717 in 1927.

Among his famous daughters were Rosalind 49239 in 1916, Wells Lady Ray 44060 in 1919, Veda 48672 in 1920, Farleton Lady Alice 47512 in 1921, and Orange Blossom 12606 in 1926.

To the above progeny may be added as outstanding, although not Cawdor Cup winners, such grand horses as Dupplin Castle 20747, Dunraven 20309, Dunure Measure 20744, and the lovely mare Cherry Blossom 52607.

Baron's Pride, paternal grandsire of Dunure Footprint, was foaled May 7, 1890. He was a noted sire of both stallions and mares. Baron's Pride was owned by Andrew and William Montgomery at The Banks, Netherhall, Scotland, who operated the largest band of Clydesdales ever assembled at one breeding establishment. Baron's Pride lived to be twenty-two years of age, and his service fees, plus options on his colts, totaled $225,000 during his stay at Netherhall.

Fairholm Footprint, grand champion Clydesdale stallion at Chicago in 1916, had as his sire, grandsire, and great-grandsire, on the paternal side, the noted stallions Dunure Footprint, Baron O'Buchlyvie, and Baron's Pride. The progeny of all three of these stallions stamp them as breed-building sires.

The Suffolk

ORIGIN The origin of the Suffolk has never been definitely determined. It is known, however, that draft horses of the Suffolk type have been bred for several centuries in Suffolk, England. The Crisp horse of Ufford, foaled in 1768, is the foundation sire to which nearly all of the representatives of this breed can be traced. They have been produced almost exclusively in the counties of Suffolk and in the neighboring county of Essex in England.

ECONOMIC IMPORTANCE Suffolk grade geldings have never appeared in

Beau Boy, a Suffolk stallion whose individuality stamps him as a rugged representative of the breed. Imported to this country by Mr. L. B. Westcott, Clinton, New Jersey. Photograph by Strohmeyer & Carpenter.

number as a source of power on city streets either in England or in the United States. They have been chiefly used in tilling the farms of Suffolk and Essex in eastern England. Their tractability, their good dispositions, their balanced conformation, and their substance—all of these characteristics commend the Suffolk as a work horse. A short-legged breed with wide, deep bodies, these horses maintain their balance and symmetry of form, when either thin or fat.

SUFFOLK CHARACTERISTICS   Suffolk horses are usually a shade of chestnut or sorrel, have occasional white markings, and, in many instances, flaxen manes and tails. Symmetry of form, dense, hard bone, clean joints, legs that are comparatively free from feather, action that compares favorably with that of the other draft breeds—these characteristics are well-marked features of the Suffolk.

In the past, lack of scale, light bone, and soft, shelly feet have been criticisms of the Suffolk, but the best representatives of the breed in recent years have been remarkably free from these defects. For many years a Suffolk six, owned by Mr. John F. Cuneo, Hawthorn Mellody Farms, Libertyville, Illinois, furnished keen competition for all of the other draft breeds at leading state fairs and national exhibitions in this country.

DISTRIBUTION   Because Suffolks have never been imported or bred in any considerable numbers in this country they have never been available here in large numbers. In fact, the area devoted to their production is limited and there is an active demand for them in several foreign countries. A study of registration and transfer figures as furnished by the American Suffolk Horse Association reflects the influence of the truck and the tractor upon the draft horse business. In 1937, 131 Suffolks were registered in this country and 97 head were transferred; in 1950, registration and transfer activities for the Suffolk in America had ceased.

Questions

1. In the heyday of the work horse business, when work horses were in big demand, was breed type or draft horse type stressed the most by the commercial buyer? Why?

2. Compare Percherons and Belgians, thinking in terms of breed type and work horse type requirements.

3. List the factors accounting for Percheron popularity.

4. List the common criticisms of Percherons.

5. List the factors accounting for Belgian popularity.

6. List the common criticisms of Belgians.

7. Name three of the most famous Percheron breed-building sires.

8. Who owned these three noted stallions? Also list the names of the farms where these noted sires stood for service.

9. Of these three celebrated stallions, which one made the most impressive record with his get in both the show ring and the stud? To support your answer, name and identify a half dozen of this stallion's most famous progeny.

10. Contrast, in detail, Shire and Clydesdale characteristics.

11. Comment at some length upon the pedigree of Dunure Footprint and upon his prowess as a sire of good Clydesdales.

12. What are the distinguishing characteristics of the Suffolk?

11

-Legged Breeds

orses may be classified under two main
and the draft breeds.
are devoted to a discussion of the light-

horoughbred, American Saddle Horses,
d stock horses, Appaloosa, Morgan, Palo-

ardbred
ney
ckney *

the Term "Breed"

als possessing distinctive characteristics
members of the same species, these characteristics be-
ing sufficiently well fixed to be quite uniformly transmitted." It is these distinctive features which give to each breed its economic importance.

Curiously enough there is scarcely a breed which does not possess at
least one distinctive characteristic in respect to which it surpasses all other
breeds.

The inherent qualities of a breed have been put there by one or more

*See Chapter Five, "Classes of Horses for Market and Show."

of three agencies; therefore, the possibilities in what can be gotten out of a breed are as definitely determined as the character of a horse's get is fixed by his ancestry. Three factors determine breed characteristics and, through them, the economic importance of the different breeds:

1. The origin in blood, which constitutes the hereditary force with which the breed is endowed

2. The environment by which these blood lines have been molded

3. The purpose for which they have been bred, constituting the ideal toward which the breeders have selected

The study of the breeds should therefore resolve itself into a consideration of the following essentials:

1. Origin: in blood, geographical
2. Development: men, methods
3. History: men, events, dates
4. Characteristics: breed types
5. Economic importance

Foundation Stock

The origin in blood is of greatest historical interest; in fact, it may be the most important of the factors which determine breed characters.

The modern breeds have been more or less composite in their origin, involving, to a greater or less degree, those breeds or stocks which had already attained distinction on account of merit. In some cases the combination of blood lines was intentional, but it was more often incidental or even accidental.

These historical horses can in turn be traced to a more limited group of common ancestors and so on until the blood lines focus in but a very few basic stocks.

Darwin believed all races of horses had descended from one common ancestry, and attributed to environment the extreme differences noted among modern breeds.

The more commonly accepted theory has been that all modern breeds trace their origin in blood directly or indirectly to one or all of three primordial stocks, the wild black horse of Flanders, the Oriental horse, and the native pony stock indigenous to Northern Europe and Asia. The last has played a more or less important part.

The Flemish horse was native to what is now a part of France, Belgium, Holland, and Germany. The country was generally low-lying, and therefore conducive to a coarse, rank, luxuriant growth of vegetation. The

King John 739, a fine type study in Arabian stallions. Note his stylish front, his balanced conformation, the set of his legs, and the quality of his underpinning. This horse, while owned by the Kellogg Arabian Horse Ranch, Pomona, California, was grand champion Arabian stallion at both the Los Angeles County and the California state fairs. Photograph by Kellogg Arabian Horse Ranch.

horse developed in this environment had somewhat the same characteristics; that is, he was large and bulky, coarse, black, sluggish and phlegmatic, and extremely hairy, with heavy mane, tail, feather, even a mustache, and tufts of hair on the anterior face of knees and points of hocks.

The Oriental horse, native to the desert regions of Northern Africa and later found in Asia Minor and Arabia, was characterized by extreme refinement, beauty of form, grace of movement, speed, stamina, spirit, intelligence, and an active, nervous temperament. The so-called Oriental group was said to consist of the Barb, the Turk, and the Arabian.

Recent researches of Professor J. Cossar Ewart of Edinburgh University and Professor William Ridgeway of Cambridge University, have shown the fountain source was neither the Flemish horse nor the so-called Oriental group.

Ridgeway concludes that all horses can be traced to one or more of three original stocks: the Libyan horse of Northern Africa, of which purebred Barbs and Arabs are typical; the common horse of Upper Asia and Europe, represented by the Mongolian pony; and the Celtic pony of Northwestern Europe.

Arabian

No horse has enjoyed a more sentimental popularity than the Arab. And the history of no other horse has been so obscured by myth and tradition.

There is every reason to believe that horses similar to the best Arabs were in Northern Africa more than one thousand years before horses were known in Arabia. The breed is composed of five strains, which in turn are believed to be derived from a single mare, Keheilet Ajuz, and the most prominent strain—Keheilan—is named after her. They are mostly bays, the fastest of any, and resemble most closely the English Thoroughbred. The Darley Arabian, the greatest foundation sire of the Thoroughbred, was of this strain.

The Arab proper, a descendant and not an antecedent of the original Libyan horse, is known as the Kohl breed, so named on account of the peculiar blue-black or antimony tint which characterizes the skin of the body.

There is much confusion in this country concerning the characteristic color of the Arab. Almost any odd color or marking, such as pure white, piebald, skewbald, or leprous or tiger spots, is attributed to Arab blood.

On the other hand, such significance of any of these colors has been absolutely denied. As a matter of fact, bay with white markings is most characteristic and, in the light of recent knowledge concerning the origin of the Arab in the Libyan horse, is most desirable. Grays are also common. Chestnuts and browns are not uncommon; blacks and even pure whites are found. It is true, too, that the whites usually show the Kohl spots about the eyes, muzzle, and elsewhere.

Although the odd colors referred to as suggesting Arab breeding are not found among the purebred Arabs, they are noted among their half-breeds, the piebalds and skewbalds especially, occurring with some degree of uniformity when the common stock of upper Asia and Europe is crossed with Arab sires.

The term "Barb" is applied to the horses of Morocco, the "Turk" to the horses of Asiatic Turkey.

The influence of the so-called Oriental blood has been well extended. The Darley Arabian, the Byerly Turk, and Godolphin Barb, with the Barb or Royal mares, are considered the real foundation of the Thoroughbred.

The Percheron owes much to the Oriental sires with which the native French mares were mated. Gallipoli and Godolphin were two of the most important of these sires. In America, the imported Grand Bashaw, a Barb

The famous Arabian Drill Team, owned some years ago by the Kellogg Ranch, Pomona, California. Note the unusual uniformity in type displayed by these eight horses. Photograph by Kellogg Arabian Horse Ranch.

brought from Tripoli, founded through his immediate descendants the Clay, Patchen, and Bashaw families of harness race horses. Zilcaadi, an Arab from Asiatic Turkey, sired the dam of Gold Dust, the founder of the Gold Dust family of Morgan trotters.

Thoroughbred

Thoroughbred is the proper name of the English Running Race Horse Breed and any other application of the term to horses is incorrect. It should not be confused, nor used synonymously, with "purebred," the adjective employed to denote the absence of any alien blood in the ancestry.

The principal foundation to which the Thoroughbred traces consists of the Barb or Royal mares, imported by Charles II (1660–1685), and the Darley Arabian imported in 1706; and the Byerly Turk, imported in 1689, and Godolphin Barb, brought from Paris in 1724. The last had been working in a water cart, a discard, no doubt, from the stable of some member of the nobility to whom he had been presented, as was commonly the custom.

Prominent families in the Thoroughbred and derived breeds can be directly traced to each of these sires. Eclipse, the most conspicuous individual in the history of the English turf; Blaze, the foundation Hackney sire; and Messenger, the progenitor of the American Standardbred, were, respectively, four, three, and six generations removed from the Darley Arabian. King Herod, a great race horse, was a line descendant of the Byerly Turk; Matchem, a noted race horse and sire, was a grandson of Godolphin Barb.

Early Racing

The first real race under racing rules was run in England in 1377 between Richard II and the Earl of Arundel. Henry the Eighth was the first king to maintain a racing stable of his own. The English sovereigns since that time have been enthusiastic patrons of the turf.

Prior to 1880, long races were common. It was not unusual to run four-mile heats and carry top weight, whereas the present custom is to sprint short distances under close handicaps, starting the horses as two-year-olds and campaigning with them for entire seasons.

Thoroughbreds were introduced into this country by the English colonists in the Old Dominion. Indeed, Thoroughbred sentiment is still very strong in that area, especially in Virginia.

The first Thoroughbred of note to be imported was Diomed, the winner of the first English Derby, the classic race in England. He was brought over in 1797. In a straight line of descent from Diomed came Sir Archy, the first truly American Thoroughbred; Boston, his grandson, conceded to have been among the greatest of the great American race horses; and the latter's son Lexington, a scarcely less remarkable performer than Boston and a most influential sire, figuring in American Standardbred and Saddle Horse families as well as in the Thoroughbred.

Thoroughbred Characteristics

The Thoroughbred represents the speed type in the extreme, and having been the first breed improved, its distinctive characters are well marked and fixed: quality and refinement in head, hair, and bone; a small, well-proportioned head; clearly defined facial features; a straight profile; a neat ear; a fine throttle; sloping shoulders; high, refined withers; muscular thighs and quarters; correctly placed legs; usually somewhat or slightly bucked knees; oblique pasterns; and shapely feet of dense texture.

Their way of going is especially characterized by being low and pointy at the walk and trot, but perfection when in motion at the gallop or the run.

Their temperament is naturally racy, and they are of such a highly nervous organization that they are likely to become "hot" and erratic. Bay and chestnut with more or less white markings are the common colors, although black, gray, and white were common among the early Thoroughbreds. Typical Thoroughbreds weigh 1,000 to 1,200 pounds and stand from 15 to 16 hands.

The Thoroughbred as a breed has largely a rich man's patronage. But

Condition is a relative term in horse make-up. In the top photograph War Admiral 145, Kentucky Derby and Triple Crown winner, is in racing condition when he won the 1937 Kentucky Derby with Charles Kurtsinger astride. In the lower photograph he is shown as he is today, in stock horse condition. Photographs by Morgan Photo Service and *Thoroughbred Record.*

the Thoroughbred is a breed of great historic importance because of its influence during the formative days of other breeds. It was the first breed improved; hence it has the purest blood lines. For it the first stud book was established. Because it was the first breed improved, the blood of the Thoroughbred has been most freely used in the improvement of other breeds and types. In all but the draft breeds the influence of the Thoroughbred may be demonstrated.

The Hackney descends from Shales, the son of Blaze, a Thoroughbred, out of a common Norfolk mare. The French "demisang" refers to the cross of the Thoroughbred on French mares. The three most important foundation sires of American horses—Messenger, Justin Morgan, and Denmark—are credited with Thoroughbred pedigrees. In addition, many hunters, a great many saddle horses, and some polo ponies are clean or part-bred Thoroughbreds.

There is a strong prejudice against the Thoroughbred in some parts of the country, where he is looked upon as merely a racing machine. But anyone familiar with the stamp of the Thoroughbred horse bred in Virginia, Kentucky, Maryland, or California, for instance, will recognize in the blood of the Thoroughbred an influence which, judiciously and intelligently used, produces most desirable results.

When the breeders of the Thoroughbred practice selection to saddle- rather than to race-horse requirements, with good disposition, size, shape, and substance as the features sought, this breed will not be so exclusively dependent on racing for its patronage.

"Blood" is a term frequently used to indicate Thoroughbred breeding. "Of the blood," "bloodlike," and "blood horse" are all expressions that refer to the Thoroughbred. This being "the blood" and this breed being altogether of it, horses carrying but a fractional percentage are designated as part-bred and the number of parts are specified as two or half-bred, in the case of the get of a Thoroughbred sire out of a common-bred mare; three parts or three quarters being used to designate the get of a Thoroughbred out of a half- bred mare. The blood is accounted for in this way even up to seven-eighths.

The Status of Thoroughbred Racing

According to the figures released by the *American Racing Manual* for the year 1951, there were 109 race meets held at 81 United States tracks. Racing programs, numbering 2,557, were attended by 23,807,892 people. The total amount of money wagered at these meetings was $1,519,038,310. In 24 states where there is legalized pari-mutuel wagering, the sport contributed the sum of $98,681,592 to state budgets.

During the year 1951, 1,695 yearling Thoroughbreds sold at public auc-

Three generations of Kentucky Derby winners.

Clockwise: *Reigh Count, winner in 1928.* Photograph courtesy *Thoroughbred Record.*

Count Fleet, winner in 1943. Photograph courtesy *Thoroughbred Record.*

Count Turf, winner in 1951. Photograph by Bert Morgan.

A fine example of winning ancestors as antecedents of winning progeny.

tion for $6,842,610, an average of $4,037 a head. A new record sum was realized for a yearling filly when Lady Lark, a daughter of the celebrated Bull Lea, sold for $60,000. Lady Lark is a sister to Twilight's Tear, the filly that was chosen Thoroughbred of the year in 1944.

The Greentree Stable, Lexington, Kentucky, owned by Mrs. Charles Shipman Payson and John Hay Whitney, led all money-winning stables in 1951 with a total of $637,432. In second position was Calumet Farm, whose earnings totaled $605,905.00.

While the total earnings of the Calumet stable were less than those of Greentree, it should be remembered that Calumet had the noted Citation, the only Thoroughbred in history to win in excess of a million dollars. Calumet also had the noted mare, Bewitch, the world's money-winning leader of her sex with a total of $462,605.

Triple Crown Winners

Three of the most noted Thoroughbred races in America are the Kentucky Derby, a mile and a quarter, raced at Churchill Downs, Louisville, Kentucky; the Preakness Stakes, a mile and three sixteenths, raced over the Pimlico Track at Baltimore, Maryland; and the Belmont Stakes, a mile and a half, raced at Belmont Park, Belmont, Long Island, New York.

The Belmont race was held the first time in 1867. The Preakness was raced the first time in 1873. The first Kentucky Derby was held in 1875.

During all the years which have elapsed since these noted races were first held only eight horses have won all three races and thereby identified themselves as winners of the Triple Crown.

TRIPLE CROWN WINNERS

Year	*Horse*	*Owner*
1919	Sir Barton	J. K. L. Ross
1930	Gallant Fox	William Woodward
1935	Omaha	William Woodward
1937	War Admiral	Samuel D. Riddle
1941	Whirlaway	Warren Wright
1943	Count Fleet	Mrs. John Hertz
1946	Assault	R. J. Kleberg, Jr.
1948	Citation	Warren Wright

WINNERS OF THE KENTUCKY DERBY AT CHURCHILL DOWNS, LOUISVILLE KENTUCKY 1875–1951

Date	*Winner*	*Jockey*	*Starters*	*Value*	*Time*
1875	Aristides	Lewis	15	$2,850	2:37¾
1876	Vagrant	Swim	11	2,950	2:38¼
1877	Baden Baden	Walker	11	3,300	2:38
1878	Day Star	Carter	9	4,050	2:37¼
1879	Lord Murphy	Schauer	9	3,550	2:37
1880	Fonso	G. Lewis	5	3,800	2:37½
1881	Hindoo	J. McLaughlin	6	4,410	2:40
1882	Apollo	Hurd	14	4,560	2:40¼
1883	Leonatus	W. Donahue	7	3,760	2:43
1884	Buchanan	I. Murphy	9	3,990	2:40¼
1885	Joe Cotton	Henderson	10	4,630	2:37¼
1886	Ben Ali	P. Duffy	10	4,890	2:36½
1887	Montrose	I. Lewis	7	4,200	2:39¼
1888	Macbeth II	Covington	7	4,740	2:38¼
1889	Spokane	Kiley	8	4,970	2:34½
1890	Riley	I. Murphy	6	5,460	2:45
1891	Kingman	I. Murphy	4	4,680	2:52½
1892	Azra	A. Clayton	3	4,230	2:41½
1893	Lookout	Kunze	6	4,090	2:39¼
1894	Chant	Goodale	4	4,020	2:41
1895	Halma	Perkins	4	2,970	2:37½

Date	*Winner*	*Jockey*	*Starters*	*Value*	*Time*
1896	Ben Brush	Simms	8	4,850	2:07$\frac{3}{4}$
1897	Typhoon II	F. Garner	6	4,850	2:12$\frac{1}{2}$
1898	Plaudit	Simms	4	4,850	2:09
1899	Manuel	Taral	3	4,850	2:12
1900	Lieutenant Gibson	Boland	7	4,850	2:06$\frac{1}{4}$
1901	His Eminence	Winkfield	5	4,850	2:07$\frac{3}{4}$
1902	Alan-a-Dale	Winkfield	4	4,850	2:08$\frac{3}{4}$
1903	Judge Himes	H. Booker	6	4,850	2:09
1904	Elwood	Prior	5	4,850	2:08$\frac{1}{2}$
1905	Agile	J. Martin	3	4,850	2:10$\frac{3}{4}$
1906	Sir Huon	R. Troxler	6	4,850	2:08$\frac{4}{5}$
1907	Pink Star	Minder	6	4,850	2:12$\frac{3}{5}$
1908	Stone Street	A. Pickens	8	4,850	2:15$\frac{1}{5}$
1909	Wintergreen	V. Powers	10	4,850	2:08$\frac{1}{5}$
1910	Donau	F. Herbert	7	4,850	2:06$\frac{2}{5}$
1911	Meridian	G. Archibald	7	4,850	2:05
1912	Worth	C. H. Shilling	8	4,850	2:09$\frac{2}{5}$
1913	Donerail	R. Goose	8	5,475	2:04$\frac{4}{5}$
1914	Old Rosebud	J. McCabe	7	9,125	2:03$\frac{2}{5}$
1915	Regret	J. Notter	16	11,450	2:05$\frac{2}{5}$
1916	George Smith	J. Loftus	9	9,750	2:04
1917	Omar Khayyam	C. Borel	15	16,600	2:04$\frac{3}{5}$
1918	Exterminator	W. Knapp	8	14,700	2:10$\frac{4}{5}$
1919	Sir Barton	J. Loftus	12	20,825	2:09$\frac{4}{5}$
1920	Paul Jones	T. Rice	17	30,375	2:09
1921	Behave Yourself	C. Thompson	12	38,450	2:04$\frac{1}{5}$
1922	Morvich	A. Johnson	10	46,775	2:04$\frac{3}{5}$
1923	Zev	E. Sande	21	53,600	2:05$\frac{2}{5}$
1924	Black Gold	J. D. Mooney	19	52,775	2:05$\frac{1}{5}$
1925	Flying Ebony	E. Sande	20	52,950	2:07$\frac{3}{5}$
1926	Bubbling Over	A. Johnson	13	50,075	2:03$\frac{4}{5}$
1927	Whiskery	L. McAtee	15	51,000	2:06
1928	Reigh Count	C. Lang	22	55,375	2:10$\frac{2}{5}$
1929	Clyde Van Dusen	L. McAtee	21	53,950	2:10$\frac{4}{5}$
1930	Gallant Fox	E. Sande	15	50,725	2:07$\frac{3}{5}$
1931	Twenty Grand	C. Kurtsinger	12	48,725	2:01$\frac{4}{5}$
1932	Burgoo King	E. James	20	52,350	2:05$\frac{1}{5}$
1933	Broker's Tip	D. Meade	13	48,925	2:06$\frac{4}{5}$
1934	Cavalcade	M. Garner	13	28,175	2:04
1935	Omaha	W. Saunders	18	39,525	2:05
1936	Bold Venture	I. Hanford	14	37,725	2:03$\frac{3}{5}$
1937	War Admiral	C. Kurtsinger	20	52,050	2:03$\frac{1}{5}$
1938	Lawrin	E. Arcaro	10	47,050	2:04$\frac{4}{5}$

Date	*Winner*	*Jockey*	*Starters*	*Value*	*Time*
1939	Johnstown	J. Stout	8	46,350	2:03$\frac{2}{5}$
1940	Gallahadion	C. Bierman	8	60,150	2:05
1941	Whirlaway	E. Arcaro	11	61,275	2:01$\frac{2}{5}$
1942	Shut Out	W. D. Wright	15	64,225	2:04$\frac{2}{5}$
1943	Count Fleet	J. Longden	10	60,725	2:04
1944	Pensive	C. McCreary	16	64,675	2:04$\frac{1}{5}$
1945	Hoop Jr.	E. Arcaro	16	64,850	2:07
1946	Assault	W. Mehrtens	17	96,400	2:06$\frac{3}{5}$
1947	Jet Pilot	E. Guerin	13	92,160	2:06$\frac{4}{5}$
1948	Citation	Eddie Arcaro	6	83,400	2:05$\frac{2}{5}$
1949	Ponder	Steve Brooks	14	91,600	2:04$\frac{1}{5}$
1950	Middleground	Bill Boland	14	92,650	2:01$\frac{3}{5}$
1951	Count Turf	Conn McCreary	20	98,050	2:02$\frac{3}{5}$
1952	Hill Gail	E. Arcaro	16	96,300	2:01$\frac{3}{5}$

Source: The American Racing Manual, 1952.

A Few Summary Statements Concerning the Kentucky Derby

DISTANCE From 1875 to 1895, inclusive, the distance was one mile and a half. In 1896, the distance was decreased to one mile and a quarter.

AWARDS TO WINNER The largest, $98,050, went to Count Turf in 1951; the smallest award, $2,850, went to Aristides in 1875.

TOTAL STARTERS From 1875 to 1952, inclusive, 822 horses started the race, the annual average being 10. The largest starting field was 22, in 1928; the smallest was 3, in 1892, in 1899, and in 1905.

JOCKEY WITH MOST WINNERS Eddie Arcaro rode the winners in 1938, 1941, 1945, 1948, and 1952. Isaac Murphy (Negro) and Earle Sande tied for second with three each. "Ike" Murphy rode the winners in 1884, 1890, 1891; Earl Sande won the race in 1923, 1925, 1930.

BREEDER WITH MOST WINNERS Tied at five are three breeders: Mr. A. J. Alexander with Baden Baden, 1877; Fonso, 1880; Joe Cotton, 1885; Chant, 1894; His Eminence, 1901; Mr. John E. Madden with Old Rosebud, 1914; Sir Barton, 1919; Paul Jones, 1920; Zev, 1923; Flying Ebony, 1925. Sir Barton was bred in partnership with Vivian Gooch; and Calumet Farm with Whirlaway, 1941; Pensive, 1944; Citation, 1948; Ponder, 1949; Hill Gail, 1952.

OWNER WITH MOST WINNERS Calumet Farm with Whirlaway, 1941; Pensive, 1944; Citation, 1948; Ponder, 1949; Hill Gail, 1952.

BEST TIME OVER MILE AND A HALF ROUTE 2:34$\frac{1}{2}$ by Spokane in 1889. Best time over mile and a quarter route, Whirlaway, 1941, in 2:01$\frac{2}{5}$. Eddie Arcaro rode Whirlaway.

Citation, a million-dollar Thoroughbred. Winner of the $100,000 Hollywood gold cup in 1951, he is the first Thoroughbred in history whose winnings total more than $1,000,000. He was foaled in 1945. His sire is Bull Lea. His dam is Hydroplane II, by Hyperion. Citation is a Triple Crown winner, having won the Kentucky Derby, the Preakness, and the Belmont in 1948. This great horse is rated by many horsemen as the best combination of individuality and performance that the breed has produced. Photograph courtesy Calumet Farm, Lexington, Kentucky. From etching by Palenske.

LARGEST NUMBER OF STARTERS   In 1928 22 entries left the chutes. The race was won by Reigh Count in 2:10⅗. The jockey was C. Lang.

SIX LARGEST MONEY WINNERS

Count Turf	1951	$98,050
Assault	1946	$96,400
Hill Gail	1952	$96,300
Middleground	1950	$92,650
Jet Pilot	1947	$92,160
Ponder	1949	$91,600

Championship Records: Men and Horses

100 Yards (world's record): Mel Patton, California.
　　Time: 9:3 seconds; rate of speed: 32.1 feet per second.
220 yards (world's record): Mel Patton.
　　Time: 20:2 seconds; rate of speed: 32.6 feet per second.
440 yards—quarter mile (world's record): Herb McKenley, University of Illinois, and George Rhoden, Morgan State College, Baltimore, tied.
　　Time: 46:2 seconds; rate of speed: 28.5 feet per second.
880 yards—half mile (world's record): Mal Whitfield, The Ohio State University, and Sidney Woodeson, England, tied.
　　Time: 1 minute, 49:2 seconds; rate of speed, 24.1 feet per second.
1,760 yards—one mile (world's record): Gunder Haag, Norway.
　　Time: 4 minutes, 1:4 seconds; rate of speed, 21.9 feet per second.
3,520 yards—two miles (world's record): Gunder Haag.
　　Time: 8 minutes, 42:8 seconds; rate of speed: 20.1 feet per second.

Quarter mile: Man o' War (3 years).
　　Time: 20:2 seconds; rate of speed: 65.3 feet per second.
One mile: Citation
　　Time: 1 minute 33:8 seconds; rate of speed: 55.9 feet per second.
　　Golden Gate Fields.
One and a half miles: Whisk Broom (6 years).
　　Time: 2:00 minutes; rate of speed: 55 feet per second.
　　Belmont Park, Long Island, 1913.
One mile: Billy Direct (4 years), world's champion pacer.
　　Time: 1:55; rate of speed: 45.91 feet per second.
　　Lexington, September 28, 1938.

One mile: Greyhound (6 years), world's champion trotter.

 Time: 1:55¼; rate of speed: 45.98 feet per second.

 Lexington, 1938.

One mile: Titan Hanover (2 years), world's champion two-year-old trotter.

 Time: 2:00 minutes; rate of speed: 44 feet per second—phenomenal speed for a two-year-old trotter.

 Record made in 1944.

One mile: Hanover's Bertha (2 years), world's champion 2-year-old trotting filly.

 Time: 2:02; rate of speed: 43.2 feet per second.

 Record made in 1929.

One mile: Knight Dream (2 years), world's champion two-year-old pacer.

 Time: 2:00⅗; rate of speed: 43.7 feet per second.

 Record made in 1947.

One mile: Ann Vonian (2 years), world's champion two-year-old pacing filly.

 Time: 2:02¼; rate of speed: 43.2 feet per second.

 Record made in 1939.

One mile: Titan Hanover (3 years), world's champion three-year-old trotter.

 Time: 1:58; rate of speed: 44.7 feet per second.

 Record made in 1945.

One mile: Little Pat (3 years), world's champion three-year-old pacer (gelding).

 Time: 1:59½; rate of speed: 44.1 feet per second.

 Record made in 1936.

Horsemen claim that a runner cannot go at maximum speed for more than a third of a mile. Therefore, in a race like the Kentucky Derby, over a distance of one and a quarter miles, a horse has to be rated if he is to do his best. Distance and the weight carried are big determining factors.

Man o' War has brushed the quarter mile in 20:2 seconds. His rate of speed over this short distance was 65.3 feet per second.

Man o' War ran a mile in 1:35. His rate of speed for the mile was 55 feet per second.

Man o' War had the longest stride ever measured—29 feet.

Over a brush and water jump, Battleship, a steeplechaser and a son of Man o' War, jumped 31 feet, landed on the run, and kept going.

Thus, in all types of horses—trotters, pacers, runners, steeplechasers, there are wide differences, both in speed and in length of stride.

The American Saddle Horse

Five-Gaited vs. Three-Gaited Saddlers

The shows have created two general divisions of American saddle horses, plain-gaited saddlers and gaited saddlers. Plain-gaited saddle horses are shown with roached manes and clipped tails. Gaited saddlers are shown with full manes and tails.

Plain-gaited saddle horses are also known as three-gaited saddlers, or walk, trot, canter saddle horses. Gaited saddle horses are known as five-gaited saddlers, American saddlers, and Kentucky saddle horses.

Gaited saddlers are the most popular in the South and the Southwest, especially in Kentucky and Missouri. The three-gaited saddlers are more in demand in the North and in the cities of the East. They enjoy wider popularity than the gaited horses because it takes less skill to train, develop, and ride them.

The Origin of the American Saddle Horse

The American Saddle Horse, as the name suggests, is an American product whose development parallels in many respects that of the American Standardbred. Both are the result of a Thoroughbred top cross, on what might be termed a native mare foundation, and in each case the descendants of one individual have constituted a family which has dominated the breed. Their respective histories are almost contemporaneous. Denmark, the Thoroughbred, whose progeny founded the saddle breed, was foaled in 1839; Messenger, another Thoroughbred, reached this country in 1788; his great-grandson, Hambletonian, foundation sire of the Standardbred, was foaled in 1849.

The Development of the American Saddle Horse

The chief differences in the development of the American Saddle Horse and the Standardbred stem from the native mares that were used, and the goals which the breeders themselves had in mind. The original American Saddle Horse was born, of necessity, on the frontier, where horses' backs were the chief means of transportation. An easy, ambling, lateral gait was cultivated, and those horses which showed greatest proficiency in this direction were selected for breeding.

On the other hand, road and vehicle construction progressed most rapidly in the vicinity of the large eastern cities; hence the breeding of the trot-

Supreme Ace 29384, whose head and neck features furnish an unusual study in saddle horse character. This stallion is owned by Mr. J. Truman Ward, Maryland Farms, Brentwood, Tennessee. Photograph courtesy Mr. Ward.

ters and road horses centered around New York City and Philadelphia, and the foundation was laid in mares which had proven themselves best adapted to trotting in harness.

Although horses were more extensively used for riding than for driving purposes in this country during the earlier period, the American Saddle Horse, in its present degree of development, is of more recent origin than the Standardbred. Furthermore, selection in the case of the American Saddle Horse has not been to a standard of performance alone; ideals in type, conformation, and quality have been sought and are as clearly marked in the prepotency of the foundation families as is performance.

The Foundation Stock

Breeders of saddle horses in this country first organized in 1891 under the name of the National Saddle Horse Breeders Association. In 1899 the name was changed to the American Saddle Horse Breeders Association. At this time, seventeen famous saddle horse sires were selected as the foundational sires of the breed. In 1902, this list of foundational sires was decreased to ten head. In 1908, it was decided that the names of all foundational sires should be eliminated with the exception of Denmark, who was designated the sole foundational sire of the breed. The horses whose names were dropped were given numbers in the list of famous deceased saddle horse sires.

It was in 1908, also, that the association started a list of famous deceased dams. Three mares had their names listed: Pekina 60, Garrett's Bettie 69, and Molly 70.

DENMARK THE SIRE SUPREME   Denmark was made the foundational sire of saddle horses because, out of 2,981 entries in the first volume of the Saddle Horse Register, 1,653 or about 55 per cent of them traced their ancestry directly to him.

Denmark mated to the Stevenson mare produced three noted sons: Gaines Denmark 61, Rob Roy 62, and Muir's Denmark 63. Gaines Denmark has been dubbed "The Denmark of the Denmark family" because, of the 1,653 entries in the first volume of the stud book that trace their ancestry directly to old Denmark, 1,647 of them trace directly through Gaines Denmark.

THE THOROUGHBRED INFLUENCE   Following publication of the first volume of the Saddle Horse Register in 1892, an analysis of the pedigrees of all entries recorded revealed the strong influence of Thoroughbred blood as follows:

Thoroughbred	3
50% Thoroughbred blood	50
25% Thoroughbred blood	296
12.5% Thoroughbred blood	343
6.25% Thoroughbred blood	152
3% Thoroughbred blood	36
Uncertain	203

The above figures are proof that Thoroughbred blood was a strong determining influence during the formative days of the American Saddle Horse.

Strains or Families of Saddle Horses

There are two famous families of American Saddle Horses, the Chiefs and the Denmarks.

Bourbon Chief 976 is the horse that gets large credit for the standing of the Chiefs. Gaines Denmark 61 gets much of the credit for the prestige of the Denmarks.

The Chiefs as a family of saddlers are characterized by scale, substance, and motion. When show horse standards are applied, they have been criticized for some plainness and coarseness about their fronts, and for some

Wing Commander 22591, sired by Anacacho Shamrock 12594 and out of Flirtation Walk 23178, has won the stallion division of the $10,000 stake at the Kentucky State Fair six times and the final division of the $10,000 stake five times in succession, the last time in 1952. Measured by the yardstick of show ring performance he has never had a peer. Earl Teater up. Photograph by John R. Horst, courtesy Dodge Stables.

coarseness in quality of coat and bone. But as a strain they have established a reputation because of demonstrated ability to work their legs, to go at speed, and to go in form.

The Denmarks, on the other hand, are characterized by their style, finish, and quality. They are criticized sometimes because they lack in size and sturdy bone.

Many of the leading saddlers today are line-bred Chiefs, line-bred Denmarks, or a cross of these two famous strains.

Gait Terminology—Definitions

"Gait" is a term used to refer to one of several ways in which progress is accomplished by the action of the locomotive organs.

Natural gaits are those that are performed by a horse instinctively and without training. Examples are the walk, trot, gallop, and, in some instances, the pace.

Acquired gaits are those which result from special training. The canter, the rack, and the slow gait are examples.

A diagonal gait is one in which the legs, in executing the gait, move in diagonal pairs. The trot is an example.

A lateral gait is one in which the legs move in lateral pairs. The pace is an example.

"High-gaited" and "high-going" are terms applied to action when a horse folds his knees, pulls his hocks, and lifts his body sensibly high from the ground.

"Hard-gaited" is the term applied when the stride lacks spring and when the rider's reactions to the various gaits tire him quickly.

"Easy-gaited" is the term applied when the rider's reactions to the various gaits are pleasant and enjoyable.

"Free-going" is a term applied when the gaits are performed in an effortless, collected manner, and action is not excessive or labored.

"Laboring action" is the term used when a horse's efforts on the move are obviously excessive.

Gait Requirements of Saddlers in the Show Ring

The gaits required of the plain-gaited saddler in the show ring are the walk, trot, and canter. The gaits required of the gaited saddler in the show ring are the walk, trot, slow gait, rack, and canter.

There are three so-called slow gaits: the stepping pace, the running walk, and the fox trot. Because the stepping pace is much showier than either the running walk or the fox trot, and because it is much easier to ride than the fox trot, the slow gait required of gaited saddlers in competition is the stepping pace. The running walk is one of three gaits required in walking horse classes. The fox trot has been practically discarded. It is not attractive to watch nor is it an easy gait to ride.

THE WALK   This gait is known as the foundation of all saddle gaits because a horse working at the flat-footed walk is doing the gait from which he may be asked to change to any other gait.

The walk is a great pleasure gait. It is the one gait that everyone can ride if he can ride at all. The walk is also a gait that lends itself to conversation if one is riding in company. The flat-footed walk is a four-beat gait that should be done with a prompt, reachy length of stride. Trueness of stride, both front and rear, and manifest folding of knees and flexion of hocks as a horse pushes himself up into the bridle should be features of this foundation gait.

The horse that dances and prances at the walk, tosses his head, and keeps up a constant duel between the bars of his mouth and the rider's hands is neither a pleasure horse nor a show horse. At the walk a horse should drop the bit in his mouth, thus permitting the rider to ride with light hands, and the horse should set his chin and walk in form.

THE TROT   The trot is a diagonal, two-beat gait which lends itself to all

Royal Irish 14186, one of the best under 15–2 walk, trot horses in the history of the show ring, a horse that was ideal for use in ladies' classes. His good looks, plus his ability at three gaits made him a real competitor. Miss Mary Fisher up. Photograph by Rounds, courtesy Dixiana Farms.

Lover's Lane 33265, sired by Anacacho Shamrock 12594 and out of Flirtation Walk 23178. Winner of the five-gaited mare stake at the Kentucky State Fair, 1948 and 1949. Note her knee and hock action as well as the expression about her front. Earl Teater up. Photograph by John R. Horst, courtesy Dodge Stables.

sorts of road conditions and can be performed better than the pace or the rack on either soft or rough ground.

Usually, saddlers on the trot are taken on the snaffle with the pressure on the curb bit released a little. A common signal used by a trainer is a "cluck" to his horse as he prepares to start off; at the same time, the rider begins to post, that is, to rise in his stirrups. The well-broken horse will trot on these signals. The less noticeable the signals used by trainers, the more finished the performance.

TROT REQUIREMENTS ARE NOT THE SAME FOR ALL TYPES OF HORSES   The requirements for the trot by five-gaited saddlers and by three-gaited saddlers are not the same. Of course, the gaited saddler and the three-gaited saddler both work their legs in diagonal pairs at the trot. So does a draft horse or a Shetland pony or a Standardbred trotter or a heavy harness horse. Yet the trot requirements for each of these types are different.

The five-gaited saddler does a diagonal trot at speed and in form. It makes no difference how fast he goes if he can maintain his form at speed. If he can fold his knees, flex his hocks, set his chin, go in form, and go collectedly, his speed is an asset on show day in competition with other gaited horses. If, as a result of too much speed, a gaited saddler extends his chin, hits on his heels in front, leaves his hocks behind him, and turns in a sprawling, uncollected performance, which happens if horses are overridden at the trot, then speed at the trot is no longer an asset but a liability.

The three-gaited saddler, in contrast to the gaited saddle horse, should trot at moderate speed and always in form. He should fold his knees, use his hocks, set his chin, and go collectedly with a balanced stride. The kind of speed that calls for quarter boots should not be tolerated in three-gaited classes.

Someone asks the question, What is meant by moderate speed at the trot for three-gaited saddlers? This question cannot be answered definitely because horses differ in the rate of speed at which they work best. But the question, How fast should a three-gaited saddler work at the trot? can be answered. When a walk, trot horse gives the impression that he is racing at the trot, he is going too fast. When he is doing a sluggardly, laboring, unanimated, and phlegmatic trot, his trot is too slow. Somewhere between these two extremes is the point where a three-gaited saddler should be rated at the trot. Three-gaited saddlers should do a four-cornered trot, folding their knees, flexing their hocks, working their legs beneath them, yet trotting on away from themselves, always in form.

The saddle horse trot is not the reachy, extended trot of the American trotter or American roadster in harness. Nor is it the trot of the heavy harness horse, where height as a feature of the stride is a prerequisite. With the light harness horse, speed is a primary requirement and extension as a feature of the stride is most important. The assignment of the light harness horse is to flatten out and trot fast in an attempt to win.

Although speed is required in gaited classes, the saddler, on the other hand, must maintain himself in good form and balance and furnish a good seat for his rider. He is not supposed to reach and sprawl at the trot, but should have all of his legs working under him, coordinating his performance at every step. To assist him, the rider should post just enough to catch the motion of his horse. It is not good form to post unduly high nor, as horsemen say, to ride "too loose" in the saddle.

THE SLOW GAITS: THE STEPPING PACE, THE RUNNING WALK, THE FOX TROT From the flat-footed walk, as previously remarked, a saddler may easily change to any of the slow gaits. The stepping pace, sometimes called the slow pace, is the most popular of the slow gaits and the one that is most commonly seen in the show ring. It is one of the easiest and most comfortable to ride of all the saddle horse gaits.

To do the stepping pace, a trainer usually takes his mount lightly on the curb bit, eases up on the snaffle reins, touches the horse with his heel, shakes his head just a little and urges him forward out of the walk, striking this slow, showy, ambling gait which is right on the edge of a four-beat gait. Although called a pace, the stepping pace of the saddle horse differs distinctly from the side-wheel pace of the American pacer. The stepping pace of the saddle horse is done slowly and is one of the showiest of all the saddle gaits. The light harness pacing horse goes at tremendous speed, with so much roll to the body that the gait is most unpleasant to ride. Roughness is a characteristic of the gait of the "side-wheeler," a lateral gait done at speed with both feet on the same side of the body striking the ground at the same time.

In the stepping pace as performed by saddlers, instead of both feet on the same side of the body striking the ground at the same time, there is just enough break in the impact of the lateral feet to create a short interval and to rob the gait of the roughness and unpleasant roll of the "side-wheeler."

The running walk resembles the flat-footed walk so far as number and sequence of hoof beats are concerned, but of course, as the name suggests, the cadence is faster. The sequence of hoof beats in the running walk is a diagonal four-beat sequence.

Running walkers are sometimes called "nodders." They keep time with their paces by the nodding of their heads, just as work mules do by the flopping of their ears. Walking horse classes are very popular at all the major shows staged in our southern or plantation states, particularly in Tennessee, where the Tennessee Walking Horse National Celebration, the greatest walking horse show held anywhere in the world, is staged annually at Shelbyville.

Sir James, five-gaited gelding owned by Mr. Leslie Atlas, Wheaton, Illinois, demonstrates his ability at the rack. The rack is also called the single-foot. Note that only one foot is on the ground. Miss Harriet Atlas up. Photograph courtesy J. A. McClasky.

The fox trot is the other slow gait and the least enjoyable of the slow gaits to ride. Saddle horse men refer to it as a "dog trot," a rather uncollected, loose-jointed trot sometimes also called a "shog," a combination of the words "shuffle" and "jog."

When a saddler strikes a stepping pace in competition, he should be held to it and made to perform the gait cleanly. He should not be permitted to push forward and shift into a rack, while other entries in the field continue at the stepping pace. When a field of gaited saddlers have been worked at the trot, they should be slowed down to a walk before being asked for the slow gait or stepping pace, which gait is usually sandwiched in between the trot and the rack. But when the horses are working at the stepping pace, it is not necessary to have them walk before asking them to rack. From the stepping pace a horse can shift to a rack with consummate ease. While the slow gait or stepping pace is a slow, four-beat gait, with a slight interval between the hoof beats of lateral feet, the rack is a fast, four-beat gait with the interval occurring between the hoof beats of diagonal feet. A well-trained saddler whose head is shaken just lightly makes the shift from the stepping pace to the rack with ease and safety.

THE RACK *The rack*, as noted above, is a four-beat gait done at speed. The rack is also called a single-foot, a term which more nearly defines it. An acquired gait, it is difficult for a horse to do, some of them even refusing to rack at all. It is hard on a horse because it is done at speed and the going can easily be too soft and heavy or the footing too rough. For a horse to be able to do this gait well the road should be smooth and the footing tolerably hard.

When you have your five-gaited horse at the walk and have him lightly in hand on the curb bit, signal the rack by increasing the pressure on the curb a little, shaking the bit in his mouth, giving him your leg, that is, grip him with the knees so that he feels the pressure, or nudging him with your heel. Saddlers are taught to rack by urging or heeling them forward and curbing them back, causing them to fly into a sort of condensed trot, which describes the rack fairly well.

To have his head, neck, and legs properly set in performing the rack, a horse should go up against the curb bit, at least lightly. He should not be allowed to fall into a swinging, side-wheel pace, for the rack is distinctly a four-beat gait, not a two-beat gait. "Paces in his rack" is a criticism of horses at the rack that display a tendency to pace and thus mix the two gaits. The gait-mixing tendency of five-gaited saddlers is sharply discriminated against, no matter whether a horse mixes his rack with the trot or whether at the rack he shows a tendency to pace. "He can rack a hole in the wind" is a statement sometimes made by trainers who commend their horses for the speed they can display at the rack.

CANTER, LOPE, GALLOP, RUN The canter is a three-beat gait performed very slowly and collectedly. It too is an acquired gait. A hind foot makes the first beat in the series, the other hind foot and the diagonal fore foot make the second beat simultaneously, and the remaining forefoot makes the third beat in the series. The body is then projected clear of the ground and a hind foot makes the first beat in a new series.

"Lope" is a contraction for the word "gallop." Although the sequence of the hoof beats is the same, the gallop and the run are gaits which differ from the canter.

The canter, the gallop, and the run, all of them three-beat gaits, may be likened to the three speeds of an automobile. "Canter" is the term used when the gait is performed under restraint and executed very slowly and collectedly.

"Gallop" is the term applied when the gait is performed at moderate speed. "Run" is the term used when a horse fully extends himself and goes fast.

However, speed is not the only difference in these gaits. The canter is an acquired gait, whereas the gallop and the run are natural gaits. They are relatively rough to ride, but the canter, when well performed, is pleasant and easy.

In doing the canter, a horse shifts his weight to his haunches and brings his hind legs well beneath him. He bounds up in front lightly, strikes the ground with his fore feet easily, supporting his weight pretty well on his hind legs instead of letting it come down hard as it does in the gallop or the run.

The canter is usually performed on the curb bit. The horse pulls in his chin, arches his neck, and sets his head a little lower than he does in the trot or the rack, but the well-trained horse does not take a hard hold on the bit at the canter. The more slowly this gait is done, if performed with promptness, life, and exactness, the better. Hence the old saying "He can canter all day in the shade of an apple tree." Although done slowly, the canter is not a lazy, listless, uncollected, loose-jointed gait. The horse that looks as though he wants to run, yet restrains himself and canters lightly on the curb at about five miles an hour, is doing the canter properly.

The show ring demands that a horse at the canter be able to lead with either fore foot. Judges require that saddlers change leads during their performance. If working in an oval arena, the right fore leg should lead in cantering to the right, the left fore leg in cantering to the left. Hence judges make it a practice to have horses at the canter work both ways of the arena. The canter is a very pleasant gait to ride when a good-mouthed horse performs it in animated, slow, collected fashion.

Gaits are requested in the following order: the three-gaited saddler in competition will be asked to walk, trot, and canter both ways of the ring; gaited saddlers will be asked to walk, trot, slow-gait, rack, and canter both ways of the ring. It should be noted that the stepping pace is sandwiched between the trot and the rack for gaited saddlers in order to place a slow gait between two fast gaits and give the horse a chance to rest a little and to catch his breath. Furthermore, as mentioned above, a horse shifts with ease from the stepping pace to the rack.

In working gaited saddlers judges will sometimes sandwich the trot in between the stepping pace and the rack. When this occurs, a horse's manners and gaits are given the acid test because each succeeding gait has a sequence of hoof beats wholly unrelated to the preceding gait. Judges who follow this plan of calling for gaits are better able to detect gait-mixing tendencies.

Important Saddle Horse Requirements

Many years ago, the officials of the American Saddle Horse Breeders Association agreed upon the following list of saddle horse qualifications. In preparing this list, these gentlemen of the early days not only aimed to include the most important qualifications of a saddle horse but also attempted to list these qualifications in the order of their importance:

1. Sure-footedness
2. A kind disposition coupled with a good mouth
3. Courage and ambition
4. Conformation of a weight carrier
5. Gaits and manners

In studying this list of saddle horse qualifications, it is well to note that sure-footedness is listed as the first requisite of a good saddle horse. This sounds reasonable, because any saddle horse that is unsure of foot is more likely to stumble, blunder, and fall, and any horse that falls is likely to injure his rider.

Saddle Horse Characteristics

In the opinions of a great many people, the beauty of the most perfect and most representative specimens of the American Saddle Horse is unmatched by any other breed of horses.

The style and finish about their fronts suggest the use of the descriptive term "class." It is a little difficult to define. In fact, it almost baffles description. We call it charm in women. We call it presence in men. We call it class in horses. But whatever you call it, it appeals to buyers and judges alike.

Symmetrical and balanced in conformation, set on legs that are a study in correctness, with a brand of quality and finish hard to match, the model American Saddle Horse leads most breeds when measured by the yardstick of good looks.

The preferred colors, chestnuts and sorrels with white markings, also enhance the beauty of the American Saddle Horse. Other colors, such as bay, black, and gray, are not infrequent nor do such colors bar good Saddle Horses from the top position in keenest competition. Highland Denmark 730, one of the most celebrated sires of walk, trot horses that ever lived, was a bay stallion with a few white markings. Rex McDonald, one of the greatest saddle horse sires in the history of the breed, the horse that made Missouri famous as a Saddle Horse state, was a black stallion. Sweetheart on Parade, in the opinion of a great many competent Saddle Horse men the greatest gaited mare of them all, was a gray.

The American Saddle Horse is a tractable, teachable, clever horse. The men who have worked with this breed of horses have artificialized them somewhat in presenting them to the public, but in spite of all this, the American Saddle Horse is still a great breed and on show day its representatives make strong public appeal in both model and performance classes. A gaited horse has five distinct jobs to do on show day. He has to walk, trot, slow-gait, rack, and canter. Any horse that can do these five jobs well must of necessity be an intelligent, clever kind of horse.

The futurity classes for saddle-bred foals and yearlings, the fine harness classes where gaited horses are shown in light harness, and, finally, the five-gaited stake for stallions, mares, and geldings on the last night of the show—all of these classes are testimony of the high esteem in which the American Saddle Horse is held.

Registrations and Transfers

According to the figures of the American Saddle Horse Breeders Association, the peak year for both registrations and transfers was 1948, when 4,477 head were registered and 5,213 head were transferred.

A study of registration and transfer figures for the years 1943 to 1948 inclusive shows a steady growth of the Saddle Horse business. There were 1,972 Saddle Horses registered in 1943 and 2,530 head transferred. Official figures for 1950 show that 3,173 saddlers were registered and 3,763 were transferred. This is a slight decrease in comparison to the peak year 1948 and due in large part to economic uncertainties arising from international tensions.

The Tennessee Walking Horse

The origin of the Tennessee Walking Horse cannot be definitely stated because, according to the best records available, this breed is of composite blood. Breed-building sires and dams of the Tennessee Walking Horse breed have pedigrees that trace to the Thoroughbred, the Standardbred, the Morgan, and the American Saddle Horse.

A study of the extended pedigrees of Tennessee Walking Horses, if traced to the foundational sires and dams of the breed, will reveal such strains, or family names, as Hals, Copper Bottoms, Slashers, Grey Johns, Bulletts, Whips,

Merry Go Boy 431336, six times grand champion at the Tennessee Walking Horse National Celebration. He was shown for six consecutive years without defeat in his class. A beautiful horse when posed for inspection, and a horse whose performance when in motion is difficult to match. He is one of the best combinations of good looks and action that the breed has produced. Photograph courtesy J. A. McClasky.

Blue Jeans, Brooks, Stonewalls, Pilots, Denmarks, and other families that are famous in horse history.

For more than a century, the breeders of Tennessee Walking Horses have selectively planned their matings with the aim of breed improvement constantly in mind. Hence the best specimens of the Walking Horse today may boast such characteristics as the endurance that was typical of their Thoroughbred and Standardbred ancestry, the docility and the balanced conformation of the Morgan, and the style, finish, and quality of the American Saddle Horse. As a result of the mingling of these various breed influences the modern Tennessee Walking Horse has been developed with breed characteristics so uniformly transmitted that he has become a separate breed entity.

The Tennessee Walking Horse, indigenous to the middle section of the state of Tennessee, originated within an area of about fourteen counties in Tennessee more than a century ago. It did not come into great public notice, however, until after the organization of the Tennessee Walking Horse Breeders Association at Lewisburg, Tennessee, in 1935.

The walkers were not universally acclaimed as show horses until the organization of the Tennessee Walking Horse National Celebration at Shelbyville, Tennessee, in 1939. Since these dates, 1935 and 1939, the growth in the popularity of the Tennessee Walking Horse, plus the expansion and growth of both the association and the celebration, has been nothing short of miraculous.

Within a period of a decade and a half, the Tennessee Walking Horse has gone to every state in this country and has won recognition on the bridle path and in the show arena all over America.

The association now has a membership of about 1,000, covering forty states. Since its organization seventeen years ago, it has registered more than 30,000 head of walking horses and has issued nine stud books. By the end of 1947, the peak year for registrations, 5,520 head of walking horses were registered. In 1950 the number of registrations decreased to 1,984 head of horses.

The Tennessee Walking Horse has been bred for utility. In the beginning, this horse, native to Tennessee, was asked to do three tasks. He was used for riding, for driving in light harness, and for tilling the fields. In other words, the Tennessee Walking Horse in the beginning had to fit into a program of sound farm economy. He was a saddle horse, a driving horse, and a work horse.

Today, however, the Tennessee Walking Horse is largely a riding horse, a pleasure mount for those who seek diversion and recreation in the saddle on bridle trails and in the open field. Also, Walking Horses are seen regularly in the show arena at our largest state and national exhibitions, where their good looks, their manners and disposition, and their distinctive gaits have won them recognition and have added to their ever-increasing popularity among horsemen everywhere.

During the Civil War, it is said that a certain Colonel Willoughby of the Southern forces wrote a letter to Colonel Andrew Jackson, in which he stated that he had a new horse whose name was Free and Easy. Then Colonel Willoughby continued, "It is a joy to ride him, for, as is his name so are his gaits."

These words of Colonel Willoughby parallel very closely the slogan of the salesmen who handle Tennessee Walking Horses: "Ride one today and you'll own one tomorrow."

Walking Horse Characteristics

The typical Tennessee Walking Horse stands about 15–2 hands in height and will weigh 1,000 to 1,200 pounds. The best specimens of the breed are balanced in conformation, are attractive about their heads, and stand squarely on clean, hard legs. They can do a flat-foot walk, a running walk, and a canter. There is a wide range in color—sorrel, chestnut, black, roan, white, bay, brown, gray, and sometimes a Palomino yellow. All kinds of head markings characterize the breed: star, snip, strip, blaze, bald. Leg markings include coronets, fetlocks, socks, and stockings. Splashes of white on the body are sometimes seen, especially in the case of roan horses. Walkers are shown with long manes and long tails; infrequently both tails and manes are white or flaxen.

Criticisms of the Breed

While Tennessee Walking Horses have much to commend them, like all other breeds they incorporate in their make-up certain features for which they are sharply criticized. The breed, measured by a quality yardstick, still needs refinement and finish. Coarseness as a feature of general make-up appears too frequently. In many instances the set of the underpinning calls for improvement. Backs need to be shortened. Long backs, splay-footedness, and sickle hocks are features which occur too often.

In 1950, there was a drop in the registration of Walking Horses of 3,536 head. The peak year for registrations and transfers of this breed, as noted above, was 1947, a boom year in which Walking Horses sold like hot cakes on a frosty morning to eager buyers at long prices. There is a possibility that some stallions were sold as prospective stock horses that should have been castrated and sold as geldings. There is also a possibility that some plain horses went to customers at values well beyond their worth. However that may be, boom days were short-lived and the registrations, as well as the transfers dropped off sharply.

Walking Horse Gaits

In the show ring, walking horses have to do three gaits, the flat-footed walk, the running walk, and the canter. The entries are worked both ways of the ring.

The flat-footed walk is a four-beat gait in which the legs work in diagonal pairs, the interval between the impact of the feet occurring between diagonal feet. A horse is supposed to walk up into the bridle, pushing himself off his hind legs and forward, with a reachy, ground-covering stride that guarantees progress, even at this slowest of the gaits. The best flat-foot walkers can make three to five miles an hour.

The running walk has the same sequence of diagonal hoof beats that characterizes the flat-foot walk, but, of course, the cadence is much faster. In reality the running walk is simply an accelerated flat-foot walk, but it is usually characterized by more overreach of the hind feet than is true of the flat-foot walk. At the running walk, the best horses will overstep fourteen to twenty-two inches. Most horses of show caliber can do five or six miles an hour at the running walk. A few of them are capable of seven or eight miles an hour at the running walk, but if form cannot be maintained at such a speed the horse is being overridden. Form should not be sacrificed for speed. The creeping, gliding, ground-covering, space-consuming stride of a walking horse doing the running walk explains in large part the thrill that the rider gets when seated on the back of a champion Tennessee walker. The gliding motion that results from the coordinated action of the best running walkers accounts largely for the ease and the comfort afforded the rider at this gait.

The canter is a slow, three-beat gait done under restraint. A hind foot makes the first beat in the series. The remaining hind foot and diagonal fore-foot make the second beat simultaneously. The remaining fore foot makes the third beat. Then the body is projected clear of the ground and a hind foot makes the first beat in a new series. The canter should be collected, characterized by height and roll, and gracefully executed, causing one to think of a rocking chair's motion. A horse should fold his knees, not canter stiff-legged, and the rider should not lift and pump a horse's head so much that the canter becomes too much of a man-made, artificialized gait.

The American Quarter Horse

Early Racing in America

The earliest form of horse racing in America was carried on in the colony of Virginia, where, owing to the lack of cleared sites large enough for formal race tracks, races were held over the so-called "race paths" that were literally hewn out of the wilderness and were usually a quarter of a mile in length. Thus Quarter Horse racing became and long remained the favored sport in Maryland, Virginia, and the Carolinas, spreading from there to the other colonies. Then, as true course racing and the Thoroughbred racehorse were introduced, the rude contests of the earliest pioneer were abandoned, retreating to the frontier as the latter was pushed ever farther westward and south-ward. Today, however, Quarter Horse racing still flourishes, especially in Texas and in the trans-Mississippi states.

Colonial Quarter Horse Racing Preceded the Thoroughbred

The colonial short-distance horse was established in the American colonies at a date too early to allow the English Thoroughbred to have much influence on his breeding. Later, when the colonial Quarter Horse was raced against the Thoroughbred, he could beat him at short distances because of his quick getaway at the start of a race.

The Quarter Horse today is known as an ideal cow horse, but in the early days of the seventeenth and eighteenth centuries, he was called the American Quarter Running Horse, a veritable speed demon for short distances. This horse was developed from the Spanish and English stock found in the thirteen colonies. The English horses that were used in the development of the early Quarter Horse were not Thoroughbreds. In fact, there were no Thoroughbreds at this time, for Godolphin Barb, one of the foundation sires of the Thoroughbred, was not taken to England until 1728.

Originally, the Quarter Horse was developed for a short-distance race horse, but as a riding horse he was always useful around the colonial cowpens. Too, he was a general utility horse, used for work during the week and raced on holidays.

First Recognition as a Breed

The Quarter Horse was recognized as an established breed by some colonial writers as early as 1665. Two hundred years later he was acknowledged to be the greatest cow horse of all time, for his original characteristics and his speed at the start provided him with everything a cow horse needs. The contribution of the American Quarter Running Horse to the development of the cow country has always been recognized and appreciated. Only in recent years, however, have the facts of history disclosed the part that was played by the American Quarter Running Horse in the development of the Thoroughbred in America.

As noted above, this colonial Quarter Horse was remarkably fast for a quarter of a mile. It must have been disconcerting to the colonial owners of English Thoroughbreds that had established themselves as greyhounds of the English turf to have them left at the post on race day by the short-legged, thick-set, close-coupled Quarter Horse of the colonies.

Janus, an imported stallion, was the only horse of his time, apparently,

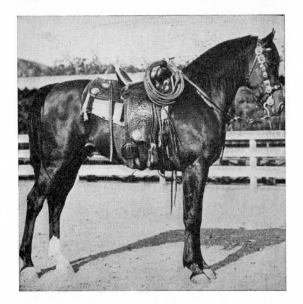

The Arabian stallion Farana 708, rigged with cow horse tack, preparatory to a cow horse demonstration. Note the set and the quality of his underpinning, his balanced conformation and the expression about his head and neck, his ears, and his eyes. For years this stallion was featured in the Sunday afternoon shows staged by the W. K. Kellogg Institute of Animal Industry, Pomona, California. A very attractive horse, but he lacks the muscle, middle and bone which the cowboy seeks in a good cow horse. Photograph by Kellogg Arabian Horse Ranch.

whose blood really influenced the development of the American Quarter Running Horse. Mr. William Anson, one of the earliest Texas stockmen to interest himself in the history of the Quarter Horse, says: "From all historical accounts and also because of the number of Januses which appear in so many Quarter Horse pedigrees, the Thoroughbred stallion Janus must have been as prolific a sire as our own Texas Steel Dust, undoubtedly the most prolific and prepotent Quarter Horse that ever stood on four legs." Today, it is agreed that there are relatively few important Quarter Horses whose pedigrees and ancestry do not trace down the line to colonial celebrities.

The Quarter Horse in Texas

In the nineteenth century, Texas had a type of horse of which it was very proud because its equal in working cattle had never been bred. Coming into Texas for the first time with that noted, bowlegged horseman and stockman, the Spaniard Cortes, horses had followed the Spanish cattle ever northward until they found what was regarded as a horse heaven on the plains of Texas. For three hundred and fifty years these Spanish horses had been working with cattle, and by the time they reached Texas, they had proved themselves capable of unbelievable feats of endurance and possessed of a "cow-horse sense" that seemed to be inbred.

The Texans, typical horsemen, would bet their last shirt on the prowess of their horses; hence the stage was set for the appearance of the noted stallion Steel Dust, one of the best Quarter Horses that ever came to Texas.

A pair of typical cow horses. They have the muscle, middle, and bone which the cowboy says are so essential in the make-up of a high-class cow horse. Photograph by Laughead Photos.

Most Quarter Horses trace to one of the two main Quarter Horse families, Steel Dust or Shilo. Steel Dust was foaled in Illinois in 1843. He was blood bay in color, stood slightly over 15 hands, and weighed about 1,200 pounds. He was brought to Lancaster, Texas, in 1846 by Mr. Mid Perry, and he died near there in 1864. Steel Dust was at least one quarter Thoroughbred because his sire, Harry Bluff, was by Short Whip and out of a Thoroughbred mare called Big Nance.

STEEL DUST PROVES HIS SUPERIORITY   The story goes that someone in

Texas had a horse that he was mighty proud of, a horse whose fame had spread because he could outrun all comers. Most of the reports give the name of this Texas horse as Shilo. Whoever the horse was, Steel Dust arrived upon the scene at the time that Shilo was attracting so much attention. It is possible that someone had brought Steel Dust into the Lone Star State for the express purpose of defeating the Texas horse, but what is more likely is that the owner of Steel Dust was just on the move through the Texas cow country.

At any rate, the records show that Steel Dust, about the middle of the nineteenth century, was matched with a champion Texas horse. Steel Dust's quiet demeanor caught the Texans off guard and his defeat of the noted Texas horse very nearly bankrupted the community. From then on the Quarter Horse was tops in Texas. Presently every Texan who had a Spanish mare wanted to breed her to a Quarter Horse stallion.

The results of mingling the blood of the eastern Quarter Horse with the blood of the Spanish cow horse, whose job for years had been to work with cattle, showed up plainly in the progeny of this new cross. The Quarter Horse and his get from these Spanish mares created a marked improvement in the conformation of the Texas cow horse without detracting from his cow sense or depreciating his stamina. The result was the best cow horse the Southwest had ever known. Now the cow horse of Texas had added weight and a fresh burst of speed without any loss of that intuitive cow sense which had been bred into the Spanish cow horse through the centuries. To this day, Quarter Horses or Steel Dusts, as they are sometimes called, are among the best stock horses in the world.

THE SHILO FAMILY   This family was founded by old Shilo, who reached Texas in 1849. Foaled in Tennessee in 1844 old Shilo was brought to Texas five years later by Mr. Jack Batchler. He was by Van Tromp, by Thomas's Big Solomon, by Sir Solomon, by Sir Archy. Van Tromp, out of the mare Barbette by Sandbeck, was a half brother to Flying Dutchman.

Sir Archy was foaled in 1797, sired by Imp. Diomed, a Thoroughbred stallion imported into Virginia in 1798.

Quarter Horse Individuality

The Quarter Horse has distinct characteristics. Types are not fixed in a few generations; hence it is not surprising to find in the pedigrees of the best Quarter Horses many animals which bear a striking resemblance when measured by the yardstick of type.

Typical Quarter Horses have small, alert ears, cleanly chiseled head features, stylish, attractive fronts with ample length of neck, long, sloping

Hired Hand, P 2495, an exceptional type study among Quarter Horse stallions, owned by King Ranch, Kingsville, Texas. This stallion is the sire of Straw Boss, one of the greatest cutting horses in the history of the breed. Photograph courtesy J. J. Dodd, for King Ranch.

shoulders, short backs and couplings, deep middles, a full, deep heart-girth, thick, muscular thighs and stifles, and heavily muscled arms, forearms, and gaskins. The best Quarter Horses stand on rather short legs that from the standpoint of set and placement are a study in correctness. Usually the proper slope of pastern accompanies the proper set of shoulder because these are correlated features in all horses. The best Quarter Horses stand on shapely feet that are full and rounding at toe and quarters, wide and deep at the heels, with hoof walls that are tough in texture.

Normally, the stance of the Quarter Horse finds him at ease with his legs well under him. This explains his ability to move quickly in any direction.

On the move, a Quarter Horse is balanced in every motion he makes. He starts, turns, and stops with noticeable ease, staging a performance which stamps him as a clever, handy, intelligent horse.

In disposition, the Quarter Horse is known for unexcelled docility. His lack of nervousness, and his quiet, even temperament, even after a display of speed in bulldogging a steer or roping a calf, are outstanding Quarter Horse characteristics. Here is a horse that is good for something instead of good for nothing.

Criticisms of the Quarter Horse

There is no breed whose representatives are all free from criticism, and the Quarter Horse, like all breeds, has his quota of faults.

Oftentimes the neck of the Quarter Horse is a trifle short and thick and too straight on top. Sometimes the head features are a little coarse. The set of his legs or the position that he takes on his legs, particularly his hind legs as viewed from the side, could be improved. Sometimes his pasterns are a little too short and straight. Thick, mutton withers are seen too frequently, and sometimes there is a lack of balance because the horse in question is high at the hips and low at the withers. Of course, these faults are not characteristic of the best Quarter Horses, but all the faults mentioned should be constantly in the minds of breeders.

All of the good features listed above, however, are important requisites in any Quarter Horse if he is to look the part of a show horse and at the same time be able to demonstrate his ability as a cow horse. Rarely does a Quarter Horse exceed 15 hands in height but because of his build, he will oftentimes weigh 1,200 pounds or more. It is this fact that led Mr. Dan Casement, celebrated ranch owner, stockman, and one of the best present-day authorities, to say that "here is more horse for the height than is found in any other breed."

The Quarter Horse vs. the Thoroughbred Type of Stock Horse

The Quarter Horse and the Thoroughbred have two different jobs to do. Both types are necessary and both are best in their respective fields.

If the legs of a Quarter Horse are lengthened in proportion to body bulk, his stability and maneuverability as a stock horse are lessened. On the other hand, if the legs of a Thoroughbred are shortened and the weight of his forequarters is increased, the concussion of the forefeet is increased to a maximum, the hazard incident to bowed or ruptured tendons is increased, and his speed and endurance over distance are greatly reduced. For these reasons the best breeders of both breeds are not crossbreeding their horses. The best Quarter Horses are produced by breeding Quarter Horse stallions to Quarter Horse mares.

Random Comments by Noted Authorities

A toast to the American Quarter Horse—"Speed to overtake the fastest calf, weight to hold the heaviest steer, endurance to work day after day and finally an inherent desire and love to work cattle."—ROBERT M. DENHARDT.

"I have schooled them as polo mounts and, because they have everything, intelligence, stamina, sure-footed action, Quarter Horses are the best type of horse a man can ride."—ALBERT HAND.

"I am confident that there is not a horse in England, nor perhaps in the

Poco Bueno, AQHA 3044, a grand champion Quarter Horse stallion in the keenest competition. He exemplifies the type sought in the best Quarter Horses. Owned at 3-D Stock Farm, Arlington, Texas. Courtesy 3-D Stock Farm.

whole world, that can excel them in rapid speed."—J. F. D. SMITH, written before the Revolutionary War.

"The immense breast and chest, enormous forearm, loin and thighs and the heavy layers of muscle are not to be found in the same proportions in other breeds."—WILLIAM ANSON.

"The Ol' Cow Hawse"

When it comes to saddle hawses, there's a difference in steeds:
There is fancy-gaited critters that will suit some feller's needs;
There is nags high-bred an' tony, with a smooth an' shiny skin,
That will capture all the races that you want to run 'em in.
But fer one that never tires; one that's faithful, tried and true;
One that allus is a "stayer" when you want to slam him through—
There's but one breed o' critters that I ever came across
That will allus stand the racket: 'tis the—Ol' cow hawse!

No, he ain't so much for beauty, fer he's scrubby an' he's rough,
An' his temper's sort o' sassy, but you bet he's good enough!
For he'll take the trail o' mornin's, be it up or be it down,
On the range a-huntin' cattle or a-lopin' into town.

A cowboy demonstrates his ability in a calf-roping contest at Fort Worth. The cow pony is on the job because the lariat is tight and the mouth of the calf is popped open. Photograph by James Cathey.

An' he'll leave the miles behind him, an' he'll never sweat a hair,
'Cuz he's a willin' critter when he's goin' anywhere.
Oh, your thoroughbred at runnin' in a race may be the boss,
But for all day ridin' lemme have the—Ol' cow hawse!

When my soul seeks peace and quiet on the Home Ranch of the blest,
Where no storms or stampedes bother, an' the trails are trails o' rest,
When my brand has been inspected an' pronounced to be O.K.,
An' the boss has looked me over an' has told me I kin stay,
Oh, I'm hopin' when I'm lopin' off across that blessed range
That I won't be in a saddle on a critter new an' strange,
But I'm prayin' every minnit if I ride that trail across—
That, I may make the journey—on my—Ol' cow hawse!
                                                    —E. A. BRINNINSTOOL

Verses like these express the love that a cowboy has for his horse as well the high regard in which these horses are held by the ranchmen of the great Southwest.

Registry Association for Quarter Horses

The American Quarter Horse Association maintains registration headquarters at Amarillo, Texas. Dr. Raymond Hollingsworth is the secretary of

First-prize tack room display in a cowboy western tack competition, Los Angeles County Fair, Pomona, California. Photograph by Jack Afflerbaugh.

the association. In the year 1950, 10,171 Quarter Horses were registered by this organization.

The stud books of the American Quarter Horse Association show that the color scheme runs about the same as it does in other breeds, except in the case of dun horses. About 10 per cent of the registered Quarter Horses are dun, a color which is unlikely to disappear from the Quarter Horse Registry because it is both potent and a favorite color of many ranchers. A good, dark pigmentation of the skin, hoofs, and eyes, such as is found in the dun horse, is especially advantageous in many ranch areas. Yellow Wolf and Yellow Jacket, both dun in color, are two of the celebrated Quarter Horses of history.

Sorrel, chestnut, bay, brown, black, gray, cream, and white are other acceptable colors for registration. Paints, Appaloosas, albinos, and multicolored horses, or glass-eyed horses are not knowingly accepted for registration.

About 99 per cent of all registered Quarter Horses trace back to some recognized Quarter Horse blood lines, 90 per cent of them having 50 per cent or more Quarter Horse blood. Forty-three per cent have a registered sire or registered dam or both. Only 10 per cent carry recent Thoroughbred blood.

Only about 1 per cent of the registered horses are of unknown breeding, but these horses are all acceptable in their conformation and performance, and although it cannot be proven, Quarter Horse blood is believed to predominate in them.

The Appaloosa

A remarkable breed of spotted horses, famed for intelligence, speed, and endurance, had been developed twenty-four hundred years ago. Revered in ancient Persia as the sacred horses of Nisaea, and in China, as the heavenly horses of Emperor Wu Ti, these beautiful animals have again come into their own through the intelligent breeding program of the Nez Percé Indians in Idaho and the organized efforts of western stockmen. In this way the heritage of this great horse has been preserved.

History

What is this "heritage" that northwestern horsemen speak of that today gives the Appaloosa the deserved title of the ideal, stock horse for rough country? To begin with, students and authorities alike state that any breed is composed of two basic ingredients, locale and use.

When Lewis and Clark entered the northwestern section of our country in 1805 they found the Nez Percé Indians in possession of the Appaloosa, the breeders of these horses castrating all animals of inferior quality. At that time the Nez Percé Indians occupied an area along the Snake and Clearwater rivers, which now forms southeastern Washington, northeastern Oregon, and a large part of Idaho. They ranged from the Blue Mountains of Oregon to the Bitterroots, often crossing into the Buffalo ranges of Montana. Thus we have their locale, a rugged, canyon-scarred vastness, a broad, mountainous expanse, the very heart of the Northwestern Plateau.

Economic Importance

The Nez Percé Indians had four fundamental, specific uses for their horses: war, hunting, traveling, and racing. They covered a great expanse of territory, year after year, generation after generation, always on horseback. The war horse of the Palouse country became the buffalo hunter par excellence. For more than a century they were trained to follow the stampeding buffalo, enter the plunging herd, and place the hunter close to his selected victim. This required a tougher, gamier, speedier horse than is needed for handling cattle on the western ranges. Only the best horses could qualify as buffalo runners.

The Nez Percé Indians, like most horsemen, held many races, from the short sprint to the distance runs of several miles, with heavy bets on their favorites. One of the popular distances for their races was about fifteen miles. They would choose some easily recognized mark, such as a lone tree or a clump of brush some seven miles away across the rolling plain. As many as thirty horses and riders would line up and dash off at full speed, rounding the distant object and returning to the starting point. Here there were no weight handicaps, no freshly watered, smoothed, and harrowed running tracks, no jockey clubs to set the rules. Winning horses in these contests were chosen to lead attacks against unfriendly, marauding tribes of Indians. And in such races were displayed the disposition, speed, and agility needed for running buffalo. By such rigorous tests the plain, mediocre horses were easily separated from the best of the breed and only the best were used as breeding stock. Is it any wonder, then, that this program developed a horse possessed of superb disposition and plenty of stamina? Careful, selective breeding thus preserved at a high level a breed long noted for speed and intelligence.

Characteristics Which Commend the Appaloosa

Rough-country cowmen are unanimous today in praising the remarkable lack of leg trouble in this colorful, ground-covering horse. They are quick to point out that his traveling gait (the Indian shuffle), a seemingly tireless kind of running walk, is a characteristic of this clean-legged horse in all but a few animals. In the idiom of the Northwest they also insist that he is the easiest-kept horse of all the present-day breeds. Since this horse was developed and maintained for centuries on natural forage, this easy-keeping trait is not surprising.

THE APPALOOSA AS A RANCH HORSE   One of the big ranches that has recognized and has taken advantage of these qualities of the Appaloosa is the 83,000 acre commercial outfit owned by the Hearst interests near San Luis Obispo, California. Although the basic crop of this ranch is beef, it has gained widespread fame during the last twenty-five years through its breeding and sale of registered Arabs, Morgans, and Thoroughbreds. Many people find it hard to believe that this outfit, operating in the old-fashioned way, still relies on the stock horse. The breed that is called on to do all the rough-country work and to handle the cattle is the Appaloosa, despite the availability of the other breeds of horses raised on the ranch.

The Hearst Ranch began using the Appaloosa in 1918, some twenty

A rodeo parade in progress at Fort Worth. This picture is proof that the cow horse still has a great following in the range territory of the Southwest. Photograph by Southwestern Livestock Exposition.

years before the incorporation of the Appaloosa Horse Club. The first Appaloosa brought to the ranch was a stallion shipped in from Wyoming. The strong preference of the cow hands for the Appaloosa, when the other breeds are kept in the same stables, points up his superiority for range work.

It is of interest, too, that the Appaloosa has won more win, place, and show money in "open" endurance races than have all the other registered breeds combined. There is no easy method of compiling the records of these contests, but every such race of sufficient note to be reported in newspapers and magazines has given the Appaloosa an insurmountable lead. It is obviously impossible even to list all such performances on record, but below is a report of one of the toughest races known, which was won by an Appaloosa in 1948.

The annual rodeo held at Omak, Washington, on the banks of the Okanogan River, staged this hazardous ride: The initial run was a mad dash down the steep slope of slide rock to the river far below. Any horses surviving this test then plunged into the rapid Okanogan River, swam to the other bank, and raced to the finish line in the rodeo arena. Here the agility, speed, and courage of the Appaloosa paid off at the prize window.

The heavyweight division of the hundred-mile endurance ride, held at Osceola, Iowa, was won in 1949 and in 1950 by Speck, an Appaloosa, owned by Mr. Glenn Wilson of Indianola, Iowa.

THE APPALOOSA AT THE SHOWS   Herculean feats of stamina and endurance, however, do not tell the complete story of this versatile breed. Mrs. W. H. Davis of Los Altos, California, decided to make a show horse of her Appaloosa stallion Domino. This horse had been ridden on the bridle paths several years before but had never been trained as a show horse. Mrs. Davis secured Pete Villa, a trainer who was an expert in the use of the hackamore and the spade bit. He started to work this fourteen-year-old stallion and within eighteen months had ridden Domino to twenty-two first places in the stiffest competitions that the shows of California could offer in stock, reining, parade, and trail horse classes.

The Appaloosa Hall of Fame should also include one of the greatest neck-reining stock horses that ever competed in the western states—Spotlight, an Appaloosa owned by Mr. Con Ruft of Maryville, California. Spotlight was agile, fast, catlike, and had an abundance of "cow-horse sense." Although Spotlight is dead, horse show audiences have not forgotten the spectacular performances that brought them to their feet time and time again.

Chief Malheur, owned by Mr. John Scharff of Burns, Oregon, is another representative of the breed that has thrilled horse show audiences. Chief's specialty was the role of pickup horse for the saddle bronc contests at rodeo events. To appreciate his training, one would have to see Chief at work. Without hackamore or bridle, Chief would edge out, after the chute gate opened, and follow the pitching bronc at a responsible distance. At the sound of the ten-second whistle or horn, Chief was right up against the bronc, helping the pickup man get the rider to safety.

THE VERSATILITY OF THE APPALOOSA   There is abundant proof that the Appaloosa is a versatile horse. A hundred years ago he was a great war horse and buffalo runner. His fine heritage as a utility horse has been preserved by the Nez Percé Indians. Today he is an outstanding stock horse, trail horse, and show horse.

How the Appaloosa Was Named

Appaloosa is an odd name. At first glance it might appear to come from one of the southeastern Indian dialects, possibly from the Georgia country. Attempts have been made to link Appaloosa through Appaluchi with Appalachian or to derive it from Opelousa in the bayou country of Louisiana, but the word belongs to the Columbia Basin, coined by the men who handled horses there, and is derived from the name of a local stream.

A small river scarcely more than a creek flows from the western spur of the Bitterroot Range and plunges into a narrow canyon a few miles above its confluence with the Snake River. Early fur traders of French-Canadian stock called this stream the Pelouse, later changed to Palouse, which might be translated rather freely as "the river with the green meadows." Anyone who has seen the Palouse below the falls, when the Snake River is in full flood, will recognize the aptness of the name.

When the wheat farmers homesteaded the land after the Civil War, the spelling was fixed as Palouse, a spelling now official on government maps. Because one of the Nez Percé Indians who lived along the stream owned a large herd of spotted horses, the white people soon came to call all such horses Palouse or "Palousez" horses. Then, no doubt, some stranger asked an old-timer the name of the strangely marked horses and received the curt answer: "A Palouse." But the stranger, unfamiliar with the term, thought it all one word and passed it along as "An Appalousey," in which form it was known to the cowboys of Montana. Charlie Russell, the famous Montana cowboy painter, so wrote the word and proved that he knew the spotted horses by painting pictures of them.

Through the ensuing years the spelling of the name has varied widely, but Appaloosa is now commonly accepted as the preferred one.

Chief Malheur 1274, noted Appaloosa stallion owned by Mr. John Scharff of Burns, Oregon. This horse is without doubt one of the greatest pick-up horses that has ever participated in the saddle bronc rodeo contests. He has thrilled thousands of spectators with his sparkling performances. Photograph by Henry H. Sheldon.

The Color of the Appaloosa

The conformation and quality requirements in the Appaloosa cow horse approach closely the form and quality requirements in Quarter Horses, but the color patterns for the two breeds are quite different.

Since Appaloosas have an unusually striking yet rather variable coat pattern, it is interesting to note that the three most popular patterns all get about the same number of breeder votes, with about as many breeders stating that they have no pattern preference as state that they prefer some specific pattern. Because of this attitude of the breeders, the breed association does not prefer any particular pattern of markings, and does not place any weight on markings in judging Appaloosas. Color patterns can be listed in several different patterns from which there are many variations.

An Appaloosa may have dark roan or solid-colored foreparts with dark spots over the loin and hips. Appaloosas of this pattern were commonly said to have "squaw spots." This pattern is one of the most common in the breed. The dark spots appear in several shapes: round, oval, pointed, leaf-shaped or diamond-shaped.

A second color pattern commonly seen is the white horse with spots over the entire body. One type of this spotting will show spots very close together on the head and neck, sometimes giving almost the appearance of a solid color. The spots will become farther separated toward the loin and hips, but will remain quite uniform in size. In the other type, spots will appear much larger over the loin and hips, becoming smaller and farther apart toward the head.

A third color pattern is found in horses with roan or solid-colored fore-parts and with white over the loin and hips. This pattern is quite common among Appaloosas.

A fourth color pattern is found in horses having a dark base color with white spots of various sizes over the body.

A fifth color pattern is a mottling of dark and white covering the body. This color sometimes resembles a roan, except for the mottling and a parti-colored skin which is in evidence about the nose and eyes.

Old-timers speak of Appaloosas as being either a red or a blue "Appa-lousey," the red applying to the chestnut, bay, and red roans and the blue to the black and the blue roans. Duns, buckskins, and Palominos with Ap-paloosa markings were not known to the early pioneers. They are the result of crossing an Appaloosa on a dun or on a Palomino.

Registration

The Appaloosa Horse Club was organized December 30, 1938, under the laws of the state of Oregon. Mr. Claude J. Thompson of Moro, Oregon, who had been raising Appaloosas for many years from his famous Painter line of stallions, undertook the task of incorporating the organization. He served as president until June, 1948.

The objectives of the organization are to collect records and historical data concerning the origin of the Appaloosa horse, to file records and issue certificates of registration for animals thought to be fit foundation stock for the breed, and to preserve, improve, and standardize the breed of spotted horses known in the Northwest as the Appaloosa.

The Appaloosa Horse Club now has its headquarters at Moscow, Idaho. Mr. George B. Hatley is secretary.

The Morgan

The Beginning

Justin Morgan, foundational sire of the breed of Morgan horses, was foaled in 1789 and died in 1821. He stood slightly over 14 hands, weighed about 950 pounds and although he was small in stature, his frame was literally weatherboarded with muscle. Because of demonstrated feats of strength in local log-pulling contests which were staged in the locality where Justin Morgan was owned, this famous stallion came to be known as "the big little horse" of the neighborhood. In these pulling contests, Justin Morgan defeated many competitors standing 16 hands and weighing several hundred pounds more.

His Pedigree

Justin Morgan was sired by True Briton, by Lloyd's Traveler, by Morton's Imp. Traveler. The dam of Justin Morgan was a mare by Diamond, by Church's Wildair, by Imp. Wildair. Justin Morgan was therefore rich in the influence of Thoroughbred and Arabian blood on both the top and the bottom side of his pedigree. A study of his pedigree proves that Justin Morgan possessed an inheritance that not only accounted for his striking individuality, but also guaranteed for him an unusual prepotency as a stock horse. In other words, Justin Morgan was bred to breed on.

His Breeder

Justin Morgan the stallion was named after the man who bred him. Justin Morgan the man was born in 1747 at West Springfield, Massachusetts, where he lived until 1788, when he moved to Randolph, Vermont. He died in the latter place in 1798.

While Justin Morgan the man owned Justin Morgan the stallion, this horse stood for service under the name Figure. In the years 1793 to 1795 Mr. Morgan stood this stallion in Randolph, Vermont, and at nearby neighboring towns. Subsequently, the horse had a number of owners, but the important point to remember is that this "big little horse" during his career as a stock horse established a type that has exerted a beneficial influence upon a number of our breeds of horses during their formative years. Because of the unusual prowess of this stallion as a stock horse in the hands of Mr. Morgan, who bred him, it was decided that the name Figure be discarded and that the stallion bear the name of Justin Morgan, his breeder.

Individuality of Justin Morgan the Stallion

Justin Morgan was a dark bay, with black legs, mane, and tail. He was a very stylish-fronted horse and the features of his head were cleanly chiseled. His dark, hazel-colored eyes were full and prominent. He had wide-set ears that were small, pointed, and erect; he was a wide-ribbed, short-backed, deep-bodied, short-coupled horse; he stood squarely on all of his legs, with shoulders and pasterns that were sloping; his action was prompt, true, and collected; his style was proud, nervous, and imposing. In summary, Justin

Congo 8354, grand champion Morgan stallion, Illinois State Fair, 1946, 1947, and 1949. A splendid representative of the breed, he has a coat like satin, is balanced in conformation and can please the judges at the walk and the trot. Owned by Mr. Roy Brunk of Rochester, Illinois. Photograph by Apperson, courtesy Mr. Brunk.

Morgan was a horse of unusual balance, a happy combination of shape, quality, substance, and style. He died from an injury at the age of thirty-two in the year 1821.

The Morgan Influence

The part played by Morgan horses in the Civil War showed them to be about as wiry as the western broncos and capable of carrying a good weight on long marches under the most difficult conditions. During the First World War, when this country was being scoured for horses for army service, much attention was given to these horses and to their performance in the cavalry.

Justin Morgan himself was an outstanding horse in military reviews and attracted much attention because of his proud, stylish personality and his sharp, incisive step when passing in review. As a trotter, he was not speedy and would probably have had difficulty in covering a mile in less than four minutes, but he had a brand of endurance that was unexcelled. At short distances, Justin Morgan was a fleet runner, best at the quarter of a mile. In his day, a century and a half ago, the race was usually on a straightaway course that either started at the tavern door or finished there. In a race it didn't take "the big little horse" very long to get under way. Again and again he met the leading horses of the community and proved himself an all-round champion, being able to outwalk, outtrot, outrun, and outpull his competitors.

Morgan horses have proved themselves worthy descendants of the sturdy little dark bay stallion that made sporting history in Randolph, Vermont, when that town consisted of little else but the tavern and a long row of hitching posts leading down toward the saw- and the gristmills. In those days, men made bets on the strength of their favorite horses. On one occasion a pulling match was announced. Some ten rods from the sawmill was a fine, big log. It was proposed that this log should be pulled to the mill.

A Mr. Evans owned Justin Morgan the stallion at this particular time. Mr. Evans bet that with three pulls, his horse could pull the log on to the logway at the mill. Jeering and hooting, his listeners willingly took the bet, for they prophesied that the log would pull the little stallion backward.

Unmindful of the ridicule, Mr. Evans hooked Justin Morgan to the log and gave him the word. The little bay went to his work. He dug in his toes and threw his weight into the collar. There was a sudden breaking; then the log began to move swiftly over the ground, nor did it stop until it had covered more than half of the required distance. Another quick pull and the load was delivered safely at the stipulated place. Evans had won his wager and the little 950 pound stallion made his name right then and there. He leaped into immediate importance as a sire and his get were in great demand. There was blood in this horse, the kind of blood that tells.

ON THE AMERICAN SADDLER   Justin Morgan was the founder of the first great American breed, the Morgan horse, and he has been of untold value in the building up of two other great American breeds, the American Saddle Horse and the Standardbred.

Of the 11,977 horses registered in the first four volumes of the Saddle Horse Register, there is a direct male trace to Justin Morgan of just a shade under 6 per cent, or a total of 714. Moreover, many of the most noted saddle show horses, as well as many of the most noted breed-building sires and dams in the history of the American Saddle Horse, have pedigrees which testify to the Morgan influence.

Following are a few of the famous saddlers which trace to Justin Morgan: Bracken Chief 2148, Glorious Red Cloud 2845, Dick Taylor 1102, Kentucky's Artist 1455, Dandy Jim 2nd 1531, My Major Dare 4424, Easter Cloud 4128—each has one cross to Justin Morgan. Jack o' Diamonds 1794, Montgomery Chief 1361, Bourbon King 1788, Emerald Chief 2132, Astral King 2805, Bohemian King 2410, Rex Peavine 1796, Kentucky Choice 3765, Kentucky's Best 5664, Golden Glow 3962, Golden Firefly 9268, Maurine Fisher 10882, and Hazel Dawn (registered as Rexola 7154)—these horses have two crosses to Justin Morgan. Golden King 3042 and Richelieu King have three crosses to Justin Morgan. Cascade 6381, Gipsy Dare 4300, Nazimova 5041, and Edna May 5703 have four crosses to the famous "big little horse."

Among the saddle horses whose names are listed in the preceding paragraph, and whose pedigrees carry one or more crosses to Justin Morgan, are many of the most noted show horses as well as many of the most noted breed-building sires and dams in the history of the American Saddle Horse.

ON THE AMERICAN TROTTER   Justin Morgan antedated Rysdyk's Hambletonian by fifty-six years. For almost three quarters of a century the Morgan led as a harness race horse, the descendants of Vermont Black Hawk long surpassing those of the famous Hambletonian. Although in recent decades, descendants of Rysdyk's Hambletonian have given name to the leading trotting horse families, seldom have any of them produced epochmaking harness race horses without some foundation of Morgan blood. It is of profound significance that George Wilkes, who heads the greatest socalled Hambletonian line, had for his dam Dolly Spanker, a mare which was credited as Morgan and whose description fits the Morgan, just as George Wilkes himself had strong Morgan characteristics.

In the Morgan Register will also be found the names of Seely's American Star and the old-time pacing star, Pilot. Without the brood mare lines springing from American Star and Pilot Jr., much of the greatness would be lost to the trotting horse families generally termed "Hambletonian," through the old custom of continuing the name of the male line. With this recognition and other direct traces to Justin Morgan, we find a distinct Morgan influence in the great present-day trotting families of Peter the Great and Axworthy, and it is not improbable that Morgan blood should have much credit for the beauty of finish and purity of gait of such record-making horses of known Morgan crosses as Uhlan, Lee Axworthy, The Harvester, and Hamburg Belle.

Also, in the Morgan Register is Tom Hal, founder of the greatest of pacing families. This family of Tennessee pacers was early made famous by such horses as Little Brown Jug, Brown Hal, Hal Pointer, and Star Pointer. After a lapse of years, it was again made prominent through Napoleon Direct. Star Pointer 1:59¼ was the first light harness horse to work a mile in less than two minutes. Napoleon Direct is the sire of Billy Direct 1:55, the champion pacing horse of the world and one of the leading sires of 2:00 minute progeny.

The Morgan as a Cow Horse

Reports from cattle-breeding states show that the Morgan is highly rated as a cow horse. Mr. Roland G. Hill of Tres Pinos, California, leading ranchman and judge of stock horses, writes: "I have been raising Morgans for thirty-five years and now breed about forty mares each year. We have large cattle ranches and use them for cow horses, save a few of the best for stallions to sell, but use most of them, and sell one now and then to the city trade. I find the Morgan the best cow horse we have ever used and I like the registered ones better than the half-breeds. We use them for the hardest kind of riding and they stand up fine."

REGISTRATIONS FOR THE LAST DECADE

1941—402	1946—599
1942—304	1947—697
1943—410	1948—469
1944—427	1949—480
1945—471	1950—479

Mr. F. B. Hills, secretary of the Morgan Horse Club, 90 Broad Street, New York City, analyzed the situation thus: "The sharp increase in registrations in 1946 and 1947 was the result of the horse situation in the state of California.

"In the early days of the last World War, there was a lot of spare cash in the hands of what is known as the 'drugstore cowboy' group in California. A great many of them decided to buy a horse and a fancy saddle, and did. This created an artificial demand and stimulated breeding and the registration of their Morgans.

"When the cost of living caught up with these people, all of their horses with their expensive tack became surplus and the whole market collapsed, with the result that breeding was abandoned in many instances and registrations were sharply curtailed. Insofar as Morgans are concerned, the jolt which was given the Morgan business during the war in California is still remembered, so the situation in the Golden Bear State is still a little uncertain and unsettled."

The Palomino

Contrary to the opinions of many people, Palominos, collectively, are neither a breed nor a type. At present they are simply a color. Individually, some are purebred, some are crossbred, and some are inbred. If they were ever a breed, no recorded proof of that fact has been established. Some horsemen believe that they are a breed; others believe they are simply a genetic enigma.

The Raider, one of the outstanding parade horses of all time. Raider was sired by a son of King's Fancy. He is out of a Palomino mare. His winnings in 1950 include parade championships at the Indianapolis Spring Show, the Parade championship at Champaign, Illinois, the parade stake at Du Quoin, Illinois, and the championship parade stake at the Indiana State Fair at Indianapolis. The Raider is owned by Mr. and Mrs. Bert Morgan of the Morgan Packing Company at Austin, Indiana. Mrs. Morgan has ridden this horse in all of his championship performances. Photograph courtesy Mrs. Morgan.

History of the Palomino

About a century ago, when the United States troops entered California in the course of the Mexican War, they found there a type of horse peculiar to the region, a horse that had been developed by the people of that area. This horse was without question a by-product, so to speak, of the Mexican horse-breeding industry that had been improved by selection until a distinct pattern had resulted.

This horse, known as the Palomino, was an offshoot in blood of the mixed Saracenic and allied strains first introduced into the New World by the Spanish conquerors under Cortes in 1519 and in many ways resembled them.

Evidently bred for beauty in color, the Palomino was of a golden hue, varying in shade of coat from gold to a soft cream or blond chestnut and with an almost white mane and tail. Broad, white strips in the face, sometimes a blazed face, and white socks or stockings were common markings of these early horses.

Generally speaking, the Saracenic or Arabian influence was quite obvious in these horses, but increased size and substance had been attained by crossing in heavier blood. Used exclusively under saddle by the Spanish and Mexican dons and great landed proprietors or ranch owners, the Palomino, while especially in demand as a parade horse, was also used for racing.

Palomino Characteristics

In height the Palomino averages 15–2 to 16 hands and in weight from 1,000 to 1,200 pounds. He is golden in color, with a light-colored, white, or flaxen mane and tail. The golden color desired is that of a newly minted gold coin. He should have dark, hazel-colored eyes and a black skin.

In general appearance, the Palomino has features which suggest the influence of Arab and Thoroughbred blood. In their pedigree many Palominos have several top crosses of Arab or Thoroughbred stallions and hence are chestnut in color, for the breeder of Palominos, if he mates a Palomino to a Palomino, has trouble in holding the golden color which is so important a feature of his horse. He has to resort to the use of a chestnut cross to get progeny whose coats are the color of a newly minted gold coin. Palominos mated to Palominos will result in light colors approaching the albino.

Registration Rules for Palominos

The Palomino Horse Breeders Association has no objection to any type that any breeder wishes to produce; hence the crosses with a number of recognized light breeds are accepted for registration if the progeny conform to the color requirement. The Palomino Horse Breeders Association does forbid the use or infusion of Shetland or draft blood and bars the use of pintos, piebalds, albinos, and other off colors. Pink- or pumpkin-skinned horses and glass-eyed horses are barred because the experience of breeders indicates that such horses do not transmit the true golden color. Palominos should be free of white spots on the body except those caused by saddle rubbing or accident. Palominos should not have stains, smudges, or smut spots on their bodies nor a dorsal stripe down their backs or zebra stripes on their shoulders, breast, and legs. A smut spot is a stained or blackened area, a kind of sooty discoloration on the coats of some horses.

Registration rules determining eligibility of Palominos to registration require that the skin of a Palomino be basically dark. A horse shall be considered to be basically dark-skinned if the color of the skin around the eyes and nose is mouse-colored, dark, or black. (However, the judging rules for Palominos under The American Horse Shows Association state in italics that "skin color shall not be considered.") Preferably the eyes should be dark hazel-brown and both eyes should be of the same color. Horses with blue, moon, pink, or glass eyes are disqualified.

No Palomino is eligible for registration in the Palomino Horse Breeders Association unless its sire or dam is registered with the organization, or unless the horse itself, its sire, or its dam is registered in one of the following recognized breed associations:

> A.S.H.B.A.—American Saddle Horse Breeders Association
> A.Q.H.A.—American Quarter Horse Association
> A.H.C.—Arabian Horse Club
> M.H.C.—Morgan Horse Club
> J.C.—Jockey Club
> T.W.H.B.A.—Tennessee Walking Horse Breeders Association
> U.S.T.A.—The United States Trotting Association

The foregoing rules and the fact that all the light-horse breeds are closely related in blood through Arab and Thoroughbred strains, the foundation of all, give the Palomino breeder a wide field in developing Palominos for riding purposes.

The Palomino as a Show Horse

Under the American Horse Shows Association rules, Palominos at the shows may compete in pleasure and parade horse classes, stock horse classes, and other saddle classes—three-gaited, five-gaited, fine harness, walking horse classes, and so on. The Palomino is a saddle horse used for pleasure purposes all over this country. He is also a stock horse in good repute in the cow country.

Pleasure horse classes for Palominos include three-gaited bridle path horses under English or Western equipment. If the number of entries do not warrant dividing this class, no differentiation shall be made because of the difference in type of equipment.

In parade classes, the entries must do a flat-footed walk and a parade gait, specified as a high, prancing trot, but not a high school gait nor the slow gait of the five-gaited saddler. The parade gait should be rated at about four miles an hour. Entries may be called upon to stop, to walk, and to parade alternately to test their manners and to determine that they are well broken and under complete control. Parade horses should be faulted for sidewise

Mr. James Franceschini, Mt. Tremblant, Quebec, owner of Dufferin Haven Farms, driving his famous Palomino four-in-hand. All of the members of this four-in-hand were bred, broken, and trained at Dufferin Haven. The offside leader in this quartet of Palominos is not only a great lead horse but an outstanding fine harness horse in the keenest competition. He was grand champion fine harness horse at the Canadian National at Toronto, 1950. Photograph courtesy J. A. McClasky.

motion, for zigzagging, for tossing the head, for fighting the bit, for carrying sour ears, and for lack of show ring manners.

A few Palominos are seen in five-gaited saddle classes at the shows, in walking horse classes, and even in the fine harness division. One of the most noted Palominos to be seen in fine harness is Far Vision, owned by Mr. James Franceschini, Dufferin Haven Farms, Mt. Tremblant, Quebec. This horse has won the fine harness stake at Devon, Pennsylvania, one of the best shows in the United States, and has demonstrated his ability to give the top fine harness horses of our country an interesting time on show day.

In stock horse classes, Palominos, like other stock horses, are judged on the following qualifications: conformation, manners, performance, rein, substance, soundness, and appointments.

There are classes for lightweight stock horses—850 to 1,100 pounds; heavyweight stock horses, 1,100 pounds and up; open stock horses; western trail horses; western pleasure horses; and the championship stock horse stake.

Western trail horses should be shown on a reasonably loose rein at a walk, trot, and lope, without undue restraint, and with special emphasis on the walk, with a loose rein. Entries will be penalized for being on the wrong lead at the lope. There will be no discrimination against the bits that are used. Horses are required to pass through and over obstacles that simulate hazards which might be found on a trail. The entries are to be judged on appointments, equipment, and neatness (silver not to count), 20 per cent; conformation, 20 per cent; performance with emphasis on manners, 60 per cent.

In a championship stock horse stake, the entries, to be eligible, must have been entered and shown in one other class in the stock horse division. The entries will be shown at a walk and at a gallop without restraint, will lope a figure eight, run at speed and stop, turn easily, and pass a rope test. To be judged on rein, conformation, manners, all-round performance, and appointments.

Registry Associations for Palominos

There are two registry associations for Palominos. One of them is the Palomino Horse Association, located at Reseda, California. The other is the Palomino Horse Breeders Association of America, located at Mineral Wells, Texas. The latter association has the larger registry.

Questions

1. Define the term "breed."
2. What three factors determine breed characteristics and through them the economic importance of the breeds?
3. Name two or three breeds of horses upon which the Arab has exerted a foundational influence.
4. Arabians, typically speaking, are of what colors?
5. Define Thoroughbred.
6. Where was the first race, under racing rules, actually conducted?
7. Thoroughbreds were first introduced to this country by what group of colonists?
8. Describe in some detail the characteristics of the Thoroughbred.
9. Name two or three American breeds upon which the Thoroughbred has exerted an influence.
10. When was the first Kentucky Derby held? What horse was the winner?
11. Name the horse that won the Kentucky Derby in 1952.
12. Name three generations of Kentucky Derby winners, telling when each horse won his race.

13. Name the greatest money-winning Thoroughbred of all time.

14. Man o' War, famous Thoroughbred race horse and sire, ran a quarter of a mile in 20:2 seconds. How many feet did he go per second?

15. Mel Patton of California holds the world's record for the 100-yard dash in 9:3 seconds. How many feet did he run per second?

16. How can you distinguish between three-gaited and five-gaited saddlers?

17. Why was Denmark made the foundational sire of the saddle horse breed?

18. Define the term "gait."

19. Name two or three natural gaits.

20. Name two acquired gaits.

21. By definition, distinguish between the terms "diagonal gait" and "lateral gait."

22. Define the terms "high-gaited," "hard-gaited," "easy-gaited," "free-gaited."

23. Discuss the walk as a saddle horse gait.

24. Why is the walk called the foundation gait?

25. Distinguish between the trot of the three-gaited and the five-gaited saddler.

26. Distinguish by definition between the running walk, the stepping pace, and the fox trot.

27. Define and discuss the rack as a saddle horse gait.

28. Define the canter, lope, and run.

29. Discuss the show ring requirements of the canter as a saddle horse gait.

30. List the gaits of the five-gaited saddler in the order in which they are requested in the show ring.

31. List the important saddle horse requirements as agreed upon by the American Saddle Horse Breeders Association.

32. Discuss the individuality of the saddle horse, stressing his most important characteristics.

33. List some of the characteristics which identify Tennessee Walking Horses.

34. What are some of the common criticisms of the breed?

35. What gaits are required of Tennessee Walking Horses at the shows?

36. What are the show ring requirements for each of these gaits?

37. In what state did the earliest horse racing occur in America?

38. Did colonial Quarter Horse racing precede or follow importation of English Thoroughbreds?

39. When was the Quarter Horse first recognized as a breed by colonial writers?

40. How many years later did the Quarter Horse come to be recognized as the greatest cow horse of all time?

41. Discuss briefly the Steel Dust and Shilo families of Quarter Horses.

42. Describe the individuality of a typical Quarter Horse.

43. List some Quarter Horse criticisms.

44. Discuss the Quarter Horse vs. the Thoroughbred type of stock horse.

45. Discuss color requirements of Quarter Horses, listing those colors that are rejected for registration.

46. What is the economic importance of the Appaloosa as a breed?

47. What characteristics commend the Appaloosa as a utility horse?

48. How was the Appaloosa named?

49. Discuss the color patterns of the Appaloosa.

50. What is the meaning of the terms "red Appalousey" and "blue Appalousey"?

51. How did the breed of Morgan horses acquire their name?

52. Comment briefly upon the individuality of Justin Morgan the stallion.

53. Discuss briefly the Morgan influence upon the American Saddle Horse and the Standardbred horse.

54. How does the Morgan rate as a cow horse?

55. Discuss Palomino characteristics.

56. Discuss registration rules for Palominos, telling what colors are desirable and what colors constitute reasons for ineligibility for registration.

57. Comment in some detail upon the requirements in Palomino parade classes.

12

The Standardbred

The Beginning

According to Mr. John Hervey, noted historian of the Standardbred horse, harness racing in this country dates from the year 1806, when official records were computed for the first time. It was then that the first trotting record was written into the books, when a 2:59 mile was trotted by a gelding named Yankee at Harlem, New York, one of the earliest centers of horse racing in America.

Yankee's performance at Harlem was the first mile publicly trotted in 3:00 minutes or better. A century later the famous Lou Dillon trotted the first 2:00 minute mile at Readville, Massachusetts, on August 24, 1903.

Present-Day Champions

Today the trotting record is 1:55¼, established by the immortal Greyhound; the world's pacing record is 1:55 flat, held by Billy Direct, champion pacing horse of all time. Before the time of Billy Direct and Greyhound, the champion light harness horse was Dan Patch 1:55¼, who held the mark for thirty-three years (1905 to 1938), when the current world trotting and pacing records were established.

Although no longer the world's champion light harness horse, Dan Patch

Greyhound 1:55¼, grand champion trotter of the world in light harness, is also the grand champion Standardbred under saddle. He was ridden to his record under saddle by Mrs. Frances Dodge Van Lennep, Lexington, Kentucky, a most accomplished horse-woman who can ride three-gaited and five-gaited saddlers, or drive a single, a pair, or a four-in-hand of heavy harness horses. Mrs. Van Lennep and Greyhound staged a thrilling exhibition. They went the first quarter in 30¾, the half in 1:00¾, the three quarter in 1:31¾, and the last quarter in 30 flat, to do the mile in 2:01¾, a record that still stands.
Photograph courtesy *Horseman and Fair World.*

was one of the greatest harness horses of all time, having performed more miles in 2:00 minutes or better than any other Standardbred horse since the sport began. According to Mr. Hervey, Dan Patch was far ahead of his time; indeed, his total number of sensationally fast miles has never been equaled.

The Pedigree of Yankee Unknown

Nothing is known of the breeding or individuality of Yankee, the first 3:00 minute trotter. This was typical of that early period when harness racing was in its infancy and the sport was not organized as it is today. Powerful influences, however, were at work toward the production of a distinctive breed, as specialized as the Thoroughbred breed of runners, whose public performances would be firmly established as a great national pastime.

GREYHOUND 1:55¼

THE CHAMPION TROTTER

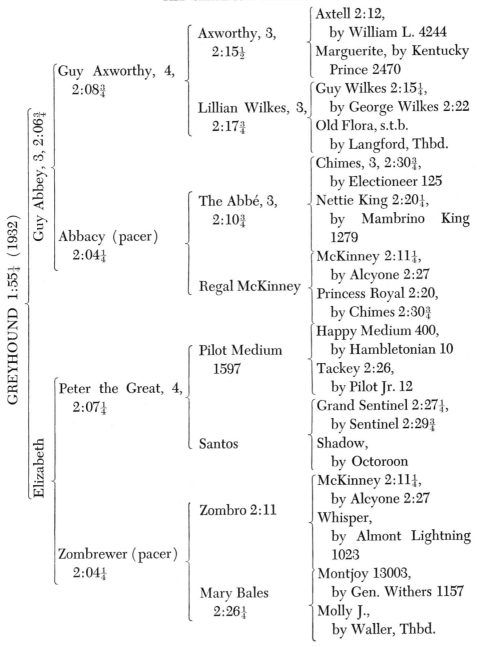

GREYHOUND 1:55¼ (1932)

Guy Abbey, 3, 2:06¾

Elizabeth

Guy Axworthy, 4, 2:08¾

Abbacy (pacer) 2:04¼

Peter the Great, 4, 2:07¼

Zombrewer (pacer) 2:04¼

Axworthy, 3, 2:15½

Lillian Wilkes, 3, 2:17¾

The Abbé, 3, 2:10¾

Regal McKinney

Pilot Medium 1597

Santos

Zombro 2:11

Mary Bales 2:26¼

Axtell 2:12, by William L. 4244
Marguerite, by Kentucky Prince 2470
Guy Wilkes 2:15¼, by George Wilkes 2:22
Old Flora, s.t.b. by Langford, Thbd.
Chimes, 3, 2:30¾, by Electioneer 125
Nettie King 2:20¼, by Mambrino King 1279
McKinney 2:11¼, by Alcyone 2:27
Princess Royal 2:20, by Chimes 2:30¾
Happy Medium 400, by Hambletonian 10
Tackey 2:26, by Pilot Jr. 12
Grand Sentinel 2:27¼, by Sentinel 2:29¾
Shadow, by Octoroon
McKinney 2:11¼, by Alcyone 2:27
Whisper, by Almont Lightning 1023
Montjoy 13003, by Gen. Withers 1157
Molly J., by Waller, Thbd.

The Imported Stallion Messenger

The greatest of these influences was a gray Thoroughbred stallion named Messenger imported from England in 1788. A successful performer upon the running turf abroad and a successful sire of runners in America, he founded here a separate and distinct breed of trotters which far surpassed all others in speed and racing quality. Many of his get became celebrated for their trotting ability. The progeny of his sons and daughters became known everywhere in speed circles as superior performers.

In seeking the causes of true breeding excellence in Standardbred horses, one finds that the best horses trace back to Messenger in the direct male line from the beginning to the present. It was from this line also that in England there had previously developed a now purely historical breed called the "Norfolk Trotter."

Messenger was imported in 1788 and died on Long Island in 1808, after getting a large progeny which relegated all rivals to the background insofar as the light harness horse is concerned.

Faster Miles a Constant Aim of the Breeder

All through the history of the sport horsemen have speculated on faster miles. As the sport developed, it was established that horses could step faster under saddle than they could hitched to the old-time high-wheeled sulkies. Finally, in 1889, driver Hiram Woodruff drove a horse named Dutchman to victory in a mile in 2:32.

The stage was now set for the appearance of the world's first 2:30 trotter in harness. This epochal animal was the gray mare Lady Suffolk, still another specimen of the inbreeding of old Messenger, as were Dutchman and many other noted brothers.

The trotting career of Lady Suffolk had been some seven years in progress when, on October 13, 1845, she trotted the second heat of a winning race in 2:29½. This record was still standing on May 5, 1849, when there was foaled at Chester, New York, a bay colt destined to become the "Great Father" of the Standardbred horse in America. This colt was Mr. William Rysdyk's Hambletonian. He was a son of Abdallah, out of the Charles Kent mare, she a daughter of the imported Norfolk trotter Bellfounder.

The Hambletonian Story

Hambletonian 10 was a dark bay stallion with black points, a small star, and white rear ankles. He stood 15–2 hands high at the withers and 2 inches taller over the coupling, a conformation that was later dubbed the "trotting pitch." His most prominent features were his large, heavy head and short neck, his immensely powerful and grandly molded hips and hind quarters. His legs were clean, his bone was rugged, and the angle of his hocks as viewed from the side was quite pronounced. His temper was kind, his intelligence great.

After Hambletonian 10 was trained for a few weeks as a three-year-old, he trotted a trial in 2:48, after which he was never hitched to a speed vehicle, but in his exercise upon the roads about Chester, he could, in stock horse condition, easily trot a mile at a 2:20 gait.

Hambletonian 10 began service as a two-year-old, when he covered a few mares free. He became a service stallion at three years and so remained to the close of his career. His popularity among the Orange County breeders was immediate. As soon as his get began racing they came at once to the front. In a few seasons more he had the lead as the sire of record trotters and the demand for his services assumed such proportions that it was impossible for him to fill it, although his fee was finally placed at $500.

Abdallah, the sire of Hambletonian 10, was the first stallion to be credited with 2:30 trotters, the first one in 1856 and three more in 1865. But Hambletonian 10 was the first to sire 2:30 trotters so consistently, ten, twenty, thirty, and finally a total of forty head. This, over a long term of years, placed Hambletonian 10 so far in the lead of all other horses as to leave them, by comparison, insignificant, and to earn for him a reputation that increased with the passing years, an identity that was to endure and in the end prove colossal.

The Record for the Mile Gradually Reduced

During the years when the get of Hambletonian 10 were fledglings, the record was being reduced by gradual stages to 2:24½ in 1865 and then to 2:20 by the little bobtail mare Flora Temple, finally by her to 2:19¾ in 1869. She was a trotting freak in the full sense of the term, for she came from sources otherwise of small repute and she was the last champion of her line.

Then Came Dexter

Flora Temple's successor to the trotting throne was the renowned Dexter, son of Hambletonian 10 and Clara, by American Star, an almost unbeatable horse that won 47 out of 51 races, and in 1867 lowered the world's trotting record to $2:17\frac{1}{4}$ over a mile track, while he posted a record of $2:19$ on a half-mile track.

Dexter, although a gelding, was sold to Robert Bonner for $35,000, the beginning of the era of high prices for trotters, prices which ultimately were to pass the $100,000 mark.

Hambletonian Influence Prevails

Dexter became the trotting king in 1867 and from that time to the present, the world's record has always been in the keeping of the Hambletonian dynasty with the sole exception of 1894 to 1900, when it was held by Alix at $2:03\frac{3}{4}$. She was not a male line Hambletonian 10, but she had three close crosses to him. The male line of Mambrino Chief, moreover, was closely allied to the Hambletonian line, because Mambrino Chief was by Mambrino Paymaster and he by Mambrino, the son of Messenger, who was also the paternal grandsire of Hambletonian.

Mambrino Chief was foaled in 1844 and was bred in Dutchess County, New York, which lies just across the Hudson River from Orange County. Mambrino Chief was taken to Kentucky in 1854, where he died in 1862. He was Kentucky's great foundation progenitor and when his mares were later crossed with the Hambletonian family through his son George Wilkes, the progeny resulting from this blend of the two strains proved an extraordinary success.

Today the pedigree of every fast-record harness horse in America, as well as most of those of foreign lands, presents a network of Hambletonian–Mambrino Chief crosses which in their totality are almost bewildering.

Other Successful Hambletonian Crosses

The Hambletonian–American Star cross was, however, the one which lifted the male line of the "Hero of Chester" into prominence and dominance through its representative Dexter. Stallions and mares produced by it were taken all over the country and exerted a breed-building influence upon the Standardbred.

Another successful cross was Hambletonian 10 upon mares by Harry

Calumet Evelyn, the only representative of the Standardbred that has both trotted and paced a mile in less than 2:00 minutes. Her record as a trotter is 1:59½. Her pacing record is 1:59¼. Her performance is without parallel in the history of Standardbred racing. It is worthy of note that her sire is Guy Abbey 2:06¾, the same stallion that sired the immortal Greyhound 1:55¼, champion trotting horse of the world. Photographs courtesy Horseman and Fair World.

E. F. Geers: ("Pop" Geers) dean of the drivers of Standardbreds, and also known as "The Silent Man from Tennessee," for he was born in Lebanon, Tennessee, on January 25, 1851. Football has had its Red Grange, "The Galloping Ghost"; golf its Bobby Jones; baseball its Babe Ruth; and tennis its Big Bill Tilden. To that exalted company harness racing adds the name of E. F. "Pop" Geers, in some respects the most remarkable of the immortals of sport.

Mr. Grantland Rice, the famous sports commentator, paid this tribute to Mr. Geers at the time of the latter's death at Wheeling, West Virginia, on September 3, 1924:

"Geers has left a memory for the younger generation of sportsmen and competitors to study and consider. He has shown beyond all debate the worth of straight shooting, square dealing, friendly helpfulness and rugged honesty; of giving his best at every start. He had no alibi and no complaint, no matter what the break against him. He had no excuses to offer, for no excuses are due when one has given 100% of what he has to give. He started straight at sunrise; he was walking straight as the sun went down." Photograph courtesy Ransom Agency.

Clay, from which came Electioneer, a stallion that revolutionized all previous conceptions of early speed in the trotter.

George Wilkes, a son of Hambletonian 10, was the champion trotting stallion of his day (2:22 in 1868) and a phenomenal sire of successful stallions, with nearly 100 to his credit. It is the male line from George Wilkes through his son William L, that has culminated in the present-day Axworthy line, from which came the reigning King of Trotters, Greyhound 1:55¼, whose performances have set the pace for all trotters produced thus far.

Another son of Hambletonian 10 was Happy Medium, whose dam, Princess 2:30, had inbred Messenger blood. He sired the first 2:05 trotter, Nancy Hanks 2:04, in 1892; his son Pilot Medium sired Peter the Great, the most prolific sire of record performers that ever lived (661 in the standard list) and the founder of the most popular and successful male line of today.

Strathmore, another son of Hambletonian 10 from a mare by North American, founded the line that produced the world's first 2:00 minute trotter, Lou Dillon, who did 1:58½ in 1903. She was by Sidney Dillon, he by Sidney, and he by Santa Claus, a son of Strathmore by Hambletonian 10.

Hambletonian Crosses Strengthen Pedigrees

Lou Dillon's pedigree is of great interest, showing in all five crosses to Hambletonian 10, a remarkable concentration of his blood considering that she was foaled almost fifty-four years ago. There are now champions among our younger trotters that show over forty Hambletonian 10 crosses.

This extraordinary dominance, surpassing everything else of the kind in any other area of horse breeding, for racing or other purposes, has led to the establishment of the Hambletonian Stake, trotted annually ever since 1926 and conducted by the Hambletonian Society, which was organized expressly for the purpose in 1924. It is for three-year-olds and is the richest harness race in the world, having on occasion approximated $75,000 in value.

Each winner of the Hambletonian Stake to date has been a male line Hambletonian stud or filly, with many collateral crosses of the blood. All other lines have been by now in effect exterminated, and in the process the Standardbred has become to all intents and purposes a Hambletonian breed.

The Individuality of the Standardbred

The Standardbred trotter and pacer of today, through a long period of selective breeding, has become greatly refined in type as compared with their ancestors of the foundation days. In many respects they approach the Thoroughbred in form, finish, and quality, while the best specimens are among the world's finest roadsters entered in the shows.

As a rule, a height from 15-2 to 16 hands prevails. It was formerly thought that in order to allow free play of the limbs, the harness horse should have unusual body length, sometimes showing as much as a hand (4 inches) greater in that measurement than in his height. But that type of conformation is no longer sought, and the champion Greyhound 1:55$\frac{1}{4}$, for example, is taller than he is long. He is also much taller than the average trotter, being almost 16-2 hands high. On the other hand, Billy Direct 1:55, the pacing champion of the world (now deceased), was at least a hand less in height than Greyhound.

Race Programs Have Changed

Through the formative years of Standardbred production, long-distance racing of the most severe type prevailed. Gradually there evolved from this the system of the best three heats in five (or more if necessary), a plan of

TABULATED PEDIGREE OF STAR POINTER 1:59¼ *

STAR POINTER 1:59¼, b h (1889)

- **Brown Hal 2:12½ (1879)**
  - **Tom Hal 16934 (Gibson's)**
    - *Tom Hal (Kittrell's)*
      - *Bald Stockings,* by *Tom Hal* (Mason's)
      - Mare, by Dare Devil
    - *Julia Johnson*
      - Adams's *Stump,* by Stump the Dealer
      - *Julia,* by Whip
  - *Lizzie*
    - *John Netherland*
      - *Henry Hal,* by *Tom Hal* (Kittrell's)
      - *Pacing mare,* untraced
    - *Blackie*
      - *John Hal,* by *John Eaton*
      - *Old March,* by *Young Conqueror*
- *Sweepstakes (1871)*
  - *Snow Heels (Knight's)*
    - *Tom Hal (Knight's)*
      - *Tom Hal,* by *Tom Hal* (Kittrell's)
      - *Pacing mare,* untraced
    - *Daughter of*
      - Glencoe (Buckett's), by imp. Glencoe
      - *Pacing mare,* untraced
  - *Kit*
    - *Traveler (McMeen's)*
      - Suggs' *Stump,* by Stump the Dealer
      - *Betsey Baker* (a double Whips)
    - *Saddle Mare*
      - Untraced
      - Untraced

* Horses printed in italics indicate pacers.

racing which was universal until after the turn of the century, when, owing to the marked increase in speed, a movement to shorten the distances began.

Today at the night meetings, where pari-mutuel wagering is a part of the program, the entries go but one dash of from six furlongs to two miles in distance. Though there is much of this odd-distance racing, even at night meetings, the route is more often a straight mile dash.

On the grand circuit and the fair circuits, the best two in three, with three heats very often the limit, is usually the rule, although dash racing has also come into considerable favor, even at the day meetings. This is done, as always, over the regulation mile and half-mile tracks, which have never been superseded.

Colt Races Are Prominent Events of Today's Race Program

Saddle and wagon racing have been discontinued, the former many decades ago. In the beginning, colt racing was unknown, for harness horses were then necessarily mature and well-seasoned animals. But with the up-building and the specialization of the light harness horse, extreme speed at an early age has resulted from a combination of inheritance and careful train-ing right from the beginning; hence the races for two-year-old trotters and pacers are features of a race program today. An example of this early speed was demonstrated in 1944, when the two-year-old trotter Titan Hanover took a record of 2:00 minutes and when the two-year-old pacer Knight Dream in 1947 took a mile record in 2:00⅖.

Champion Trotters and Pacers Produced in Many States

Although the breeding of Standardbreds centers in Kentucky, as in the case of the Thoroughbred, one of the strong points of the Standardbred is the fact that champions can be and have been bred in all parts of the United States as well as Canada.

Of the four successive world champions since the trotting record was placed below 2:00 minutes, the first, Lou Dillon 1:58½, was bred in Cali-fornia; the second, Uhlan 1:58, in Massachusetts; the third, Peter Manning 1:56¾, in Illinois; the fourth, Greyhound 1:55¼, in Kentucky. The pacing champion, Billy Direct 1:55, was bred in Tennessee. Titan Hanover, cham-pion two-year-old trotter, and Knight Dream, champion two-year-old pacer, were both bred in Pennsylvania.

Numerous other states have produced 2:00 minute performers; Canada has sent out Winnipeg 1:57¾, a champion pacing gelding.

The Trainer Contribution

A powerful influence in the evolution of the trotter and the steady re-duction of the speed limit, aside from the great work of the breeders, has been that of the trainers and drivers, many of whom have been breeders as well.

The immense improvement in their methods and skill as compared with those of the formative period has contributed greatly to progress, to the improvement of gaits, and to manners most particularly.

The First 2:00 Minute Mile

The first light harness horse to cover one mile in two minutes was the famous Star Pointer, a member of the noted Hal family of Tennessee pacers. He established his record of 1:59¼ over the Readville, Massachusetts, track in 1897.

Mr. E. F. Geers, one of the most noted trainers of light harness horses that ever lived, had a great deal to do with the development of the Hal family of Tennessee pacers, and because a number of them exhibited such sensational bursts of speed in training, Mr. Geers predicted that some day a light harness horse would go a mile in two minutes. In fact, he even went so far as to say that the first horse to accomplish the feat would be a member of the Hal family. On that historic day at Readville, Massachusetts, in 1897, Star Pointer made the Geer prophecy come true.

The 2:00 Minute Mile a Criterion of Speed

The long-anticipated mile in two minutes created a tremendous sensation, and although a mile in two minutes is still the last criterion of speed in light harness horses, such a performance no longer creates the furor that attended the pioneer mile by Star Pointer, the son of the old mare Sweepstakes.

Today it requires a Titan Hanover, crashing into a new speed bracket as the first 2:00-minute, two-year-old trotter, to create a sensation that parallels that of the first 2:00 minute performance by an older horse in 1897.

At present there are 182 records of horses that have trotted or paced a mile in 2:00 minutes or better. Actually there are only 181 horses in the 2:00 minute list because Calumet Evelyn has paced and also trotted a mile, in less than 2:00 minutes. She is the only Standardbred in the history of the breed that has performed such a feat.

Few Mares Are Dams of 2:00 Minute Speed

During the more than five decades which have elapsed since that first history-making mile by Star Pointer, the trotting and pacing nurseries have seen thousands of brood mares come and go, but only 155 of them have been able to follow Sweepstakes into that exclusive brood mare sorority where one finds listed the names of the dams of 2:00 minute harness horses. Only 156 mares are the dams of 2:00 minute speed.

Billy Direct 1:55, the champion pacing horse of the world. His sire is Napoleon Direct 1:59¾. His dam is Gay Forbes 2:07¾. Billy Direct is by a pacing sire and out of a pacing mare. As a two-year-old he paced in 2:04¼. As a three-year-old he had a record of 1:58. As a four-year-old he paced to the world's record of 1:55. He has sired three of the seven winners of the Little Brown Jug Pace at Delaware, Ohio. During his lifetime, he proved himself to be one of the greatest sires of pacing speed that the breed has produced.
Photograph courtesy *Horseman and Fair World.*

Only 16 mares are dams of two or more 2:00 minute trotters or pacers.

These 16 brood mares are responsible for no less than 41 trotters and pacers in the 2:00 minute test. They have to their credit 23 2:00 minute trotters and 18 2:00 minute pacers. These 16 multiple dams constitute a very select list of brood mares whose influence entitles them to a place on the list of the royal mares in Standardbred horse production in this country.

There are 57 trotters on the 2:00 minute list of all time. These 16 multiple dams are the mothers of 23 of the 57 2:00 minute trotters.

There are 125 pacers on the 2:00 minute list of all time. These 16 multiple dams are the mothers of 18 of them.

In addition, 9 other 2:00 minute trotters are direct descendants of these 16 mares, giving them, therefore, titular credit to 32 2:00 minute performers

BILLY DIRECT 1:55
THE CHAMPION PACER

BILLY DIRECT, 2, 2:04¼; 3, 1:58; 4, 1:55 (1938)

- Napoleon Direct (pacer) 1:59¾
  - Walter Direct (pacer) 2:05¾
    - Direct Hal (pacer) 2:04¼
      - Direct, p, 2:05½, by Director 2:17
      - Bessie Hal, by Tom Hal 16934
    - Ella Brown (pacer) 2:11½
      - Prince Pulaski, Jr., by Prince Pulaski 01471
      - Fannie Brown, by Joe Bowers
  - Lady Erectress
    - Tom Kendall
      - Erector 2:25, by Director 2:17
      - Winnie Davis, by Parkville 6050
    - Nellie Zarro
      - Hal Pizarro, by Don Pizarro, p, 2:14¾
      - Daughter of Bay Tom, p, 2:23
- Gay Forbes (pacer) 2:07¾
  - Malcolm Forbes 47353
    - Bingen 2:06¼
      - May King 2:20, by Electioneer 125
      - Young Miss, by Young Jim 2009
    - Nancy Hanks 2:04
      - Happy Medium 400, by Hambletonian 10
      - Nancy Lee, by Dictator 113
  - Gay Girl Chimes 2:28¼
    - Berkshire Chimes 2:17¾
      - Chimes 2:30¾, by Electioneer 125
      - Berkshire Belle 2:22½, by Alcyone 2:27
    - Miss Gay Girl
      - Gay Boy 29429, by Allerton 2:09¼
      - Electric Bell, by Electricity 2:17¾

at the trotting gait, more than half of the present list of 57 2:00 minute performers.

    Eighteen of the 2:00 minute pacers listed are foals of the same 16 multiple dams. In other words, about one seventh of the 125 2:00 minute pacers are out of the 16 multiple dams. In addition, 13 other 2:00 minute pacers are descendants of these sixteen mares, giving them titular credit to 31 performers at the pacing gait, 63 for both gaits, more than one third of the 182 performers in the 2:00 minute list.

The names of these sixteen mares and the names of their immediate 2:00 minute progeny are listed below:

The Multiple 2:00 Minute Dams of All Time

1. Roya McKinney 2:07½ (*dead*)
   - SIRE, McKinney 2:11¼
   - DAM, Princess Royal 2:20

   Progeny:
   Rose Scott 1:59¾ (trotter)
   Highland Scott 1:59¼ (pacer)
   Scotland 1:59¼ (trotter)

2. Miss Bertha Dillon 2:02¼ (*dead*)
   - SIRE, Dillon Axworthy 2:10¼
   - DAM, Miss Bertha C 2:10¼

   Progeny:
   Hanover's Bertha 1:59½ (trotter)
   Miss Bertha Hanover 2:00 (trotter)
   Charlotte Hanover 1:59½ (trotter)

3. Margaret Arion 2:10½ (*dead*)
   - SIRE, Guy Axworthy 2:08¾
   - DAM, Margaret Parrish 2:06¼

   Progeny:
   Protector 1:59¼ (trotter)
   The Marchioness 1:59¼ (trotter)
   His Excellency 1:59¾ (trotter)

4. Margaret Parrish 2:06¼ (*dead*)
   - SIRE, Vice Commodore 2:11
   - DAM, Lady Layburn 2:23½

   Progeny:
   Arion Guy 1:59½ (trotter)
   Margaret Castleton 1:59¼ (trotter)

5. Dell Direct (pacer) 2:03½ (*dead*)
   - SIRE, Merry Direct 2:06¾
   - DAM, Dell Kinney

   Progeny:
   Dell Frisco 1:59¾ (pacer)
   Edna Brewer 2:00 (pacer)

6. Margaret Spangler (pacer) 2:02¼ (*dead*)
   - SIRE, Guy Axworthy 2:08¾
   - DAM, Maggie Winder 2:06¼

Progeny:
    Chief Counsel 1:57¾ (pacer)
    Blackstone 1:59½ (pacer)
    King's Counsel 1:58 (pacer)

7. Even Song 2:08¾ (*dead*)
                                { SIRE, Nelson Dillon 2:05¼
                                    DAM, Faffolet 2:23¾

Progeny:
    Love Song 1:59 (trotter)
    Volo Song 1:57¾ (trotter)
    Victory Song 1:57⅗ (trotter)
    Peter Song 2:00 (trotter)
    Gay Song 1:59¾ (trotter)

8. Helen Hanover 2:04¾
                                  { SIRE, Dillon Volo 2:11½
                                    DAM, Helen Dillon 2:08¼

Progeny:
    Atlantic Hanover 1:59¾ (pacer)
    Ensign Hanover 1:59⅘ (pacer)
    Hayes Hanover 1:59⅘ (pacer)

9. La Paloma (pacer) 2:01¾ (*dead*)
                                  { SIRE, Walter Direct 2:05¾
                                        (pacer)
                                  DAM, Kay's Ess 2:30

Progeny:
    Her Ladyship 1:56¾ (world's champion pacing mare)
    Carty Nagle 2:00 (pacer)

10. La Petite 2:20¼
                                  { SIRE, Lee Axworthy
                                      DAM, Alice Belwin 2:10¾

Progeny:
    Lee Hanover 1:59½ (pacer)
    Dusty Hanover 1:59 (pacer)

11. Iosola's Worthy 2:03¼
                                  { SIRE, Guy Axworthy 2:08¾
                                    DAM, Iosola Great 2:15¼

Progeny:
    Long Key * 2:00 (trotter)

---

* These three 2:00 minute (or better) trotters (Long Key, Scotland's Comet, and Algiers) are all by different sires. In this respect as a brood mare, Iosola's Worthy stands alone.

Scotland's Comet * 2:00 (trotter)
Algiers * 1:58⅘ (trotter)

12. Justissima 2:06¼

{ SIRE, Justice Brook 2:08½

{ DAM, Clarie Toddington

Progeny:
 Calumet Adam 1:59¾ (pacer)
 Nibble Hanover 1:58¾ (trotter)

13. Gay Forbes 2:07¾ (pacer)

{ SIRE, Malcolm Forbes

{ DAM, Gay Girl Chimes 2:28¼

Progeny:
 Billy Direct † 1:55 (Champion pacing horse of the world. Hence his dam, Gay Forbes, has a special distinction.)
 Forbes Direct 2:00 (pacer)

14. Earl's Princess Martha 2:01¾

{ SIRE, Protector 1:59¼

{ DAM, Mignon 2:17

Progeny:
 Rodney 1:57⅖ (trotter)
 Egan Hanover 1:59 (trotter)

15. Marion Scott 2:10¼

{ SIRE, Peter Scott 2:05

{ DAM, Peach Blossom, by Constantine

Progeny:
 Calumet Evelyn 1:59¼ (pacer)
 Calumet Evelyn 1:59½ (trotter)

16. The Worthy Miss Morris 2:04½

{ SIRE, Guy Axworthy 2:08¾

{ DAM, The Great Miss Morris 2:07¼

Progeny:
 Speed King 2:00 (trotter)
 Robert Morris 2:00 (trotter)

* See footnote on the preceding page.
† Billy Direct is now dead, but he sired nine in the 2:00 minute list, with some additional prospects in his last few crops of foals.

Source: These data on the multiple dams courtesy *The Horseman and Fair World.*

Leading Standardbred Sires Indebted to These Sixteen Multiple Dams

The debt of leading stallions to this group of multiple dams of 2:00 minute speed is quite revealing. Of the eight stallions that have sired four or more 2:00 minute performers, only one, Single G, is not indebted to them for at least one of his fast list. Volomite, 2:00 minute leader among sires, owes nearly half or eleven out of twenty-three, to them. Peter Volo owes seven out of ten of his get to these mares. Billy Direct 1:55, champion pacing horse of all times, and Scotland 1:59¾ are sons of the mares themselves.

Leading Standardbred Nurseries Indebted to These Sixteen Multiple Dams

The use that is being made of the blood of these dams in the leading stallion barns of the country is another evidence of their contribution to the Standardbred strain. For example, at Hanover Shoe Farms at Hanover, Pennsylvania, are four sons and four grandsons of these mares. Walnut Hall Farm, Donerail, Kentucky, has three sons and a grandson. Two Gaits Farm, Indianapolis, Indiana, has two grandsons, and Bonnie Brae Farm at Wellington, Ohio, has a grandson. Descendants of these mares are owned at Siskiyou Farm, Ladd, Illinois; Ankabar Farm, Washington, Illinois; Gainesway Farm, Lexington, Kentucky; Fairmeade Greenacres Farm, Wilmington, Ohio. In fact, their blood through both male and female channels is an integral part of the breeding plan at almost all of the leading light harness nurseries in the nation.

All of these sixteen mares had quite respectable records—thirteen of them in the 2:10 list, eight of them under 2:05. Many of them were truly great race horses, seven of them taking their best records as colts. La Paloma, Dell Direct, Margaret Spangler, Iosola's Worthy, Miss Bertha Dillon—all were race horses of sterling quality that won numerous races against the best horses of their day. Furthermore, the dams of these sixteen mares, with only two exceptions also had standard records.

Breeding Does Count

If one learns anything from the careers of these mares, it is that rigid selection on both sides of the pedigree is necessary if one is to reduce uncertainty in the breeding of trotters, a most uncertain pursuit at best.

The records of these mares indicate that if one has a well-bred mare who has proved speed in her pedigree and who also has the needed degree of gameness and racing quality, then, if she is bred to a stallion possessing the same qualifications, he may expect offspring that can go to the races and give a good account of themselves in keen competition.

The 2:00 Minute Sires

One hundred and eighty-two 2:00 minute performers have been sired by 80 different stallions. Among the 182 2:00 minute race horses, there are 57 trotters and 125 pacers. Only 17 stallions have a total of 3 2:00 minute performers to their credit. Their names are listed as follows:

THE 2:00 MINUTE SIRES

Sires		Trotters	Pacers	Total
1. Volomite	2:03¼	10	13	23
2. Peter Volo	2:02	7	3	10
3. Scotland	1:59¼	6	4	10
4. Billy Direct	1:55	0	9	9
5. Abbedale	2:01¼	0	6	6
6. Guy Abbey	2:06¾	3	1	4
7. Guy Axworthy	2:08¾	4	0	4
8. Single G	1:58½	0	4	4
9. Bert Abbe	1:59¼	0	3	3
10. Bunter	2:04¼	1	2	3
11. Dillon Axworthy	2:10¼	1	2	3
12. Grattan Royal	2:06¼	0	3	3
13. Hal Dale	2:02¼	0	3	3
14. Napoleon Direct	1:59¾	0	3	3
15. Peter Scott	2:05	2	1	3
16. Sandy Flash	2:14¼	1	2	3
17. Spencer	1:59¾	3	0	3

Source: These data on the 2:00 minute sires courtesy of *The Horseman and Fair World.*

The Story of Volomite 68580, the Premier Standardbred Sire

More than a century has passed since the birth of the immortal Hambletonian 10, the foundation sire of the Standardbred breed. He was foaled May 5, 1849, at Chester, New York.

Three generations of breed-building Standardbred sires. From the top down: *Peter the Great, Peter Volo,* and *Volomite. The first photograph shows Peter the Great in 1898, after winning the $10,000 Kentucky Futurity for three-year-olds in 2:12¼. During his career as a stock horse, 661 of his progeny were entered in the standard list. Peter Volo 2:12 ranks next and has 533 progeny in the standard list. Volomite 2:03¼, the greatest sire of 2:00 minute speed in the history of the breed, is the sire of 23 head in the 2:00 minute list. Ten of them have been trotters and 13 of them have been pacers.* Photographs courtesy *The Harness Horse* and Walnut Hall Farm.

At no time since the foundational days of the breed has there been such a sire of speed as Volomite 68580, premier sire at the present time of 2:00 minute performers in light harness. Volomite stands for service at Walnut Hall Farm at Donerail, Kentucky.

The stallion Volomite is the sixth in a consecutive line of champions, starting with the great "Father of the Tribe," Hambletonian 10. As a sire of race winners of extreme speed, of 2:00 minute performers at both gaits and of champions at various ages, Volomite 2:03¼, a great race horse himself, stands alone—the greatest in the history of the breed he represents.

Volomite is a product of Walnut Hall, where he was foaled in 1926. He took the trip with the farm yearlings to the Old Glory Sale in New York City

VOLOMITE 2:03¼

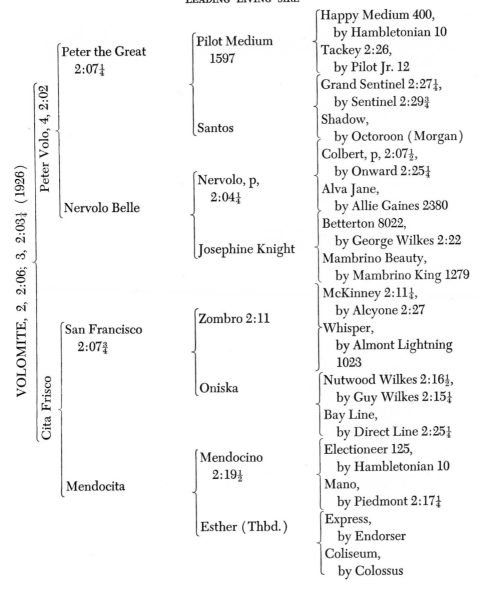

in 1927, where he was sold to the Walter Cox stable. He was one of the top two-year-old trotters in 1928 and won, among other events, the Junior Futurity at Lexington.

The following year on the grand circuit, the major part of the three-year-old trotting talent was in the stable of Walter Cox. Volomite was a good winner in this class and he showed so much speed that he was chosen to represent the stable in the $10,000 Charter Oak Stake at Hartford, Connecticut, going

Good Time, famous pacing stallion, winner of The Little Brown Jug, Delaware, Ohio, 1949, is the champion money-winning Standardbred horse of all time. His winnings total $318,792.86. He is owned by W H. Cane of Goshen, New York. His driver has been the veteran reinsman, Mr. Frank Ervin. Good Time will start his stud career in 1953, at Castleton Farm, Lexington, Kentucky. Courtesy Standard Bred Publication, Harrisburg, Pennsylvania.

out of his class to take on the crack aged trotters. Volomite won the stake, the first time in history that a three-year-old won an important all-age event.

Volomite finished his three-year-old season in 1929 with a record of 2:03¼. Then he was consigned again to the Old Glory Sale. When the hammer fell, he was on his way once more to Walnut Hall and for over two decades has been a reigning figure there; in addition he has been the pace setter among the sires of extreme speed everywhere.

Volomite is the leading sire not only of 2:00 minute trotters, but also of 2:00 minute pacers, having to his credit ten 2:00 minute trotters and thirteen 2:00 minute pacers, his grand total being more than the total of the second and third sires combined.

The three fastest of Volomite's trotters—Victory Song, Volo Song, and Algiers—took their best records in races. The champion three-year-old pacer Chief Counsel 1:57¾ paced 1:58¼ in a race, and his brother King's Counsel, when he raced to a 1:58 record, equaled the world's race record for pacers.

Volo Song established the world's race record for trotting stallions at

1:57¾ in 1944; three years later his brother Victory Song shaded the record with a race mile in 1:57⅗.

The fastest mile by a trotting mare in 1948 was the 1:58¼ of Full Bloom, a daughter of Volomite. The pacing record for four-year-olds in 1948 was 1:59⅗ by Poplar Byrd, and the fastest mile by an aged trotting stallion was the 1:58⅖ of Victory Song, two sons of Volomite.

The number of 2:05 performers in 1949 totaled 58 trotters of which 11 were by Volomite; and 101 pacers, 12 of them by Volomite. In 1950, of the 59 2:05 trotters, 4 were by Volomite and 4 of the 28 pacers were likewise by him.

Race-winning get determine the real standing of a sire. At the "Hambletonian Trot" held at Goshen, New York, the most valuable stake of the harness horse world, on four different occasions the winner has been by Volomite. Volo Song won the Hambletonian in 1943, Yankee Maid in 1944, Chestertown in 1946, and Lusty Song in 1950. In addition, His Excellency, Princess Peg, and Victory Song, all sired by Volomite, have been heat winners in the Hambletonian. Tara, a daughter of Volomite, was the best three-year-old in 1934, but she was not eligible to the Hambletonian. Later she raced to a 2:00 minute record and was sold for export.

In 1946, grand circuit racing was inaugurated on the Pacific Coast where the major trotting event has been the $50,000 "Golden West Trot." Kaola by Volomite won the inaugural event. In 1947, Algiers by Volomite was the winner, and shortly following his victory was sold for $70,000 to Walnut Hall Farm, of Donerail, Kentucky, and Gainesway Farm of Lexington, Kentucky.

One of the striking features of the stud career of Volomite has been his ability to sire both trotters and pacers of 2:00 minute speed. Ten of his 2:00 minute performers have been trotters. Thirteen of them have paced a mile in 2:00 minutes or under. Volomite has undoubtedly established a stud record toward which other Standardbred sires will have to strive for a long time.

Registration of Standardbred Horses

In the United States, all Standardbred horses are registered through The United States Trotting Association, an organization which issues proper application blanks and mating certificates as well as valuable information on current ownership of sire and dam and their records.

According to the association's rules, for a horse to race in one of its sanctioned meetings he must have been registered through these official channels if foaled in 1937 or thereafter. This does not preclude older horses from being registered through the association, however. In fact, the registration of older horses is earnestly advocated and encouraged for several reasons: It is a sound investment for the owner of an older mare or horse to have his property registered because proper identification of his horse protects his interests at all times; registration of horses, regardless of age, guarantees prospective buyers and owners against any fraudulent transactions and misrepresentations; finally, the process of registration gives owners, breeders, and The United States Trotting Association a clear and concise history of the blood lines of any particular horse. This in turn aids greatly in the choice of blood lines for future matings, and thus leads to the ultimate goal of improvement.

Standardbreds, regardless of gait, can be registered as Standard or non-Standard. All progeny of established blood lines are placed in the former classification, as are also all horses registered through their bona fide performance on the track. Speed at either gait renders them eligible to Standard registration.

A non-Standardbred horse is the untried or little-known trotter or pacer whose blood lines are not clear or whose proof of ancestry has been lost. Or he may be a horse that has not performed too well on the track, but is made eligible to compete in sanctioned race meetings so that eventually he may win the right, by proof of speed and behavior, to proper registration.

In every case of requested registration, both for the Standard and non-Standard, all applicants must provide a true statement of breeding, which is checked in detail by The United States Trotting Association's registration department for accuracy and authenticity. The applicant must also provide the association with authorized mating certificates which are further proof of mating by given sires and dams at exact dates.

In conclusion, therefore, a Standardbred horse may be defined as any horse that is registered, or is eligible to registry, on the books of the United States Trotting Association.

Prices for Standardbred Horses

The highest-priced trotter ever sold at auction was Algiers 1:58⅘, sold in 1947 at the dispersal of Baker Acres Farm, near Chicago. Bidding started at a high figure for this great son of Volomite 2:03¼, for he is one of the most perfectly bred and flawless individuals in the history of the sulky sport, as well as one of the greatest race horses of all time. The final bid was $70,000, made by Walnut Hall and Gainesway Farm, on a co-owner basis.

At the Harrisburg sale, also in 1947, a yearling named White Hanover, from the Hanover Shoe Farms consignment, brought the highest price ever paid for a yearling, selling to a California patron of the sport for $42,000.

Other yearlings that have sold for outstanding auction prices in recent years are Victory Song, $37,000; Bombs Away, $36,500; Flying Song, $35,100; and Mighty Song, $30,000.

HIGH-PRICED HARNESS HORSES OF ALL TIME

Price	Horse and Record	Sire	Purchaser	Year of Purchase
$125,000	Arion 2:07¾	Electioneer	J. Malcolm Forbes, Milton, Mass.	1891
105,000	Axtell 2:02½	William L.	W. P. Ijams, Terre Haute, Ind., J. W. Conley, Chicago F. T. Moran and A. E. Brush, Detroit	1889
75,000	Director 2:17	Dictator	A. H. Moore, Philadelphia	1890
72,000	Imperial Hanover	Spencer Scott	McIntyre Hollins, Virginia	1949
70,000 *	Algiers 1:58⅘	Volomite	Walnut Hall and Gainesway Farm, Mrs. H. W. Nichols, Lexington, Ky.	1947
60,000	Anteeo 2:16½	Electioneer	S. A. Brown & Co., Kalamazoo, Mich. M. R. Bissell, Kalamazoo, Mich.	1896
60,000	Dan Patch 1:55¼	Joe Patchen	M. W. Savage, Minneapolis, Minn.	1903
51,000	Bell Boy 2:19¼	Electioneer	George H. Hopper, and J. H. Clark, Unionville, Ohio	1888
51,000	The Harvester 2:01	Walnut Hall	C. K. G. Billings, New York City	1911
50,000	Hoot Mon 2:00	Scotland	Castleton Farm, Lexington, Ky.	1946
50,000	Dr. Spencer 1:59¼	Spencer	Orsi Mangelli, Milan, Italy	1946

* Record at auction.

Price	Horse and Record	Sire	Purchaser	Year of Purchase
$50,000	Allen Winter 2:06½	Ed Winter	H. M. Konoplin, Moscow, Russia	1908
50,000	Hamburg Belle 2:01¼	Axworthy	H. M. Hanna, Cleveland, Ohio	1909
50,000	McKinney 2:11¼	Alcyone	William Simpson, Cuba, N. Y.	1904
50,000	Peter the Great 2:07¼	Pilot Medium	Stoughton A. Fletcher, Indianapolis, Ind.	1916
50,000	Stamboul 2:07½	Sultan	E. H. Harriman, Arden, N. Y.	1892
50,000	Belwin 2:06¾	McKinney	W. M. Wright, Lexington, Ky.	1924
45,000	Nancy Hanks 2:04¼	Happy Medium	J. Malcolm Forbes, Milton, Mass.	1890
42,000 *	White Hanover	Spencer Scott	S. A. Camp, Shafter, Calif.	1947
41,000	Sunol 2:08¼	Electioneer	Robert Bonner, New York City	1888
40,000	Chestertown 2:00⅖	Volomite	W. M. Smith, Hollywood, Calif.	1946
40,000	Acolyte 2:21	Onward	W. E. Campbell, Kiowa, Kans.	1886
40,000	Maud S 2:08¼	Harold	Robert Bonner, New York City	1884
40,000	Major Delmar 1:59¾	Delmar	E. E. Smathers, New York City	1902
37,000	Victory Song 1:57⅖	Volomite	Castleton Farm, Lexington, Ky.	1944
36,500	Bombs Away 2:04½	Volomite	Castleton Farm, Lexington, Ky.	1944
36,000	Pocahontas 2:17¼	Cadmus	Robert Bonner, New York City	1884
35,100	Flying Song 2:01	Volomite	Castleton Farm, Lexington, Ky.	1947
35,000	Antevolo 2:19½	Electioneer	Clairview Farm, Clairview, Mich.	1898
35,000	Dexter 2:17¼	Hambleto-nian 10	Robert Bonner, New York City	1867
33,000	Rarus 2:13¼	Conklin's Abdallah	Robert Bonner, New York City	1879

* Record for yearling.

Price	Horse and Record	Sire	Purchaser	Year of Purchase
$32,000	Bingen 2:06¼	May King	J. Malcolm Forbes, Milton, Mass.	1895
32,000	Goldsmith Maid 2:14	Abdallah 15	Henry N. Smith, Trenton, N. J.	1875
30,000	Lady Thorne 2:18	Mambrino Chief	Henry N. Smith, Trenton, N. J.	1870
30,000	Uhlan 1:58	Bingen	C. K. G. Billings, New York City	1909
30,000	Mighty Song	Volomite	Castleton Farm, Lexington, Ky.	1945
30,000	Smuggler 2:15¼	Blanco	H. S. Russell, Milton, Mass.	1873
30,000	Blackwood 2:21½	Rockwood	Harrison Durkee, New York City	1860
30,000	Prince Wilkes 2:14¾	Red Wilkes	George A. Singerly, Philadelphia, Pa.	1885
30,000	Peter Scott 2:05	Peter the Great	Henry Oliver and Robert McAfee, Pittsburgh	1914
30,000	Guy Richard 2:02¾	Guy Axworthy	James P. Berry, Hartford, Conn.	1924

Source: These data courtesy of the United States Trotting Association.

The Hambletonian Stake

Harness racing's counterpart to the famed Kentucky Derby is the Hambletonian Stake sponsored and originated by the Hambletonian Society, organized in 1923 to promote interest in the sport and to stimulate the market for Standardbreds.

This three-year-old trotting classic was first held at Syracuse, New York, in 1926, with a purse of $73,451, the highest purse ever offered in its twenty-two years of existence. Although this event is now annually presented at Goshen, New York, the Hambletonian has been raced over several different courses, including Lexington, Yonkers, and Syracuse. However, it has grown to be an integral part of Goshen, located in the low, sloping hills of Orange County, New York, and will evidently remain there as a fixture.

Through the efforts of the Hambletonian Society, this race has perhaps gained more notoriety and publicity than any other event the harness world has ever known. The scene of some of the sport's most hotly contested races, it has come to be the yardstick of success for trainers. And when a driver wins the Hambletonian he is at the top.

Some of the most revered names in sulky racing have been connected with this famous mile race of three heats. Among the champion trotters who have won their way to the winners' circle to be crowned rulers of the three-year-old trotting class for the year are such familiar names as Hoot Mon, holder of the time record of 2:00 minutes for the event, set in winning the 1947 race. Other winners are the immortal Greyhound, greatest trotting horse of all time, who won the event in 1935, with the famous Mr. "Sep" Palin in the sulky; Rosalind 1:56¾, world's champion trotting mare; Spencer 1:59¾, one of the great Standardbred sires of our day; and the first winner of the event, Guy McKinney 1:58¾.

When the names of a few of the trotters which have won the Hambletonian are listed, it is most appropriate that the names of some of the drivers should be mentioned. Mr. Ben White, who has won this event four times during its short history, is the leading driver and is sometimes referred to as "Mr. Hambletonian." Mr. Henry Thomas, another very successful reinsman, has driven three Hambletonian winners. Mr. H. M. ("Doc") Parshall, Mr. Palin, and Mr. Tom Berry, have two winners apiece to their credit.

The Little Brown Jug Society

Strange enough, until 1943 there was no feature race for three-year-old pacers, long termed the forgotten class of the light harness racing world.

This seeming lack of recognition and failure to provide a big race for juvenile pacers was finally realized by a group of horsemen from Delaware, Ohio, who now enthusiastically sponsor an annual grand circuit meeting over their half-mile track. Headed by Mr. Joseph Neville, a prominent attorney in Delaware, this group organized the Little Brown Jug Society for the purpose of sponsoring a "big" race for three-year-old pacers.

In 1944, a nation-wide contest was conducted by this Ohio group to select a name for the event. The name finally chosen was Little Brown Jug, in honor of the famous world champion pacer of years ago. With the selection of a name, a great event was born, and with subsequent promotion and organization, the three-year-old pacer's lot in the harness field was established. Today the event carries an estimated purse of $50,000, with every indication that it will be increased to a peak of perhaps $70,000 or $75,000.

In 1944, the first event finally leading up to the staging of the Jug was conducted as a preview pace. The same practice was repeated in 1945. In 1946, the first Little Brown Jug race was held for foals of 1943 and was won

Meadow Rice, illustrious pacing son of the Widower, beats Thunderclap, famous pacing son of Chief Counsel in the second heat at Sedalia, Missouri, 1952. Time 2:00⅕. An unusual study of pacers in action. Note that neither horse has a foot touching the ground.
Courtesy *Harness Horse*, Harrisburg, Pennsylvania.

by the chestnut colt Ensign Hanover 1:59⅘, a great pacing son of Billy Direct, the champion pacer of the world.

The second annual midwestern pacing classic sponsored by the society in 1947 was won by Forbes Chief, son of Chief Abbedale. The third Brown Jug event in 1948 was won by Knight Dream 1:59, a son of Nibble Hanover.

In 1949, Good Time 1:58⅘, a son of Hal Dale 2:02¼, won the race. Good Time, out of the Volomite mare On Time, is the champion winning pacer of all time, having rolled up in three years' earnings a grand total of $157,904.33. Good Time is one of the most popular pacers ever to appear on the grand circuit. He has a manner all his own. He even paces when he walks.

In 1950, Dudley Hanover won the fifth Little Brown Jug race. This colt is by Billy Direct 1:55; his dam is Vivian Hanover by Guy McKinney.

In 1951, Tar Heel won the sixth Brown Jug event in 2:00 flat, setting a new record in the most famous of all pacing classics. Tar Heel is out of Leta Long 2:03¾, she by Volomite. It is worthy of note that three of the seven Brown Jug events have been won by the get of Billy Direct.

In 1952, Meadow Rice, a son of the famous pacing sire, The Widower, was the winner of the Little Brown Jug.

The table on the next page shows how the record for trotters was lowered from the first horse trotting the mile in 2:10 to the present-day record.

TROTTING RECORDS, OLD AND NEW

Name	Color, Sex, Age	Sire	Track	Year	Driver	Time
Jay Eye See	bl – g —	Dictator	Providence, R.I.	1884	E. D. Bither	2:10
Maud S	ch – m – 10	Harold	Cleveland, O.	1884	W. W. Bair	2:09¾
Maud S	ch – m – 10	Harold	Lexington, Ky.	1884	W. W. Bair	2:09¼
Maud S	ch – m – 11	Harold	Cleveland, O.	1885	W. W. Bair	2:08¾
Sunol	b – m – 5	Electioneer	Stockton, Calif.	1891	C. Marvin	2:08¼
Nancy Hanks	b – m – 6	Happy Medium	Independence, Ia.	1892	Budd Doble	2:05¼
Nancy Hanks	b – m – 6	Happy Medium	Terre Haute, Ind.	1892	Budd Doble	2:04
Alix	b – m – 6	Patronage	Galesburg, Ill.	1894	Andrew McDowell	2:03¾
The Abbot	b – g – 7	Chimes	Terre Haute, Ind.	1900	E. F. Geers	2:03¼
Cresceus	ch – h – 7 –	Robert McGregor	Cleveland, O.	1901	G. H. Ketcham	2:03¾
Cresceus	ch – m – 7	Robert McGregor	Columbus, O.	1901	G. H. Ketcham	2:02¼
Lou Dillon	ch – m – 5	Sidney Dillon	Readville, Mass.	1903	Millard Saunders	2:00
Lou Dillon	ch – m – 5	Sidney Dillon	Memphis, Tenn.	1903	Millard Saunders	1:58½
Uhlan	bl – g —	Bingen	Lexington, Ky.	1912	Charles Tanner	1:58
Peter Manning	b – g – 6	Azoff	Lexington, Ky.	1922	T. W. Murphy	1:56¾
Greyhound	gr – g —	Guy Abbey	Lexington, Ky.	1938	S. F. Palin	1:55¼

Thus fifty-four years elapsed while the trotting record was being lowered from 2:10 to 1:55¼.

PACING RECORDS, OLD AND NEW

Name	Color, Sex, Age	Sire	Track	Year	Driver	Time
Johnston	b – g – 6	Joe Bassett	Chicago, Ill.	1883	Peter V. Johnston	2:10
Johnston	b – g – 7	Joe Bassett	Milwaukee, Wis.	1884	John Splan	2:10
Johnston	b – g – 7	Joe Bassett	Chicago, Ill.	1884	John Splan	2:06¼
Direct	b – h – 6	Director	Independence, Ia.	1891	George Starr	2:06
Hal Pointer	b – g – 8	Tom Hal	Chicago, Ill.	1892	E. F. Geers	2:05¼
Mascot	b – g – 7	Deceive	Terre Haute, Ind.	1892	W. J. Andrews	2:04
Flying Jib	b – g —	Algona	Chicago, Ill.	1893	John Kelley	2:04
Robert J	b – g – 6	Hartford	Ft. Wayne, Ind.	1894	E. F. Geers	2:03¾
Robert J	b – g – 6	Hartford	Indianapolis, Ind.	1894	E. F. Geers	2:03¾
Robert J	b – g – 6	Hartford	Indianapolis, Ind.	1894	E. F. Geers	2:02½
Robert J	b – g – 6	Hartford	Terre Haute, Ind.	1894	E. F. Geers	2:01½
John R. Gentry	b – h – 7	Ashland Wilkes	Glens Falls, N.Y.	1896	W. J. Andrews	2:01½
John R. Gentry	b – h – 7	Ashland Wilkes	Glens Falls, N.Y.	1896	W. J. Andrews	2:00½
Star Pointer	b – h – 8	Brown Hal	Readville, Mass.	1897	D. McClary	1:59¼
Dan Patch	br – h – 7	Joe Patchen	Brighton Beach, N.Y.	1903	M. E. McHenry	1:59
Dan Patch	br – h – 7	Joe Patchen	Memphis, Tenn.	1903	M. E. McHenry	1:56¼
Dan Patch	br – h – 8	Joe Patchen	Memphis, Tenn.	1904	H. C. Hershey	1:56
Dan Patch	br – h – 9	Joe Patchen	Lexington, Ky.	1905	H. C. Hershey	1:55¼
Billy Direct	b – h – 4	Napoleon Direct	Lexington, Ky.	1938	Vic Fleming	1:55

Source: These trotting and pacing records courtesy of the United States Trotting Association.

Fifty-five years elapsed while the pacing record was being lowered from 2:10 to 1:55. It took the trotters fifty-four years to lower the mile record from 2:10 to 1:55¼. Johnston, bay pacing gelding, worked the first 2:10 mile in 1883. Jay Eye See, black trotting gelding, trotted the first 2:10 mile in 1884. Billy Direct became champion pacer of the world in 1938. Greyhound became champion trotter of the world in 1938. Both world records were made on the historic mile track at Lexington.

GROWTH OF STANDARDBRED SPORT

Year	Total Purses	Number of Horses Starting	Memberships	Registration of horses
1943	$ 1,313,028.87	3,773		
1944	2,634,977.58	5,029		
1945	3,445,906.13	5,679		
1946	6,290,600.00	7,757	5,918	2,418
1947	7,528,870.98	8,563	7,352	3,247
1948	9,805,079.05	9,323	7,353	3,460
1949	11,362,785.09	9,798	7,821	4,140
1950	11,527,711.94	10,281	8,411	4,364
1951	13,119,753.57	11,187	8,731	4,879
1952	16,052,773.31	11,922	9,776	
				(1st 11 months)

Source: The United States Trotting Association.

Terminology Used in Harness Racing

BLOWOUT   The workout or warm-up heat which both trotters and pacers receive before the first heat of a race.

BREAK   A term used when a trotter or a pacer in a race stops trotting or pacing and starts to run.

CHECK REIN   That part of the harness which aids in setting a horse's head in the position at which he races to best advantage.

CLASS RACE   A term used for a race in which the eligibility of the horses to compete is determined by the amount of money they have won. A horse starts his racing career in the 2:30 class and is moved into faster classes in accordance with the money he has won. For example, a race of 2:14 class trotters is set up for horses which have not won $3,250. When a horse has won more than $25,500, he is placed in the highest or fastest classification and is known as a free-for-all horse.

ELBOW BOOTS   Protectors worn on the elbows of light harness horses which at speed go with a bold, high stride in front.

FIRE-WAGON   A term used by racehorse men in referring to a racing sulky.

FREE-LEGGED PACER   Any pacer that races without hopples.

GAITING STRAP   A strap used to reduce the space in which the horse works between the shafts of a sulky.

HEAD POLE   A cue stick running from the horse's head to the back pad of the harness. It keeps a horse headed straight down the track and helps to control the tendency to side rein or to go sidewise.

HOPPLES   A pair of leather straps each of which is designed in the form of a loop that encircles a lateral pair (front and rear) of a pacer's legs. These loops are adjustable and may be of use in keeping a pacer from overreaching, thereby hitting himself, throwing himself off stride and out of balance, and breaking. The word "hopples" is pronounced and is oftentimes spelled "hobbles."

JOG CART   A sulky, narrower and with longer shafts than those in a racing sulky. Jog carts are used for training sessions and workout drills.

JOGGING   A slow warm up of several miles, oftentimes with the horse going the wrong way of the track.

KNEE BOOTS   Protectors for the inside of a horse's knees so that if he hits a knee, the injury will not be so painful that he is thrown off stride, and so breaks his stride. Some horses will pound their knees when thrown off balance, particularly when making the turns of a track.

MARTINGALE   A standing martingale is a strap which runs from the bellyband to the noseband of the bridle and makes it impossible for a trotter or pacer to carry his nose too high and race up into the air, so to speak.

POLE   The position occupied by a horse in a race that is closest to the inside rail of the track.

RUNNING MARTINGALE   A bifurcated strap, looped at the single end to receive the bellyband, bifurcated at the other end, with rings at the end of the bifurcations, to receive the lines which run from the rings of the bridle to the driver's hands. Running martingales help to set a horse's chin and to keep his head in position.

SCORING   A term that refers to the limbering-up process, when horses are worked up and down the stretch before the actual start of the race.

SHADOW ROLL   A large roll that resembles a sheepskin which is placed across a horse's nose just below his eyes, making it impossible for him to look down and see the shadow of an approaching horse alongside of him. Oftentimes the shadow of an approaching horse scares the horse in the lead and causes him to make a break. Shadow rolls are sometimes called shadow jumpers.

SHIN BOOTS   Protectors worn on rear legs, to prevent speedy-cut injuries in the case of overreaching trotters or cross-firing pacers.

TOE WEIGHTS   Brass weights weighing from one to four ounces, and about as large around as a half dollar, placed on the toe of the hoofs of the front legs to balance and improve a horse's stride.

TOW RING or TOE RING   A small circle around which a trainer walks a horse in cooling him out.

TRAILING   A horseman's expression used to mean that a driver has got his horse right in behind the leader in the favorite spot, with a horse ahead of him to set the pace and break the wind. This coveted spot is also referred to as the "two-hole position."

Questions

1. In what year was the first official record made of a trotting race in the United States?

2. What horse among all Standardbred horses has performed the most 2:00 minute miles?

3. Name the present-day champion trotter of the world. What year was the record made?

4. Name the present-day champion pacer of the world. What year was the record made?

5. What gray imported Thoroughbred stallion exerted a tremendous influence upon the speed of the Standardbred in America?

6. Name the world's first 2:30 trotter in harness.

7. Name the sire known as the "Great Father" of the Standardbred horse in America.

8. Name two or three of his sons that proved to be great sires.

9. Describe the individuality of the present-day Standardbred stallion.

10. Discuss the change that has taken place in race programs.

11. What are the advantages of the two- and three-year-old colt races which feature today's programs?

12. How many mares are multiple dams of 2:00 minute speed?

13. Name the multiple dam that leads this famous brood mare group.

14. Name the only Standardbred stallion, mare, or gelding that has a record at both the trotting and pacing gait of less than 2:00 minutes. What are the records at both gaits? What is the breeding of the only Standardbred that has ever performed this feat?

15. What stallion is the leading sire of 2:00 minute trotters and pacers?

16. Comment at some length upon his prowess as a sire.

17. What is the highest-priced light harness horse of all time?

18. Where is the Hambletonian Stake held?

19. Where is the Little Brown Jug Race held?
20. Name the first light harness horse to go a mile in 2:00 minutes.
21. What is a class race?
22. What is a head pole?
23. What is a shadow roll?
24. In a race, what is meant by the pole horse?
25. What are toe weights?

13

The Hackney

Heavy Harness Horses

The Hackney is the breed which has furnished the great majority of our best heavy harness horses. Hard roads in England antedated hard roads in America. For years, heavy English vehicles rolled along on top of hard stone roads easily, while American vehicles much lighter in weight were drawn laboriously and oftentimes hub-deep through the mud. Therefore, England and America developed different types of harness horses because these horses had different jobs to do. The horses, the tack, and the vehicles pulled were fashioned to suit the circumstances under which they had to be used.

Since the English have had hard roads for many years, the heavy harness horse hitched to a heavy vehicle has been their choice. Elsewhere in this text I have used an expression which will bear repetition here: "The Englishman's idea of driving handsomely has been to drive heavily."

Heavy Harness Required for Heavy Vehicles

When heavy vehicles such as a phaeton, a coach, or a heavy gig appear in a horse show arena, they have to be pulled over soft tanbark footing that in many instances is altogether too deep. The soft footing of itself is a great handicap to the horse and, of course, when he is hitched to a heavy vehicle he is asked to operate under a severe disadvantage. Therefore it is

Spartan King, grand champion Heavy Harness Gelding at such leading shows as the Canadian Royal at Toronto, Canada, and Devon, Pennsylvania. This famous gelding has been driven by his owner, Mr. James Franceschini, Dufferin Stock Farm, Toronto, Canada. Note that he can fold his knees, flex his hocks, set his chin and go collectedly. Photograph courtesy J. A. McClasky.

necessary that the harness by which the horses are put to these vehicles be correspondingly heavy.

Hackney History

The name of this breed immediately distinguishes it. The word "hackney" is a very old one, and has come to denote both a general purpose horse and the vehicles which he draws. In England the word was specifically applied to a type of harness horse midway between the light and the heavy sorts.

The word "hack" was much used in referring to riding horses in early days and is still in common use by horsemen. In the show classifications at the present time there are classes for road hacks, three-gaited park hacks, hunter hacks, bridle path hacks, the qualifying term in each instance suggesting the job which the entries in each class are supposed to do. During the formative days of the breed's development, the Hackney might have been described as a heavier strain of the old-time Norfolk trotter, so-called as a result of having originated in the county of Norfolk in England.

The two adjoining counties of Norfolk and Suffolk are the most easterly counties of England and are located directly opposite Belgium and Holland, which were the regions where the "great" and other heavy draft breeds of Europe were evolved in the Middle Ages. In Norfolk, which is the more northern county, the breeders made liberal use of Thoroughbred stallions crossed on the native mares. By means of a selective and refining process, these matings resulted in the Norfolk trotter and his derivative, the Hackney. In Suffolk, however, the emphasis of breeders was quite different for they made liberal use of seed stock from Belgium and Holland; the result was the Suffolk punch, a horse whose type was drafty in the extreme.

FOUNDATION STOCK The Hackney, as a distinct type, did not emerge until comparatively recent times. Its patriarch, or most important foundational sire during the formative days of the breed, was the stallion Blaze, foaled in 1873. This horse was a grandson of the Darley Arabian, the same Blaze from whom imported Messenger, the foundational sire of the American Standardbred trotter, was also directly descended.

The Hackney became specialized for use in the British hackney coach service of the eighteenth century, and, hitched to vehicles of many kinds, was later used by members of the well-to-do classes in their road driving. Horses were needed in the road service, and Hackneys were bred with that object in view, the road-driving assignment calling for a horse that was full-made as compared with a horse designed for racing, yet featuring in make-up the characteristics of finish, quality, substance, and speed, all of which were stressed as important requirements of horses whose job it was to pull a coach over the highways.

THE BREEDERS' GOAL The aim of the breeders was to produce a horse of medium size and weight, 15 to 15–2 hands in height and weighing 900 to 1,100 pounds. Of course, the round-ribbed, full-bodied horses, the easy-keeping kind that stood correctly on their legs and could swing off at a smart trot were the horses most in demand as power units hitched to a coach. The preferred colors for horses in the coaching service were bay, brown, and chestnut with white trimmings. Before the advent of the carriage, these horses were occasionally used under saddle as well as for some light agricultural work.

The Place of the Hackney in America

Before the great tidal wave of motor development, the Hackney was a very popular horse in both England and America. In the former country the breed was very actively promoted and publicized, and had a stud book of its own. Many choice Hackneys were imported to America and used for park

driving, for exhibition at the shows, and for breeding. In this country, however, they encountered strong competition from the Standardbreds and their
derivatives.

Today, the Hackney in this country is used for purposes of show only.
City planning boards are still including bridle paths in our parks and bridle
trails in suburban territory on the outskirts of our large cities where saddle
horses can be ridden in safety. That is to say, provision is still being made
for those horse owners who seek pleasure and recreation on horseback. But
motor cars and motor trucks have driven harness horses off the public
highways.

Heavy Harness Horses at the Shows

There is no question about the pleasure which the spectator experiences
in watching heavy harness classes at the shows. Such classes contribute interest because they diversify a show program. Furthermore, a bold, high-
stepping, heavy harness horse, going with his chin set and in form, rigged
in harness that glistens and shines, and drawing a vehicle such as a phaeton,
whose design suggests dignity and elegance, appeals to most show audiences.

In show competition, there are maiden, novice, limit, and amateur
classes for both single and pairs of heavy harness horses. There are gig classes,
tandem classes, and four-in-hand classes, where four matched horses in park
harness are hitched to a park drag or where the four horses are hitched to a
road coach, in which latter instance the horses are rigged with road harness
and need not be matched in color but they should have substance and be
able to go at a brisk trot.

Most shows include a class for a lady's single harness horse, mare, or
gelding hitched to a phaeton. In all classes, ladies to drive, a horse's manners
are paramount. All-round, animated action at a park pace is very important,
but speed is not required. Horses must stand and back quietly and must not
take a hard hold of the bit when in motion. The entries in such classes are to
be judged on manners, conformation, quality, and performance. Appointments in these classes usually count 40 per cent.

Eligibility of Entries to the Various Show Classes

A maiden class is open to horses or drivers which have not won a first
ribbon at a recognized show in the particular division in which they are
shown.

Custom Maid 4543, grand champion Hackney pony, American Royal Livestock Show 1950, Kansas City, Missouri. This pony won every ladies' class and every amateur class in which she participated in 1950. Her stake winnings included Tulsa, Dallas, Shreveport, South Shore Country Club, Chicago, Maywood, Milwaukee, and Indianapolis. Photograph courtesy J. A. McClasky.

A novice class is open to horses or drivers which have not won three first ribbons at a recognized show in the particular division in which they are shown.

A limit class is open to horses which have not won six first ribbons at recognized shows in the particular division in which they are shown.

For horse show purposes, an amateur is one who rides or drives for pleasure and for the love of the sport and who draws no profit from the sport, either directly or indirectly.

Registration of Heavy Harness Horses and Ponies

Registrations and transfers of heavy harness horses and hackney ponies are handled by the American Hackney Horse Society, 42 Broadway, New York City. Mrs. J. Macy Willetts is secretary of this organization.

Questions

1. What breed has furnished the great majority of heavy harness horses?
2. Of what country is the Hackney breed native?
3. Does the qualifying term "heavy harness" apply to the horse or to the harness he wears?
4. What is the derivation of the term "hackney"?
5. How did the Hackney originate?
6. What is the place of the Hackney in America today?
7. Discuss heavy harness horse requirements as fixed by the shows.
8. What requirements should be emphasized in heavy harness classes, ladies to drive?
9. What heavy harness horses are eligible to a maiden class, a novice class, a limit class?
10. The term "amateur" is applicable to what group of exhibitors at horse shows?

14

Horse Breeding

The Glory of the Horse

You say that he rates a back number—
  A creature of days that are past;
That his glory and records lie buried—
  'Neath the things which old Time has o'er-cast.

I listen and note what you're saying—
  As one does or should do of course;
But no one can keep me from paying—
  My tribute, heart deep to a horse.

America! What pen can reckon—
  The deeds of the horse in our land;
Where paths scarcely trodden did beckon—
  Still beckon the hoof and the hand.

O'er the rough Alleghenies he bore you—
  O'er the prairies and plains with high zest;
Worked for you, slaved for you, fought for you,
  He gave to this country the west.

So—when in a moment of scoffing—
  You pick my old friend for your mark;
Just count me aside in the offing—
  Unconcerned with your whiffet-like bark.

297

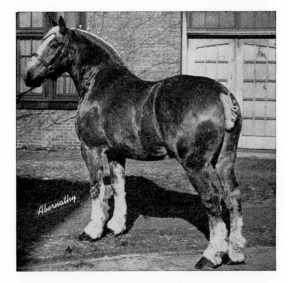

Firestone, a great type study in Belgian geldings. This horse has been grand champion gelding at the Chicago International three times, the last time in 1950, all breeds competing. He was bred and exhibited by Meadow Brook Farms, Mrs. A. G. Wilson of Rochester, Michigan, owner. Photograph courtesy J. F. Abernathy.

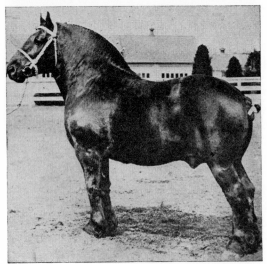

A splendid study in Percheron stallion type. Note the depth and thickness of body, the ruggedness of bone, and the set of the legs. This is Lynnwood Don 231169, former grand champion at the Chicago International. Owned by Lynnwood Farm, Carmel, Indiana. Photograph courtesy Charles J. Lynn.

> For—though the cars fill this earth with their gases
> And the airplanes whiz on in their course;
> In the progress and spread of the masses
> He's Immortal—God Bless Him—The Horse!
> —ANONYMOUS

The foregoing verses remind us that work horses at one time were an economic necessity, both in the city and on the farm. Before the coming of the automobile and the truck, horses played an important role in agriculture and industry.

It was during this period that draft stallions sired most of the horses that were sold for use on city streets and that were retained for work on the farm.

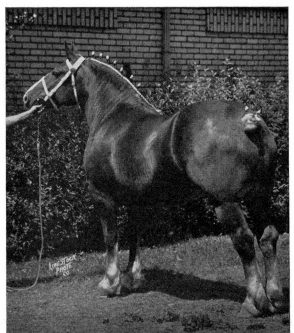

An unusual study in Belgian brood mare type. This mare has the thickness typical of the breed. Note the fullness of her heart, the depth of her flanks, the thickness of hindquarters, and the ruggedness of her bone. This mare, shown by Mr. H. C. Horneman of Danville, Illinois, has been champion at nearly all the large state and national shows in the Midwest. Photograph courtesy Cook and Gormley.

Today, the situation is greatly changed. Trucks have driven horses from city streets and tractors have supplanted them completely as sources of power on many farms.

Nevertheless, it is appropriate that we devote some space in this text to a brief study of the draft breeds, because of the great contribution that draft horses have made to the agricultural and industrial economy of this country, and because of the fact that stallions of the draft breeds continue to sire the bulk of the work horses that appear on the open market. Moreover, draft stallions sire all the entries in the draft horse hitch classes that appear in competition today at our state and national shows.

"Draft horse type" is a term which refers to the sum total of those features which should be included in the make-up of a commonly accepted ideal draft stallion, mare, or gelding.

Important Considerations in Judging Drafters

Weight

1. Other things equal, weight adds value.
2. Weight increases the resources upon which a drafter draws in the performance of his tasks.
3. Weight gives stability on the feet and makes possible maximum effort.

Low-setness

The closer the center of gravity to the base of support, the more stable the equilibrium. The more stable a work horse is on his legs and feet, the more power he can exert.

Width

1. Width is largely a matter of bony framework and skeleton. Power results from muscular activity. The skeleton is the foundation upon which the muscular system is based. Therefore, the skeletal foundation should be ample.

2. Width adds stability on the feet. Stability of equilibrium makes for power. Power is the thing we seek in a work horse.

3. Width of rib and depth of rib provide heart, lung, and digestive capacity.

4. Short backs, close couplings, and deep middles are a combination of features which makes possible the best kind of unit of transmission; that is to say, a short unit of transmission functions best in transmitting forward the power generated in the hind legs to the point of application, which is the collar.

Substance

The amount of muscle and bone indicates substance or the lack of it in a horse. We need sufficient muscle wrapped up in the hide of a horse to give him the balance sought in good horses, either thin or fat. If the big fat is needed to give a horse the depth and thickness necessary to provide balance as a feature in his make-up, he is not a real horse. The big fat costs money to put on and it has to come off before a horse is in proper condition for hard work.

Of course, the kind of bone—that is, the quality of bone as well as the quantity of bone—should be considered in appraising the value of a horse. "The most of the best" should be a guidepost when we think of bone as an indicator of substance in horses and when we estimate the tenure of service to be expected from a horse's bone.

Feet

The feet of the draft horse quite commonly go wrong in one way and the feet of light-leg horses quite commonly go wrong in another way. During the height of the horse business, flatness was one of the prevailing foot ailments of work horses that tramped the city streets, whereas in light-leg horses contraction of the feet and navicular disease are much more common ailments.

The ideal foot for the drafter should be big in proportion to body bulk, should be wide and deep at the heel, should be full and rounding at toe and quarters, and should have enough arch of sole and strength of hoof wall to oppose flatness. I have never seen feet beneath a work horse that can be criticized for being too large when they were properly leveled, trimmed and dressed for show. On the other hand, I have seen thousands of work horse feet that are too small, too narrow, and too upright.

Action

The drafter has always done most of his work at the walk. Three features of the stride contribute to a work horse's efficiency at this gait. Length of stride is important. This refers to the distance from imprint to imprint of the same foot. Trueness or directness of stride is necessary to eliminate interference. Promptness of stride is necessary to ensure against loss of time in taking a single step.

The Drafter as the Horse for the Farmer

It is not surprising that the drafter was commonly referred to as "The farmer's horse."

1. The seed stock with which to launch a breeding project, either commercial or purebred, was much more readily available.

2. Since performance requirements for drafters were much fewer than performance requirements for light-legs, the law of variation was less of a stumbling block to breeders of draft horses. As the number of requirements in a satisfactory foal are decreased, the number of chances of having a good foal are increased.

3. There is less element of risk incident to raising drafters than in the production of light-legs. For example, because they are less hot-blooded, drafters are not so likely to get into the barbed wire. Furthermore, if both the draft colt and the light-leg colt get into the wire, the injury sustained may not impair the service of the drafter working at the walk, whereas the same injury may completely incapacitate the trotter or pacer for racing or the saddle horse for show.

4. At the peak of the business, when work horses fitted into a sound program of farm economy, draft colts, in comparison to light-leg colts, were the farmer's preference because they became self-supporting or partially

self-supporting, at an early age. It was common practice to work well-grown, two-year-old draft colts for half-day sessions and three-year-old drafters for full-day sessions.

5. The prices which breeders received for draft colts constituted a greater percentage of the amount paid by the ultimate purchaser than was true for light-leg colts. That is to say, the range between the price paid to the breeder and the price paid by the ultimate user of drafters has always been narrower than the price spread for light-leg horses. The middleman often gets a much higher price for a light-leg colt than does its breeder. The latter in many instances does not have the time or the money to grow, develop, and train light-leg foals. Hence the man who trains and develops them into potential race winners or stake winners on the tracks and at the shows is in a position to demand long prices from purchasers in quest of a colt that can win.

Launching the Horse Breeding Project

A knowledge of judging is a prerequisite to the successful establishment of a herd. The intelligent selection of animals for mating purposes is also based upon judging.

Herd Establishment

It is doubtful if the prospective breeder of horses should attempt the production of purebreds unless he has had experience with grades. To begin with, purebreds may prove too disappointing and costly and for the following reasons:

1. The investment connected with launching any horse breeding enterprise is high in comparison with other kinds of farm livestock. For example, grade mares cost more than grade brood sows. Purebred saddle mares cost more than purebred brood sows.

2. The turnover is slow in comparison with other kinds of livestock. The period of pregnancy is eleven months. Horses do not have a full mouth until they are five years of age. Hence it takes approximately six years to produce a mature horse.

3. The element of risk is greater in handling pregnant females (brood mares) than in handling the same number of other pregnant females, cows, sows, or ewes. Unsoundness as a determining factor in the success of a horse breeding project is much more important than it is in cattle, sheep, and swine production.

4. The rate of reproduction is low in comparison with that of other kinds of livestock. Under average farm conditions, only about 50 per cent of the mares bred actually produce and save their foals. Under average farm conditions only about 60 per cent of the mares bred settle to service. Eight to 10 per cent of the foals are lost because of dystocia (difficult parturition), navel ill, or pernicious scours.

Thus because of high investment, slow turnover, the element of risk, and the low rate of reproduction, even when trade in them was brisk, horses were never considered a primary source of livestock income on most farms. They were considered as a side line or an occasional source of income and at one time were considered an economic, dependable, and flexible source of farm power. For the four reasons mentioned, grade drafters, even in the peak times of the horse industry, made a stronger appeal to the average farmer than did purebreds or any kind of light-leg horses.

Foundation Stock, Selection of Purebred Stallions and Mares

Selection of the stallion, the single most important step in the establishment of a herd, is based upon three important considerations:

1. He must be considered as an animal representing and transmitting the characteristics of an ancestry.

2. The horse must be considered as an individual.

3. He must be considered as the progenitor of offspring.

Stallion selection, therefore, is based upon pedigree, individuality, and get. Brood mare selection is based upon pedigree, individuality, and produce.

Pedigree as a Factor in Selection

Learn all that you can of the sires and the dams whose names appear in the ancestry of the purebred stallion or mare which you are considering for purchase. It is unreasonable to believe that you can breed from a stallion or a mare characteristics which have never been bred into it. The breeding of livestock may be likened to the checking privilege on a bank. The checking privilege is denied you unless you have made a deposit.

Proving a Pedigree

In March, 1946, The Ohio State University purchased the saddle stallion Genius Stepper 19557 from Mr. George Gwinn of Danville, Kentucky. The purchase of this stallion was one of the first steps incident to launching a saddle horse breeding project at the university. Pedigree and individuality were

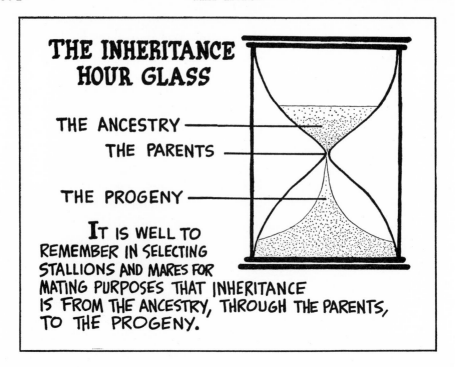

THE INHERITANCE
HOUR GLASS

THE ANCESTRY ————

THE PARENTS ————

THE PROGENY ————

It is well to
remember in selecting
stallions and mares for
mating purposes that inheritance
is from the ancestry, through the parents,
to the progeny.

the two signposts which were read carefully preceding the purchase of this stallion as a prospective stock horse. He had not been used as a stock horse before the time that the university purchased him; hence there was no opportunity to inspect his get.

The Pedigree of Genius Stepper 19557

The names of the many famous saddle horses appearing in the pedigree of Genius Stepper constituted one of the real reasons why it was thought that he was a good potential stock horse.

First, Genius Stepper is sired by the immortal King's Genius 9500, the most famous son of the celebrated Bourbon King 1788, a stallion whose stud earnings, plus the sale of his colts, earned for Mr. Allie Jones, his owner, a half million dollars and made Mr. Jones one of the most well-to-do residents of Bourbon County, Kentucky.

King's Genius ranks as one of the greatest show horse–stock horse combinations in the history of the American Saddle Horse. None can approach his record. No other stallion was ever shown so often or shipped so far as King's Genius. He was a veritable iron horse. In 1933, for example, when King's Genius was at his peak as a show horse, he was shown at Denver, Colorado; Miami, Florida; Ft. Worth, Texas; the Ohio State Fair, Columbus; the Kentucky State Fair, Louisville; the World's Fair, Chicago; the National

Genius Stepper 19557, sired by King's Genius 9500 and out of a granddaughter of Rex Peavine 1796. Study his pedigree. He is bred to breed on. Owned by The Ohio State University. Photograph courtesy J. F. Abernathy.

Horse Show, New York City; and the Chicago International. King's Genius won the stallion division at all of these and at six of them he won the gaited grand championship. King's Genius made this record in 1933 after a heavy stud season in 1932, when he served sixty-eight mares.

King's Genius defeated every horse he ever met in competition except Carnation Chief 10660, Chief of Longview 9704, and Sweetheart on Parade 20872. He defeated the famous Belle Le Rose 17659 twice, and he also defeated Dickery Dare 12536, Totokonoolah 11791, America's Dream 11492, and My Golden Dawn 20708—all horses who made their mark in their day.

King's Genius was exhibited in twelve states—from Michigan to Texas and from New York to California. His famous progeny include such horses as Bourbon Genius, Leatherwood King, Emily Genius, In Society, and dozens of others too numerous to include here.

Bourbon King, the sire of King's Genius, is the horse whose daughters, when mated to Rex Peavine 1796, resulted in progeny so outstanding that the Bourbon King–Rex Peavine cross has come to be known as the "Golden Cross" in saddle horse breeding.

NAME AND NUMBER GENIUS STEPPER, 19557

BREED AMERICAN SADDLE HORSE

DATE OF BIRTH JUNE 3, 1941

BREEDER ROGER A. SELBY

PORTSMOUTH, OHIO

SIRE KING'S GENIUS 9500

DAM QUEEN STEPTOE 19137

SIRE — KING'S GENIUS 9500
- BOURBON KING 1788
  - BOURBON CHIEF 976
    - HARRISON CHIEF 1606
    - BELLE BY LATHAM'S
  - ANNIE C. 3025
    - KING 2196
    - KATE BY RICHLIEU
- PRINCESS EUGENIA 6558
  - CHESTER PEAVINE 3184
    - REX PEAVINE 1796
    - MISS MADISON 4685
  - QUEEN OF LINCOLN 6557
    - WOODS' EAGLE BIRD 1014
    - NOT REG. BY SILVER KING

DAM — QUEEN STEPTOE 19137
- REX STEPTOE 9817
  - REX PEAVINE 1796
    - REX MC DONALD 833
    - DAISY 2ND 2229
  - GEN. CUSTER MAY 10574
    - GENERAL CUSTER 1403
    - RUIE MAY 9139
- ELOISE BOURBON 14396
  - BOURBON KING 1788
    - BOURBON CHIEF 976
    - ANNIE C. 3025
  - ELOUISE 3371
    - HIGHLAND DENMARK 730
    - NANCY LEE 476

On the bottom or maternal side of his pedigree, Genius Stepper is out of the mare Queen Steptoe 19137, a granddaughter of Rex Peavine.

The second dam of Genius Stepper is Eloise Bourbon 14396, a daughter of Bourbon King.

The third dam of Genius Stepper is Elouise 3371, a daughter of Highland Denmark 730, a stallion which has sired some of the longest-necked, finest, and best-motioned walk, trot horses in the history of the breed. Highland Denmark 730 is the sire of Lord Highland, and Lord Highland is the sire of the famous Roxie Highland, a mare that sold for $27,500, and, in the opinion of many good horsemen, the best walk, trot show mare in history.

The fourth dam of Genius Stepper is Nancy Lee 476, by Monte Cristo, 59 and he by Montrose 106, the first saddle horse of the breed to sell for $5,000.

The foregoing comments are proof that Genius Stepper has some famous "kinfolks" and, measured by the pedigree yardstick, is a potential stock horse.

INDIVIDUALITY AS A FACTOR IN SELECTION—FEATURES TO KEEP IN MIND

Draft type	Saddle type
Breed type	Breed type
Sex type	Sex type
Age	Age
Color	Color
Size or scale	Size or scale
Conformation	Conformation
Quality	Quality
Condition	Condition
Constitution—feeding and breeding capacity	Constitution—feeding and breeding capacity
Substance (bone and muscle)	Substance (bone and muscle)
Action	Action
Soundness	Soundness

The Individuality of Genius Stepper

This stallion features in his make-up many of the characteristics that are sought in the best saddle horses. His feet and legs are a study in correctness; he is a very stylish, masculine-fronted horse; he is a happy combination of size, shape, and quality. At the trot, he can push himself off his hocks and up into his bridle and, while he is doing it, remind his audience of his fa-

King's Genius (deceased), sired by Bourbon King 1788 and out of Princess Eugenia 6558, granddaughter of Rex Peavine. Sons of Bourbon King crossed on daughters of Rex Peavine represent what is known as "The Golden Cross in Saddle Horse Production." King's Genius was one of the greatest show stallions and one of the greatest sires in American Saddle Horse history. Note his action at the trot. Chester Caldwell up. Photograph by Haas, New York.

mous sire, King's Genius. In color he is a red sorrel with a few white markings.

Get as a Factor in Selection

Get and produce are the best signposts of all to guide one in selecting breeding stock, but in many instances inspection of get or produce is an impossibility because the stallion or mare changing hands is not of breeding age. Hence the purchaser has to depend upon pedigree and individuality as his guides.

Three generations of Saddle Horse champions. From the top down: Edna May's King 8672, winner of the five-gaited championship, Kentucky State Fair, 1924.

Anacacho Shamrock 12594, winner of the gaited stake, California State Fair, 1938, also winner of the gaited stake at the Pacific International, Portland, Oregon, 1939.

Wing Commander 22591, winner of the gaited stake at the Kentucky State Fair in 1948, 1949, 1950, 1951, 1952, the only American Saddle Horse in history to win this coveted honor five years in succession. A study of the show and the stock careers of this trio of saddle stallions is proof that breeding does count. Photographs by Revel English and John R. Horst.

Choice of a Breed

In the draft horse area in Ohio, Percherons and Belgians have occupied the center of the stage for years. Both breeds have been popular, one of them selling as readily as the other if the offering was choice. Clydes and Shires, with their hairy legs, have been almost wholly without a breeder following in Ohio for the last quarter of a century.

Among the light-leg breeds, American Saddle Horses and Standardbreds are extremely popular in Ohio, a highly urbanized state in which live many people of considerable wealth. Enough of them are interested in saddle horses to make the saddle horse industry one of the leading light-leg industries of the state. The number of people riding horseback, the number of shows held annually in the state, the number of entries in the Ohio-owned classes at the shows are all testimony of the large following of the American Saddle Horse there.

Age at Which Stallions and Mares Should Be Bought

This question must be answered in terms of the needs and conditions of each specific case. Foals and yearlings, both stallions and mares, can be purchased more cheaply, but the purchaser has to assume the risk incident to owning and growing them. Two-year-old and three-year-old stallions, bred right, made right, and old enough for service cost more money. Old, proven sires are rarely available.

Mares four years of age and up to ten years, safe in foal, are the quickest way of getting into the horse breeding business. Diseased generative tracts in the case of old mares make them risky buys. Healthy young mares are better risks than "agey," tried failures.

If one cannot buy a good foundation mare, he should seek to improve the strain he has by breeding only to a high-class stallion. This stallion should include in his make-up those features which are sought in the best work horses if the stallion is a draft stallion, or those features sought in the best saddle horses if the plan is to launch a saddle horse breeding project.

Sureness and soundness as a breeder are stallion essentials. Do not let a low service fee determine the choice of the stallion to which you mate your mare. Such practice may be and oftentimes is costly in time and money.

The time to start to sell the progeny is when you mate your mare. Breed to a horse whose identity is known. In the end, the difference in price of three-year-olds ready for service may more nearly determine profit and loss than will the difference in service fees in the beginning. For example, a stallion breeds one hundred mares in a season and settles sixty of them. If these sixty colts are worth $50 a head more as three-year-olds than the get of an unknown stallion, then a good stallion has added $3,000 to horse values in a community.

Improvement vs. Propagation as an Aim of the Breeder

"Breeding is the regulation of the progeny through the control of the parents with the view of improvement." The aim of the breeder should be either to maintain levels of excellence already attained or else to improve

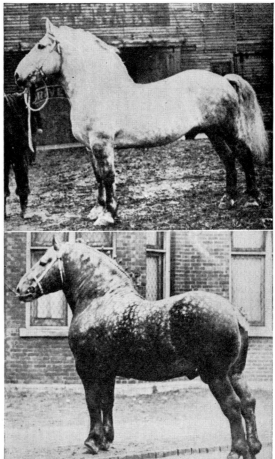

Breeding vs. the propagation of Percherons.

Above: A grade Percheron stallion that stood at a service fee of $5 and bred 252 mares in a single year.

Below: A purebred Percheron stallion, grand champion at the Indiana and Illinois state fairs and with about as good a pedigree as Percherons can have. The patrons of one stallion were simply propagating the species but the patrons of the purebred were trying to breed better Percherons. Lower photograph courtesy J. F. Abernathy.

those levels of excellence. Breeding has been defined also as the "direction of reproduction." Rats propagate themselves, sundry and miscellaneous matings resulting in progeny, but with no intent to improve the progeny.

When to Breed

Breeders of purebreds prefer winter and spring foals because it is common practice to reckon the age of show colts from the first day of January of the year shown. For example, fall colts of 1952 will be barred from the yearling classes at the fall shows of 1953. To be eligible to foal classes at the fall shows of 1953, entries must be dropped on or after January 1, 1953.

Spring foals are preferred to winter foals because the mortality rate is lower.

Spring foals have the advantages of warm weather, sunshine, and grass.

Winter foals require the best housing and much additional care.

A pasture scene at Hanover Shoe Farms, Paoli, Pennsylvania, one of the leading Standard-bred nurseries in America. Photograph courtesy Hanover Shoe Farms.

Thoroughbred brood mares and foals at pasture, Calumet Farm, Lexington, Kentucky. Photograph courtesy Calumet Farm.

Exercise is more of a problem with winter foals.

Summer foals are handicapped by the heat, the flies, and the short grass seasons.

Fall foals are handicapped by cold weather and artificial housing conditions during the suckling period; moreover, they usually have some evience of barn staleness not seen in spring foals. And as noted above, the good ones are ineligible for the foal classes on the basis of age at the shows the following year. Hence the fall foals, and the very late summer foals do not have a ready sale, this being particularly true of the purebred foals good enough to show.

At one time fall draft foals were favored by a few farmers because the fall season was not so much of a rush season as was the spring and the foals interfered but little with the work of the dams. With the situation in horse production as it is today, however, it is best to have the foals arrive on or after January 1 of the year they are to be shown. Because weather conditions in many areas are inclement during January, February, and sometimes March, it is best as a usual thing not to have the foals arrive until late winter or early spring, so that the wait for sunshine, warm weather, and grass will not be too long. This statement applies to all kinds of foals.

Miscellaneous Breeding Terms

Breeding has been defined as an attempt to regulate the progeny through the selection of the immediate parents. Of course there are two aims to be kept in mind in connection with the launching of any livestock breeding project. Any constructive breeder aims to maintain or else improve the levels of excellence already attained in a herd or flock.

Mr. Harry Strauss, of Reisterstown, Maryland, who during his lifetime became one of the most constructive breeders of Polled Shorthorn cattle in the history of the breed and who also served as president of The American Shorthorn Cattle Breeders' Association, once said to his fellow breeders in an annual meeting: "To breed Shorthorns is good; to breed good Shorthorns is better; to breed better Shorthorns is an achievement."

These words should be a goal of attainment for all breeders of livestock for they are applicable clear across the field of livestock breeding. All constructive breeders of livestock must have an aim.

Two great forces are involved in breeding livestock: heredity, by means of which characters are transmitted from generation to generation; and variation, the agency through which new characters are introduced.

The natural tendency in reproduction is toward variation or the production of unlike individuals, with heredity acting as a brake or check opposing variation. The more intense the hereditary force, the less marked the variation.

The strength of the hereditary force, so far as the specific character is concerned, is determined by the extent to which that character is represented in the ancestry. The greater the number of individual ancestors which possess it, and the greater the degree in which it is possessed, the stronger the likelihood of its being transmitted.

Heredity, therefore, is not a matter which involves only the individuals mated; it involves all the ancestors of the individuals.

The germ plasm, which is the union of the two sex cells, is the physical basis of heredity. It represents not only the characters of the ancestry which are dominant in this generation, and will therefore be manifested by the individual developed from the germ plasm, but also the potential characters of the entire ancestry, which may remain recessive in this generation and not be manifested in this particular individual, but may, in the next succeeding generations, become dominant, some in one individual descendant and some in another. Thus the unlikeness of brothers may be accounted for.

Transmission is therefore not from the individual parent but from the ancestry through the parent. The individual displays but a part of the characters which he inherits; consequently he is capable of transmitting characters which he apparently does not possess. All the possibilities of transmission can be learned only by a study of the ancestry.

Because unknown individuals in the ancestry introduce unknown possibilities into the progeny, the purebred parent, the known excellence of whose ancestry is established, has another advantage over the grade parent. A superior but short-bred individual may happen to manifest all the good qualities of his or her ancestors but transmit none of them. A lack of uniformity in the ancestry is sure to result in a miscellaneous progeny.

Pedigree is but a record of the ancestry, and the value of the pedigree, provided it is complete in recording all ancestors of the first five or six generations, depends upon the merit of the individuals recorded.

Prepotency is the breeding power of a stallion or mare measured by the degree with which their likeness is transmitted to their get or produce.

Fecundity is the reproductive power, measured by the regularity with which progeny are begotten by the sire or produced by the dam.

Line breeding is the mating of two individuals having a common ancestor, that ancestor being a few generations removed. It is practiced for the purpose of intensifying the hereditary force derived from certain individuals. It is an alternative to inbreeding.

Inbreeding is the mating of brother and sister, sire and daughter, son and dam, thus eliminating all but the blood from certain individuals. It is rarely practiced by horse breeders.

Crossbreeding is the mating of purebred individuals that are representatives of different breeds.

Hybrid is a term applied to the progeny resulting from the crossing of representatives of different species. The common equine hybrid is the mule, resulting from the mating of a Jack with a mare.

Jennet, or jenny, is the female ass to which the jack is mated to maintain the species. "Jinny" is the term used in common parlance. When a stallion is mated to a jennet, sometimes called the inverse cross, the resulting progeny is called a hinny.

The Nick, a term commonly used by horse breeders in referring to a mating that results in a foal that is superior to either parent. It is supposed to be due to a special affinity of hereditary forces which results in a most harmonious blend or union. A mare may produce good colts to the service of one stallion, but mated with another stallion may result in utter failure in terms of the excellence of the get.

Atavism and reversion are terms referring to the reappearance of the type of remote ancestors or to certain features that suggest the type of remote ancestors.

Atavistic characters refer to a harking back in appearance to a very remote ancestor. The line back, the leg stripes, and the breast stripes sometimes seen in horses are examples of atavistic inheritance.

Reversion suggests resemblance to an ancestor not so far removed in type as in cases of atavism.

A *purebred* is one whose sire and dam are both registered. The "purity" of the breeding depends upon the eligibility rules of the respective registry associations. Literally, a purebred is one in whom there is no trace of alien blood, but such a degree of purity is approached only by the oldest breeds, such as the Thoroughbred and the Arab.

Grading up is the mating of common-bred mares to purebred stallions, or the reverse, producing half-breds. When the half-breds are mated to purebreds, the percentage of increase of the pure blood will follow the proportions of three quarters, seven eighths, and so on, for each successive generation. A horse so bred is called a "grade," and the greater the number of generations through which the grading-up process has been carried, the higher the grade.

A *scrub* or mongrel is one whose fractional breed identity cannot be established.

Top cross refers to the male line of ancestors—the sire's sire, his sire, and thus on back.

Dams, first, second, third, and fourth dams, represent the female line of ancestors—the dam's dam, her dam, and so on.

Brothers in blood are the progeny of mating full brothers with full sisters, the same stallion with full sisters or the same mare with full brothers. In each case the mating results in progeny whose pedigrees after the first generation are identical.

Gelding, an unsexed male castrated at an early age.

Stag, the term applied to an unsexed male, castration having occurred late enough in life to have made it possible for the secondary sex characters to have developed about the head and neck.

Staggy-fronted, studdy-fronted, synonymous terms applied sometimes to heavy-necked mares.

Yeld, the term applied to a brood mare that is not carrying a foal, that is to say, a mare that may be open for a year. The shows sometimes feature classes for yeld mares to which only mares not in foal are eligible.

Barren, the term applied when mares are incapable of procreating themselves, that is, they do not secrete functional egg cells.

Sterile, the term applied when stallions are incapable of procreating themselves, that is, they do not secrete functional sperm cells.

Longevity, a term suggesting procreational productivity over a long period of years.

Single cryptorchid (or ridgling), the term applied to a stallion that has retained one testicle in the abdominal cavity, the testicle having failed to descend to the scrotum.

Double cryptorchid, a stallion (usually sterile) in which both testicles are retained undeveloped in the abdomen.

Hermaphrodite, an individual in which the sexual organs of both sexes are more or less completely represented but, of course, are sterile.

Questions

1. Comment upon the status of the work horse today.
2. List the important type considerations in judging drafters.
3. List three reasons why weight is an important feature in work horses.
4. Why should work horses be low-set?
5. Give three or four reasons why width is an important requirement in the work horse.
6. Define the term "substance." Why should substance characterize work horse make-up?
7. Discuss the importance of good feet as a requirement in the best work horses.
8. Comment upon action as a work horse requirement.

9. List four reasons, why, for so many years, the drafter was the horse in which farmers were most interested.

10. Why is a knowledge of judging a prerequisite to successful herd establishment?

11. List five reasons why the average person should have some experience in commercial horse production before attempting the production of purebreds.

12. Why is the selection of the stallion the single most important step in launching a purebred project?

13. Upon what three important considerations is the intelligent selection of a stallion based?

14. Comment upon pedigree as a factor in selecting stallions.

15. What items of importance would you keep in mind, under the heading of individuality, as a factor in selection?

16. What about the importance of get as a factor in selecting stallions?

17. Discuss the choice of a breed as a problem in launching the horse project.

18. Comment upon age as a problem in selection of the stallion.

19. Discuss breed improvement vs. propagation as the aim of a breeder.

20. Discuss the advantages and disadvantages of spring foals; fall foals.

21. Define the term "breeding."

22. Comment upon heredity and variation as forces involved in breeding livestock.

23. Discuss the germ plasm as the physical basis of heredity.

24. Define these terms: pedigree, prepotency, fecundity, line breeding, inbreeding, cross breeding.

25. What is a hybrid?

26. By definition, distinguish between a jennet and a hinny.

27. What is the meaning of the term "atavism"? "reversion"?

28. Define these terms: purebred, grade, scrub, top-cross, brothers in blood.

29. Give the meaning of these terms: gelding, stag, yeld, barren, sterile, longevity.

30. What is the meaning of these terms: single cryptorchid, double cryptorchid, hermaphrodite.

15

Feeds for Horses

Important Factors to Consider in Choosing a Ration

Availability

Since horses have the slowest rate of turnover in the livestock business, farm-grown feeds should be used as much as possible in order to reduce to a minimum the feed bills incident to their growth and maintenance. Pasture, legume hays, and forage crops should be utilized as a method of cutting production costs in the breeding of horses.

The period of pregnancy in horses is eleven months. In the old days, city users of horses did not want to buy green-mouthed horses. They wanted a work horse at least five years of age that could stand the wear and tear incident to a life on city streets. A farmer breeder, therefore, had to spend six years in the production of a five-year-old gelding for the city user of horses. Since the breeder of such a gelding could not afford to purchase high-priced mill feeds over a period of five years to get a work horse ready for the city streets, he had to use home-grown feeds.

Standardbred horses, both trotters and pacers, are not raced until they are two years of age. The shows do not provide performance classes for saddle horses until they are three years of age. These are but two examples of the comparatively slow turnover in all areas of horse production which is the reason why maximum use of home-grown feeds be practiced in producing horses. A much greater use of high-priced mill feeds is possible in feeding dairy cows and swine because in both dairy and swine production a quick financial turnover is possible.

Suitability

Disappointing results are in store for the horse breeder who attempts the use of feeds that are not suitable for horses. Moldy feed of any kind cannot be fed to horses safely. Mold in quantity will cause digestive disturbances which kill horses. King's Genius, one of the most noted gaited stallions that ever lived, died from a case of indigestion due to some moldy hay that was fed to him by a negligent caretaker.

Moldy feed may cause brood mares to abort. Coarse, dry, stemmy timothy hay will not furnish the protein and the calcium necessary for the growth of foals, yearlings, and two-year-olds. These examples are just a few of many that can be cited in a discussion of suitable feeds for horses.

Palatability

There is a wide range in the palatability of feeds. Dusty oats and hay are not as palatable as clean oats and hay.

There are at least two reasons why many horses eat crushed oats with more relish than they eat whole oats. When oats are run through a crusher, the dirt and dust particles are blown out of the ration, leaving a clean ration which is more palatable. Second, the oat kernel is crushed and its mealy smell makes the feed more palatable.

Linseed meal is much more palatable than cottonseed meal as a feed for horses. Horses do not relish cottonseed meal as such. Therefore it can be fed much more successfully in combination with other feeds, such as crushed oats or corn and cob meal.

Bulkiness

The equine digestive tract cannot handle roughage in any such quantity as can the bovine digestive tract. Horses can easily be fed too much hay or roughage. If allowed to eat all the good hay they will consume, horses often eat too much, with labored breathing and a tendency to tire quickly as the result. This difference between horses and ruminants is doubtless due chiefly to the relatively small size of the simple stomach of the horse, in comparison with the fourfold stomach of a ruminant. Some bulk in the ration of the horse, however, is a guarantee against impaction and colic, especially in the case of the greedy eater. Ravenous eaters will not gorge themselves so easily on crushed oats as on whole oats because the crushed oats are more bulky. Greedy eaters will suffer more frequently from impaction if fed shelled corn than they will when the corn is offered as ear corn and they have to shell it themselves.

Variety

There are at least two advantages which result from variety in the ration. Horses, like people, eventually get tired of the same ration day after day. Variety whets the appetite and tickles the palate. Variety in the ration also provides a means of cutting costs.

Cost

Those who are engaged in any phase of livestock production must of necessity watch the costs. The slower the money turnover in the business, the more careful the operator must be in watching the costs. Any livestock project must be both productive and profitable if it is to be permanent.

Concentrates for Horses

Facts about Oats

Analysis: Dig. prot. 9.4%; t.d.n. 71.5%; calcium 0.09%; phosphorus 0.33%; nut. ratio 1:6.6

1. Next to corn, oats are one of the most extensively grown cereals in America.

2. There is wide variation in the weight of a bushel of oats. Southern oats, because of their long awn or beard, may weigh only twenty pounds a bushel. Pacific oats may weigh fifty pounds a bushel.

3. Oats by weight are 30 to 45 per cent hull, 30 per cent on the average.

4. Clipped oats are heavier than the ordinary run of oats because the hull has been clipped off the bearded end.

5. Oats are higher in protein and calcium than corn; hence as a grain ration alone, oats are preferred for foals and growing colts.

6. The hull of oats gives such bulk to the ration that horses rarely suffer from gorging. This is an advantage of oats as compared to corn.

7. Oats are inferior to corn for fattening. Oat hulls are 30 per cent fiber and their feeding value is but little above that of oat straw.

8. If in eating whole oats a horse has a tendency to bolt his feed, his eating can be retarded by placing corn cobs in the trough or by feeding chopped hay with the oats to add bulk.

9. New or musty oats are dangerous and if fed may cause colic.

10. Whole oats get the call over ground oats as a feed for horses. Ground oats are dusty and should be fed wet or dampened.

11. Crushing or bruising oats is advocated when feeding large numbers of horses.

Crushed oats have the following advantages:

1. Oats that weigh 32 pounds to the bushel will almost double their bulk when crushed.

2. Crushing makes the nutriment of the oat kernel completely available. Oats do not pass through the digestive tract whole.

3. Crushing gives oats a mealy, palatable smell as a ration.

4. Crushing cleans oats thoroughly, for the fan on the crusher blows out most of the dirt.

5. Crushing oats will save one sixth of the oats bill when horses are fed in large numbers. When Hoster Brewery Company in Columbus owned 325 head of horses, it installed an oats crusher and claimed that the crusher saved one sixth of the oats bill.

Facts about Barley

Analysis: Dig. prot. 9.3%; t.d.n. 77.79%; calcium 0.06%; phosphorus 0.38%; nut. ratio 1:7.5

1. Barley is used quite extensively on the Pacific Coast.

2. Barley grains are hard and small; hence they should be crushed or rolled.

3. Ground barley forms an unpleasant pasty mass in the mouth when it is mixed with the saliva.

4. The question is often asked what feed value barley has in comparison with oats as a ration for horses. At the Wisconsin Station, barley was fed one horse in a team; oats was fed to the other. Barley was considered worth 10 per cent more than oats pound for pound when fed with mixed clover and timothy as the roughage. On the other hand, Shephard compared whole barley with whole oats as a feed for horses in North Dakota. Whole barley was not quite so valuable, pound for pound as whole oats. Also, there was more trouble from colic when it was fed.

Facts about Corn

Analysis: Dig. prot. 6.8%; t.d.n. 82%; calcium 0.02%;
phosphorus 0.28%; nut. ratio 1:10.3

1. Corn is the leading grain crop grown.

2. It is the great energizing, heat-giving, fat-furnishing food for ani-mals on the farm.

3. The corn kernel is palatable because of its oil and its physical char-acter. Upon mastication, it is broken into tasty, nutty, palatable particles relished by livestock. It is unlike wheat, which becomes a sticky, pasty dough in the mouth.

4. Corn lacks protein and mineral matter, especially calcium. A ton of the grain contains only 0.2 pound of calcium.

5. Furthermore, the crude protein of corn is unbalanced, since 58 per cent of it is the protein zein, which lacks some of the amino acids necessary to life and growth.

6. Corn is also lower in phosphorus than oats, wheat, barley, or rye, having only 0.28 per cent phosphorus.

7. Yellow corn is rich in vitamin A. Yellow varieties of corn and varieties with yellow endosperm (the inner, starchy part of the kernel) are good sources of vitamin A. Egg fat, butterfat, kidney fat, and all green-leaved roughages are rich in vitamin A.

8. There are three kinds of corn; dent, flint, sweet. In dent corn, the starch is hornlike and floury. In flint corn, the starch is hornlike and flinty. Sweet corn has much glucose, which is changed to tough, horny starch.

9. Fifty-six pounds of dent corn shelled or 70 pounds of ear corn (well dried) make a bushel. In such a bushel of corn, there will be about 14 pounds of cobs or about a quarter of the weight in cobs. The proportion of cob to corn varies from below 20 per cent to 40 per cent. Cobs are about 30 per cent fiber.

10. Shelled corn stored a year has about 10 to 14 per cent water. Newly husked corn may run to 35 per cent water.

11. Seventy pounds of ear corn (dried) make a bushel. However, in the fall of the year, during harvest or a little later, buyers may demand seventy-five or eighty pounds ear corn a bushel because of the moisture contained in new corn.

12. To grade No. 1, corn must not exceed 14 per cent moisture. Number 2 grade must not exceed 15.5 per cent moisture, No. 3 grade, not over 17.5 per cent; No. 4 grade, not over 20 per cent; and No. 5 grade, not over 23 per cent. Corn containing more than 23 per cent water must be sold as sample

grade. Twenty to 25 per cent of moisture in corn is the upper limit for safe storage. When the water content of corn falls to 12 per cent, shrinkage practically ceases.

13. Moldy corn is injurious to horses and sheep.

14. The flinty or horny endosperm (or horny starch) at the sides and the back of the kernel of dent corn forms nearly half the total weight. About 88 per cent of this portion is starch, with but 10 per cent protein, less than 1 per cent fiber, and but a trace of fat and minerals. The floury endosperm (or floury starch) at the tip of the kernel, and partially surrounding the germ, forms about one fourth of the kernel. It is even higher in starch content than the flinty endosperm, but carries only 7.8 per cent protein. The hulls and tip caps, which make up 7 per cent of the kernel, are also composed largely of carbohydrates, but they contain less starch and about 15 per cent fiber. The hornlike gluten layer (8 per cent of the kernel), just under the hull, contains about 22 per cent protein; the germ (12 per cent of the kernel) carries nearly as much protein and about 35 per cent fat and oil. As this analysis suggests, corn is an excellent fattening feed, but deficient in protein and minerals.

15. Methods of feeding corn:

   a. On the cob—the common farm method

   b. Shelled

Does not keep as well. The horse can bolt his feed more easily. It costs money to shell it. In the old days, when it was fed as part of the ration to city horses, shelled corn was more easily stored.

   c. Ground corn

If ground, corn should be ground coarsely or cracked. Moores & Ross Milk Company for years fed a combination of cracked corn and crushed oats as the grain ration. In feeding ground corn there is always the danger of impaction or colic.

   d. Corn and cob meal is preferable to ground shelled corn because the cobs add bulk and lessen the danger of impaction. In a test at the North Carolina Station, Burkett found corn and cob meal pound for pound the equal of shelled corn. In a Minnesota trial, corn and cob meal was not as palatable as oats, but the weights of the horses were maintained on a slightly smaller amount of corn and cob meal.

Facts about Bran

Analysis: Dig. prot. 13.7%; t.d.n. 67.2%; fat 5%; phosphorus 1.29%; calcium 0.14%; nut. ratio 1:3.9

1. Bran is twice as bulky as oats.
2. Horses like it.
3. Bran whets the appetite.
4. Bran is mildly laxative (speeds up the bowels).
5. Bran is low in calcium. Legume hay fed chopped or whole will make good the calcium deficiency in bran.

CALCIUM AND PHOSPHOROUS CONTENT OF LEADING ROUGHAGES

Timothy hay: calcium 0.23%; phosphorus 0.20%
Alfalfa hay: calcium 1.47%; phosphorus 0.24%
Red clover hay: calcium 1.21%; phosphorus 0.18%
Soybean hay: calcium 0.96%; phosphorus 0.25%

In the heyday of the business a bran mash Saturday night was common practice in work horse stables because it helped to take care of the idle-day feeding difficulties. A straight bran mash or half bran and half oats, either whole or crushed can be fed. Bran is excellent as part of the ration for foals, brood mares, and stallions. In a New Hampshire trial, equal weights of bran and ear corn were the equivalent of equal parts of ear corn and oats when fed with mixed clover and timothy hay to work horses.

Facts about Linseed Meal

Analysis: Dig. prot. 30.8%; t.d.n. 77.2%; calcium 0.39%; phosphorus 0.87%; nut. ratio 1:5

1. Linseed meal is rich in protein (35.4 per cent all analyses, old process) and rich in fat (5.8 per cent).
2. It has laxative properties.
3. It adds bloom and finish in fitting horses for show.
4. Fed in the spring, it helps to loosen a horse's winter hair coat. One to one and a half pounds daily is the limit to feed for two reasons, the price and the laxative effect. This amount will balance a ration of ear corn and timothy hay for work horses.

At the Kansas Station 1,170 pound artillery horses were daily fed

4 pounds oats
6 pounds ear corn
1 pound linseed oil meal
12 pounds prairie hay

The linseed oil meal balanced this ration and was cheaper than bran.

At the Iowa Station three teams of farm horses were daily fed

  1 pound linseed oil meal
10 pounds shelled corn
12 pounds timothy hay

This much oil meal proved too laxative for horses at summer work.

At the Iowa Station big draft teams were daily fed

1 pound linseed oil meal		10 pounds oats
4 pounds oats		6 pounds corn
12 pounds ear corn	*vs.*	16 pounds mixed clover and timothy
16 pounds timothy hay		hay

The ration with the oil meal was just as satisfactory a ration and cheaper.

Facts about Cottonseed Meal (43 per cent protein grade, Texas analysis).

One of the most common sources of protein in feed for animals.

> *Analysis:* Dig. prot. 34.2%; t.d.n. 72.6%; calcium
> 0.19%; phosphorus 0.96%; nut. ratio 1:1

Cottonseed meal is a feed that has been used widely in the South as a protein concentrate for horses and mules. Cottonseed meal lacks vitamin D, the vitamin that prevents rickets. This vitamin is necessary to assimilate and utilize calcium and phosphorus in feed. Vitamin D from some source is necessary in the ration during pregnancy and lactation. Moreover, cottonseed meal has little or no vitamin A. Although it has been fed successfully in greater quantity, a common safe rule to follow is one pound daily for one thousand pounds of live weight. In Texas trials a daily ration of two pounds was fed for long periods successfully to more than 90 animals, including work stock, brood mares, growing colts, and in the following ration:

  7.5 pounds ground ear corn
  3 pounds cottonseed meal
12 pounds Johnson grass

In these trials pasture was provided during a considerable part of the year and a mineral supplement supplying calcium was included in the ration.

At the Mississippi Station in a 305 day trial with work mules, cottonseed meal was fed at the rate of three pounds for one thousand pounds live weight. Cottonseed meal might prove poisonous to some animals in excess of this amount. Horses do not relish it when it is fed alone. It is more palatable mixed with whole oats, crushed oats, bran, or corn and cob meal.

In starting horses on cottonseed meal, it is a good plan to start with about a quarter of a pound daily, increasing the allowance as horses become accustomed to it. Palatability of cottonseed meal is increased by "blackstrap" molasses diluted with water and poured over the feed.

In the Texas experiment 1 pound of cottonseed meal was palatable to 95 per cent of the horses. There was no difficulty in getting work horses and mules, brood mares, yearlings and two-year-old mules to eat two pounds daily, but about 5 per cent of the horses and mules fed were slow in acquiring an appetite for it. Mares receiving two pounds of cottonseed meal in their ration were good sucklers and raised vigorous foals.

Facts about Molasses

Cane molasses (blackstrap) is well liked by horses and mules. Even when molasses is more costly than grain, one quart daily of blackstrap is fed as an appetizer to fit horses for show because it whets the appetite of the "picky," choicy, fastidious eaters.

The sprinkling of molasses diluted with water (one gallon of molasses to ten gallons of water) over hay increases the hay appetite, keeps down dust, and helps prevent cases of impaction. Undiluted molasses smears the muzzles and the sides of animals in fly time. The practice of using molasses in mixed feeds is quite common. Such mixtures usually contain about 20 per cent of molasses in summer, about 30 per cent in winter.

In feeding trials, molasses has proved a satisfactory substitute for part of the grain ration, but its mussiness, its tendency to attract too many flies, its tendency to increase sweating and to make horses soft and easily winded explain why it is not more popular as a feed for work stock.

A rather common daily allowance on Louisiana plantations is two quarts or six pounds an animal. Work mules weighing twelve hundred pounds at hard work will eat:

> 6 pounds corn and cob meal or oats
> 6 pounds molasses
> 3 pounds alfalfa hay

It was found that feeding up to nine pounds of molasses to a mule increased sweating and decreased the endurance of the animal in hot weather. A satisfactory ration including molasses for work mules in moderate weather at moderately heavy farm work is:

> 3 pounds corn and cob meal
> 3 pounds ground alfalfa
> 9 pounds molasses

Because molasses replaced some corn in this mixture, feed costs were reduced.

BEET MOLASSES   Because of its laxative properties, beet molasses must be fed in limited quantities. For driving horses, two and a half pounds is the limit daily.

Hard-worked horses, 130 head owned by the Budapest Transportation Company years ago, were fed the following ration for every one thousand pounds of live weight:

> 4 pounds beet molasses
> 5½ pounds of wheat bran
> 5½ pounds of corn meal
> unlimited hay (timothy)

Watering Horses

An ample amount of water is essential, ten to twelve gallons or eighty to one hundred pounds daily for each horse, depending upon the type of horse and the work he is doing. Water consumption of horses depends upon temperature, the kind of work, and the nature of the feed. More water is consumed when legume hay is fed than when the hay is from the grasses.

Extensive tests have shown that horses may be watered before, after, or during a meal with no interference with digestion or absorption of feed. Individual circumstances and convenience should therefore govern. Insist on regularity and systematic procedure. Always use judgment and care in watering warm horses following severe exertion.

Salt for Horses

Horses are very fond of salt. They thrive best when regularly supplied with it. Horses at hard work require more salt than idle horses because salt is excreted in the sweat.

In supplying salt to horses the free-choice system is a good one, either flake salt from a box or a piece of block salt in the feed box.

An allowance of 1.7 ounces to 2 ounces of salt a head daily is ample.

In a Michigan experiment horses having free access to flake salt consumed on the average 1.8 ounces a head daily. Consumption of individual horses varied from 0.27 ounces to 3.2 ounces daily.

Mules in a Mississippi experiment consumed an average of 0.04 ounces of brick salt per thousand pounds of live weight daily.

Vitamin Requirements of Horses

No special attention need be given to the vitamin supply of mature work horses, except perhaps brood mares, because the requirements of such horses for vitamins A and D are apparently low and there seem to be no deficiencies in ordinary rations.

Foals, on the other hand, sometimes develop rickets because of a lack of vitamin D, calcium, or phosphorus. If a foal shows symptoms of rickets, it should be given an ounce of cod-liver oil a day or, better, an equivalent amount of a vitamin D concentrate. It should also be allowed access to bone meal or a suitable mineral mixture, in addition to receiving plenty of good legume hay or good pasture. When a foal is on well-fertilized pasture, or when it is fed plenty of good legume hay, there will be no deficiency of vitamin A, vitamin D, or calcium, all of which are needed in liberal amounts for growth.

The vitamin requirements of brood mares will be met if they are fed good legume hay or mixed hay.

Minerals for Horses

Mineral requirements for horses have been investigated but little. However, practical experience and our general knowledge of nutrition indicate that mature work horses, with the possible exception of brood mares, do not require the addition of any minerals except common salt to ordinary rations which contain a normal amount of good hay. This is because their needs for calcium and phosphorus are but little higher than for mere body maintenance. In Iowa tests with work horses, the addition of a mineral mixture (supplying calcium, phosphorus, and iron) to a ration of oats, corn, timothy hay, and common salt did not save feed or make a marked difference in the condition of the horses.

It is important, however, that growing colts have an ample supply of calcium and phosphorus as well as sufficient vitamin D to enable them to develop strong, sound bones. Likewise, pregnant mares and mares nursing foals require much more calcium and phosphorus than do other mature horses. Well-cured legume hay or mixed hay high in legumes is therefore the best roughage for colts and brood mares during the winter season.

Whenever horses must be fed rations that are deficient in either calcium or phosphorus, care must be taken to supply a suitable mineral mixture or supplement.

If calcium is the only mineral lacking, one ounce daily of ground lime-stone or other calcium supplement for each head will correct the deficiency.

If phosphorus is lacking, one ounce daily of steamed bone meal or some other safe source of phosphorus should be added to the ration of each animal. If both calcium and phosphorus are lacking, a mineral mixture that has wide use is two parts ground limestone, two parts steamed bone meal, and one part salt.

In areas where there is a deficiency of iodine, brood mares should be fed iodized salt during at least the latter half of pregnancy to avoid the danger of goiter in newborn foals. One ounce of potassium iodide in three hundred pounds of the mineral mixture has proved effective in controlling goiter.

At Minnesota, mares in foal were fed one gram of potassium iodide crystals in a bran mash on Saturday nights.

At Purdue, during the winter months, mares in foal were fed this mixture:

> 500 pounds finely ground deodorized steamed bone meal
> 15 pounds iron oxide
> 300 pounds powdered limestone
> 5 pounds powdered anise seed

Brood mares were fed one and a half pounds of this mixture to each one hundred pounds of grain. Usually the grain was dampened to get the minerals to stick to it and so not be wasted.

Pasture as a Feed for Horses

Meadow land and land in pasture, whether in rotation or permanent pasture, particularly the latter, are much less subject to erosion than land in tilled crops such as corn.

Perennial grasses provide a most effective means of building up the organic matter and structure of soils.

Most of our productive soils have been built up under a cover of grass. By means of a permanent pasture, the livestock farmer can hold on to his productive topsoil and keep it from washing away, particularly where the land is rolling or even somewhat hilly.

Good pasture generally furnishes the most economical feed for live-stock. Furthermore, animal health is less of a problem when stock is at pasture than when it is housed or closely confined.

Years ago, Charles F. Curtiss, former Dean of Iowa State College, stated: "Grass is the basis of successful animal husbandry in every successful livestock region on the face of the globe. The grass lands are entitled to first consideration on every good stock farm. Can the yield of any other crop be doubled so quickly and at so little expense? Increase the acreage of grass lands rather than decrease this crop. The farm will thereby carry more stock and the manure will enrich the cultivated fields and increase the yield of crops."

Good Pasture of Basic Importance in Any Horse Production Project

There are four basic requirements of good pasture:

1. An ample supply of palatable grasses during the grass-growing months of the year.

2. An abundant supply of good fresh water.

3. Fences of a kind that reduce to a minimum the likelihood of injury to horses.

4. Adequate shade.

Colonel E. B. White, at one time the owner of Selma Farms at Leesburg, Virginia, and rated one of the most constructive breeders of Percheron horses that ever lived, placed great emphasis upon good pastures as a prerequisite to breeding the best Percherons. His horses grazed on bluegrass pastures that were underlaid with limestone. The rainfall in his area was usually adequate; therefore the Percherons at Selma Farms had access to lush pastures during the pasture season. Grown on a limestone foundation, these pastures made a great contribution to the bone of the Percherons that grazed there. Competing exhibitors who showed their horses against Colonel White's Percherons always commented upon the amount of bone displayed by the entries from Selma Farms. And Colonel White always believed that his limestone, bluegrass pastures accounted for the rugged bone in his horses.

For a water supply, Colonel White depended upon a spring located part way up the side of the mountain. From this spring, clear, cold water flowed by gravity system through pipes into all the pastures and horse paddocks on the farm.

All fences at Selma Farms were built with locust posts and chestnut rails. There was no barbed wire on the farm. Mr. White has been heard to say that fences made from locust posts and chestnut rails are expensive in the beginning, but that such fences would last for sixty years, a fact which made them a cheap fence after all as well as a fence that reduced to a minimum risks of injury to horses.

Oak trees growing in the pastures at Selma Farms furnished an abundance of shade where Percherons were protected from the sun on the hottest days of summer. Therefore, the pasture layout at Selma Farms featured four of the most important pasture requirements: grass, water, fences, and shade.

Pasture should be well drained, free from swamps and bog areas. Pastures which are flooded in the winter or early spring should not be used for horses until midsummer or late summer. Stagnant ponds and isolated posts that have nails or sagging pieces of wire should be eliminated in all pastures to which high-priced horses have access. Trees for shade should be available, but if there are no trees for shade, open sheds should be provided for protection from the sun and the flies during the hot summer months. Satisfactory shed equipment makes it possible to house horses in the daytime and turn them out at nights.

Pastures: The Basis of Success in Light-Leg Horse Production

Noted Thoroughbred, Standardbred, and American Saddle Horse nurseries stress the importance of pastures and pasture management as a determining factor in successful horse production.

Mr. Lawrence B. Sheppard, Sr., of Hanover Shoe Farms, York County, Paoli, Pennsylvania, one of the top Standardbred nurseries in the United States says: "I believe bluegrass pasture to be probably the best all-purpose pasture grass for horses, everything considered, with as many legumes as possible growing with it. However, I wish to state that bluegrass pastures may be good and they may be poor. So, I wish to re-emphasize again that grass of any kind can only be as good as the soil on which it grows. Nearly all land will produce some grass, but the quality of that grass will vary tremendously and so will the stock grazed upon it."

How to Establish a Bluegrass Pasture

Since Hanover Shoe Farms have bred, fed, grown, and developed so many champion trotters and pacers, the results are proof that their management methods must be sound. Again Mr. Sheppard expresses himself on methods of establishing a bluegrass pasture:

"There are many ways to establish bluegrass. Probably the best and the surest way is to sow it with a small-grain nurse crop (I prefer wheat in our country in the fall) together with some timothy. The usual amount of fertilizer is applied to the grain seeding, that is to say, 300 or 400 pounds of 20 per cent superphosphate on wheat. Red clover and some more bluegrass is sown on the wheat in the early spring, when the ground is honey-combed from freezing. The spring rains and the frost seem to cover the seed so we do not do anything to cover it. After the wheat harvest, the pasture is left alone and about all you will see that fall is clover. We sometimes clip the weeds and the high wheat stubble, using care to set the mower at least six inches high.

"The following year we usually have a bumper crop of red clover hay mixed with a little timothy. We like to cut our hay as early as possible, as that conserves the protein and the vitamin content. A field can be left another year for hay if you do not need the pasture too badly. If so left, you will probably cut a crop of pretty good mixed hay, but with far more timothy.

"However, if you need the pasture you can turn your horses in the first hay year, a month or six weeks after the hay has been taken off and have pretty good pasture for a short while, although it does not take them long to eat off the clover that has come in, and the timothy and bluegrass are not very well established. The following year will be your poorest pasture year for that field, but the next year it should be fairly good, improving each succeeding year as the blue grass is then beginning to take full charge of the situation.

"I am a strong believer in mowing or clipping permanent pastures. Blue grass seems to spread from the roots, and keeping it cut seems to cause it to struggle for existence by spreading. It also keeps down weeds which are the constant enemy of all permanent pasture. Clipping keeps the grass from becoming coarse and less palatable and tends to cause more even grazing by the stock. By starting early in the spring and keeping at it constantly, we usually do not have to rake the grass to prevent matting or smothering. But if we are having a good spring and the grass gets ahead of us as much as two weeks, we then have to haul it off, which always hurts my feelings, because I can see all of that good lime and fertilizer going with it."

Some Common Reasons Why Pastures Are Low in Production

The agronomists tell us that about 55 or 60 per cent of the total land area of the United States is in pasture. They also tell us that about 85 to 90 per cent of this pasture was established without the aid of man. In too many cases farmers, instead of feeding their pastures, have robbed and exploited them. In many instances the pasture acreage on farms has been left as pasture because it has been too rough, too poorly drained, too weedy, sour, and unproductive to be used with profit in the production of cultivated crops.

In too many instances, also, farmers have not taken any pride in their pastures. Pasture is not thought of as a cash crop, like corn, oats, wheat, or soybeans. Farmers that would be ashamed and apologetic about a weedy cornfield seem to be quite undisturbed about a pasture which grows more weeds than grass.

The Advantages of Good Pasture

Good pasture offers to livestock men, horsemen, cattlemen, sheepmen, and swine growers the cheapest and the most economical source of feed. In many instances experimental data show that livestock and livestock products can be produced on pasture at from one fourth to one half the cost of producing them by barn feeding.

It has been shown also that in years when prices for livestock and livestock products are low, profitable production is possible only when an abundance of good pasturage is available through the entire growing period.

Pasture reduces labor costs in handling all kinds of livestock. In the case of horses, where exercise is a primary essential if horses are to stay sound in their legs, it can be stated truthfully that pasture almost completely solves the exercise problem.

Of course pasture is the best insurance against the menace of soil erosion. The heavy, fibrous root system of the perennial pasture grasses is the most effective means known of holding the soil in place. Various researchers have established the fact that land with a slope of more than 15 per cent should remain in pasture or forest indefinitely.

The Stages of Diminishing Permanent Pasture Production

Nature did not provide soils with an inexhaustible supply of plant food materials which could be drawn upon indefinitely by plants. Year after year, phosphorus, nitrogen, lime, and potassium have been removed by the livestock grazing the pastures and have been sold away from the farm in the form of livestock and livestock products. As a result pastures which were once productive have become impoverished to the extent that they are no longer able to support a vigorous growth of forage. During the period of exploitation, pastures in the humid areas of the United States have gone through five different stages, each followed by a lower production of forage of inferior quality. These stages are listed herewith:

1. DEPLETION OF ORGANIC MATTER, LIME, AND PHOSPHATE   An abundance of calcium and phosphorus is essential to a vigorous growth of both grasses and legumes.

2. LOSS OF POTASSIUM   The depletion of available potassium in the soils of permanent pastures to a point where it becomes a limiting factor is not as rapid as in the case of calcium, phosphorus, and nitrogen, primarily because there is a greater reserve in most soils. Also very little potassium is used in the animal body.

3. FAILURE OF LEGUMES   With this failure comes a further decrease of organic matter and nitrogen in the soil. In the northern humid portion of the United States, white clover is the natural companion crop of Kentucky bluegrass. However, it thrives only on moist soils, reasonably high in available phosphorus, potassium, and calcium. When the white clover fails, the supply of organic matter and nitrogen in the soil fails.

4. ENCROACHMENT OF INFERIOR WEEDS AND GRASSES   As the available nitrogen, phosphorus, potassium, calcium, and organic reserve of the soil continues to diminish, the yield decreases. The turf becomes thin and more open. Then unpalatable weeds and inferior, low-yielding grasses capable of rapid growth at low levels of soil fertility begin to make their appearance in the turf or sward.

5. EROSION   Erosion represents the final stage in the deterioration of permanent pastures. In this stage, the fibrous-rooted grass plants have been thinned out to a point where they are no longer effective in holding the soil against moving water.

Steps in Pasture Improvement

Methods recommended for improving permanent pastures in any of the corn belt and bordering states are pretty much the same.

1. TEST AND TREAT THE SOIL   Test to determine the need for limestone and phosphorus. The testing and the sampling should be thorough enough to determine the soil needs accurately. County agents will give directions for taking samples and will help in making the tests. Then apply sufficient limestone to correct the acidity. Generally, the best time to do this is in the fall (August and September), although it can also be done during the winter and early spring.

2. DISK THOROUGHLY   After applying the limestone, tear up the sod thoroughly with a disk cultivator, spring-tooth harrow, or quack-grass digger. This will mix the limestone with the soil and will also help to make a good seedbed. Do not worry about the grasses in the field. Do a good job of tearing up the sod. Late summer or early fall is the best time to disk in order to give the limestone sufficient time to correct the acidity and to permit the seeding of grasses.

3. SEED HEAVILY   In renovating pastures, a good seedbed is difficult to prepare; therefore use plenty of seed. Sweet clover is used widely as the main legume in the central corn-belt states—Illinois, Indiana, and Ohio— and can be depended upon to improve permanent pastures. It grows well in a variety of soils and is one of the best legumes for adding nitrogen and organic matter to the soil. Where damage by the sweet clover weevil is expected, the addition of alfalfa, alsike, or red or mammoth clover seed to the

sweet clover is advisable. A good growth of clover will supply the nitrogen needed by the grasses.

On many fields, especially those which have a fair stand of grass, seeding sweet clover alone is sufficient if the sweet clover weevil is not present. Sow at least ten pounds of sweet clover seed to an acre in the early spring on a prepared seedbed and harrow or roll the seed in. Be sure to inoculate the seed. On the better soils of the central corn-belt states, particularly those whose soils test medium in available phosphorus, red clover and alfalfa can be added to advantage at the rate of four pounds an acre of each. In those areas where lespedeza will grow, adding four or five pounds of lespedeza to the ten pounds of sweet clover is a good practice.

4. CONTROL GRAZING   The improved pasture should not be grazed until well into the summer in order to allow the new seedings to become well established. If the reseeded area is part of a larger field, fence it temporarily to keep the stock off. The date when grazing may safely be permitted will vary from July for a good growing season to August 15 for a less favorable one. Even then allow only moderate grazing and discontinue it by September 15 in order to allow the plants to make a good growth for the winter.

5. CLIP WEEDS   Soil treatment which improves the growth of grasses and legumes helps to control weeds. Since livestock prefer the better pasture plants, however, the weeds gain an advantage. It is therefore helpful to clip pastures once or twice a year. Cut annual weeds, such as ragweed, wild barley, downy brome, and white top before the seed is formed. Perennials such as iron weed or vervain can be controlled most effectively by cutting when the flower buds are first visible. If the weeds can be controlled by setting the mower eight to ten inches high, the grasses and the legumes will have the best chance to grow.

Clipping pastures in which sweet clover is an established part of the mixture requires considerable care if the second-year plants are not to be injured. Two clippings are sometimes advisable. The first clipping can be made in May. The mower bar should be eight to ten inches high, so as to leave several branches on the plants and thus avoid serious injury or death. The second cutting can be made in late July or August soon after the sweet clover has set seed.

Summary Statement

The foregoing discussion of pasture as a feed for horses has stressed the importance of adequate pasture as a means of cutting production costs in that area of livestock production where money turnover is the slowest. The leading Thoroughbred, Standardbred, and American Saddle Horse nurseries in this country all advocate a sound pasture program.

Staffed as the agricultural colleges are today with extension men and county agents, there is no real reason why the neglect of pastures should continue to constitute one of the major faults in livestock farming, or why farmers of the present day should have the mistaken notion that land can be improved by "permitting it to go to grass."

A stream does not rise above its source. Just so our pastures and our livestock cannot be any better than our soil.

Questions

1. List and discuss a half-dozen important factors in selecting a ration, making it perfectly clear why each factor mentioned is important.

2. Comment at some length regarding oats as a concentrate for horses.

3. Comment upon barley as a concentrate for horses, telling in what form this grain can be fed to best advantage.

4. Discuss corn as a concentrate for horses, stating in what form it can be fed most satisfactorily; also make clear what nutrients it furnishes and what nutrients it lacks as a feed for horses.

5. List the advantages of bran as a feed for horses. Bran is low as a source of supply for what mineral?

6. Discuss the advantages and disadvantages of linseed meal as a feed for horses.

7. List the advantages and disadvantages of cottonseed meal as a feed for horses.

8. Cottonseed meal lacks what vitamin?

9. How can the palatability of cottonseed meal as a feed for horses be increased?

10. What use is made of blackstrap molasses as a feed for horses?

11. In what ways is blackstrap molasses fed?

12. Compare the maximum pounds of blackstrap molasses with the maximum pounds of beet molasses that it is advisable to feed horses daily.

13. What constitutes good practice in watering horses daily?

14. How may salt be fed to horses and in what quantity daily?

15. If a colt shows signs of rickets and vitamin D deficiency in the ration, how would you correct such a vitamin deficiency?

16. If both calcium and phosphorus are lacking in a ration, suggest a mineral mixture that could be used satisfactorily to correct the mineral deficiency.

17. Why is good pasture very important as a source of feed in connection with any horse project?

18. List four basic requirements of a good pasture field.

19. Why is pasture the basis of success in light-leg horse production?

20. How would you establish a bluegrass pasture?

21. Name several of the most common reasons why pastures are low in production.

22. Itemize the advantages of good pasture in any phase of livestock production.

23. Outline the steps of a sound plan for pasture improvement.

16

The Cost of Feeding Horses

Price Data, Farm Products 1918 to 1933

The figures in the table opposite are proof that the law of supply and demand still operates as a factor in fixing prices. These figures for a period of fifteen years, a decade and a half, from 1918 to 1933, show that prices on farm work chunks fluctuated less than did prices on other farm products.

The wide fluctuations in feed prices during these years also prove that to estimate the cost of keeping a horse for a year one must know the amounts of feed necessary to maintain him and then figure the cost at current prices.

A good farm chunk cost $100 in 1918. In 1933, fifteen years later, a good farm chunk cost $75, horse prices receding about $25 a head over a period of fifteen years.

But let us see what happened to prices on some other farm products during the same fifteen years. The price of corn went from $1.85 to 12¢ a bushel. Oats went from 84¢ to 9¢ a bushel. Wheat toppled from $2.20 to 40¢ a bushel. Good beef cattle fluctuated in price from $12.10 to $4.50 a hundred. Pork skidded from $16.30 to $3.00 a hundred.

In 1918, it took only 54 bushels of $1.85 corn to buy a $100 farm chunk. In 1933, it took 625 bushels of 12¢ corn to buy a $75 farm chunk.

In 1918, it took only 118 bushels of 84¢ oats to buy a $100 gelding. In 1933, it took 833 bushels of 9¢ oats to buy a $75 gelding.

In 1918, it required only 45 bushels of $2.20 wheat to buy a $100 grade farm gelding. In 1933, it took 186 bushels of 40¢ wheat to buy a $75 gelding.

338

COST OF A FARM CHUNK, IN DOLLARS, AND IN OTHER FARM PRODUCTS, 1918 TO 1933 INCLUSIVE, CHICAGO MARKETS

Year	Price Farm Work Chunk	Corn Bush-els	Price	Oats Bush-els	Price	Wheat Bush-els	Price	Native Beef Cattle Weight	Price per Cwt.	Hogs Weight	Price per Cwt.
1918	$100	54	$1.85	118	$0.84	45	$2.20	826	$12.10	613	$16.30
1919	110	68	1.62	145	0.76	45	2.45	696	15.80	625	17.60
1920	100	63	1.58	110	0.91	40	2.50	716	13.95	667	15.00
1921	90	115	0.78	184	0.49	44	2.06	1,034	8.70	957	9.40
1922	90	176	0.51	204	0.44	65	1.39	1,276	7.05	1,139	7.90
1923	90	120	0.75	191	0.47	69	1.30	984	9.15	1,077	8.35
1924	80	97	0.82	151	0.53	64	1.24	846	9.45	1,126	7.10
1925	80	60	1.34	129	0.62	39	2.03	879	9.10	769	10.40
1926	80	95	0.84	178	0.45	42	1.92	829	9.65	724	11.05
1927	90	108	0.83	163	0.55	60	1.50	882	10.20	753	11.95
1928	90	96	0.94	150	0.60	61	1.47	647	13.90	1,084	8.30
1929	100	102	0.98	175	0.57	69	1.45	796	12.55	1,093	9.15
1930	85	92	0.92	177	0.48	66	1.29	667	12.75	872	9.75
1931	80	109	0.78	235	0.34	96	0.83	833	9.60	1,046	7.65
1932	80	200	0.40	286	0.28	114	0.70	1,176	6.80	2,000	4.00
1933	75	312	0.24	441	0.17	153	0.49	1,500	5.00	2,380	3.15

Farm Prices, Magnolia, Illinois (first week in January 1933)

Year	Price Farm Work Chunk	Corn Bush-els	Price	Oats Bush-els	Price	Wheat Bush-els	Price	Native Beef Cattle Weight	Price per Cwt.	Hogs Weight	Price per Cwt.
1933	75	625	0.12	833	0.09	186	0.40	1,666	4.50	2,500	3.00

Source: Iowa Horse and Mule Breeders' Association.

In 1918, it took only 826 pounds of beef at $12.10 a hundredweight to buy a $100 work horse. In 1933, it took 1,666 pounds of beef at $4.50 a hundredweight to buy a $75 work chunk.

In 1918, 613 pounds of pork at $16.30 a hundredweight would buy a $100 horse. In 1933, it required 2,500 pounds of pork at $3.00 a hundredweight to buy a $75 work horse.

Chicago Prices vs. Farm Prices, 1918 and 1933

Study for a moment the two lines of figures showing the extreme range in values of farm products over a period of fifteen years. This table of figures shows very plainly what can happen to values and how wide the range in prices may become in a short period of time.

CHICAGO PRICES AND FARM PRICES, 1918 AND 1933

	Cost of a Farm Chunk	Corn per Bu.	Oats per Bu.	Wheat per Bu.	Beef per Cwt.	Hogs per Cwt.	Mixed Hay a Ton
Chicago prices, 1918	$100	$1.85	$.84	$2.20	$12.10	$16.30	$30.00
Farm prices, 1933	75	.12	.09	.40	4.50	3.00	3.00

Source: Iowa Horse and Mule Breeders' Association.

Cost of Feeding a Work Horse for a Year

A common question is, What does it cost to feed a work horse a year? To answer this question one must know, first, what quantities of feed are required. Also, in determining the cost of feeding a work horse for a year, one must know the size of the horse, the number of days he works, the number of days he is idle, the kind of work he has to do, the amounts of feed he requires, and the cost of the feed at the time.

For example, let us compute the cost of feeding a Moores & Ross Milk Company horse, whose work assignment on the streets of Columbus used to be for 365 days a year. The horse's job was pulling a milk wagon. First, let us use feed values as of the year 1933. The weight of the horse to be fed is sixteen hundred pounds, and he is to consume 16 pounds of grain daily, 1 part by weight of cracked corn, 5 parts by weight of crushed oats. This horse is also to consume 18 pounds of mixed hay daily. This horse, therefore, is to eat about 1 pound of grain and 1.1 pounds of hay per hundredweight.

Moores and Ross Milk Company bought its feed supplies in quantity and in 1933 paid the following prices: shelled corn, 28¢ a bushel; oats, 21¢ a bushel; baled mixed clover and timothy hay, $7 a ton.

Daily cost of this ration:

2.66 pounds corn @ 0.5¢	1.33¢
13.33 pounds oats @ 0.65¢	8.66¢
10 pounds hay @ 0.35¢	6.30¢
Daily cost of feed	16.29¢

365 days at 16.29¢ = $59.45, or cost of feed for one year (1933).

If a milk wagon horse was kept idle on Sunday, his feed was reduced by half, as a precaution against azoturia or Monday morning's disease. With 52 idle days for a horse during the year, the feed bill was cut to 8.14¢ for each of these days, or a total for Sunday feeds of $4.23. When this amount is deducted from the above total the yearly feed bill of a milk wagon horse was $55.22 in 1933.

If we figure daily feed costs on the same horse, using 1918 feed prices in Chicago, the figures would be as follows:

2.66 pounds corn @ 3.3¢	8.7¢
13.33 pounds oats @ 2.6¢	34.6¢
18 pounds mixed hay @ 1.5¢	
($30 a ton)	27.0¢
Daily feed cost	70.3¢

365 days at 70.3¢ daily = $256.59 or cost of feed for one year (1918).

For a horse that was idle on 52 Sundays of the year, with daily ration cut in half, deduct $18.27, hence the yearly feed bill on a horse fed as indicated was $238.32 for the year 1918. Fifteen years later, in 1933, it would have cost only $55.22 to feed the same milk wagon horse. The same work horse could have been fed for $183.10 less in 1933 than in 1918 because of fluctuations in the price of feed. It would have cost more than four times as much to feed this work horse in 1918 as it did in 1933.

Annual Feed Cost of Average Farm Work Horse

In the heyday of the work horse business, Wayne Dinsmore, secretary of the Horse Association of America, assembled figures to show that the average farm work horse at medium work and working 120 days a year, could be kept on 3,000 pounds of grain, 5,000 pounds of roughage (half legume roughage and half carbonaceous roughage), and the necessary pasture.

Let us compare the feed costs of maintaining such a farm horse for 120 days in 1918 and in 1933 on 3,000 pounds grain (1,500 pounds oats, 1,500 pounds ear corn) and 5,000 pounds roughage (2,500 pounds alfalfa, 2,500 pounds timothy).

Feed Prices, 1918—(Chicago)

Ear corn @ $1.85 a bushel
Oats @ $0.84 a bushel
Alfalfa @ $30.00 a ton
Timothy @ $20.00 a ton

1,500 pounds ear corn @ 2.6¢	$39.00
1,500 pounds oats @ 2.6¢	39.00
2,500 pounds alfalfa @ 1.5¢	37.50

2,500 pounds timothy @ 1.0¢	$ 25.00
8 months' strawstack, cornfield,	
pasture @ $2.50 per month	20.00
Total feed expense	$160.50

Feed Prices, 1933 (Farm Prices)

1,500 pounds ear corn @ 0.17¢	$ 2.55
1,500 pounds oats @ 0.28¢	4.20
2,500 pounds alfalfa @ 0.25¢	6.25
2,500 pounds timothy @ 0.15¢	3.75
8 months' strawstack, cornfield,	
pasture, meadow aftermath	
@ 50¢ per month	4.00
Total feed expense	$20.75

It cost more than seven times as much to feed a farm work horse in 1918 as it did in 1933.

Sample Work Horse Rations

The rations that follow have proved satisfactory. Their cost today can be figured at current prices.

Ohio Station (1907)

The weight of the horses averaged 1,500 pounds.

One horse in each team was fed 15 pounds of ear corn and 17 pounds of mixed hay daily.

One horse in each team was fed 15 pounds of oats and 17 pounds mixed hay daily.

The horses on ear corn, 1 pound of corn per hundredweight of horse, did just as well in every respect as did the oat-fed horses eating 1 pound of oats per hundredweight of horse, with both horses eating mixed hay (clover and timothy) as the roughage, at the rate of 1 pound of mixed hay per hundredweight of horse.

A satisfactory work horse ration, therefore, for horses weighing 1,500 pounds at medium farm work is as follows:

15 pounds ear corn with 17 pounds mixed hay, daily,

or

15 pounds oats with 17 pounds mixed hay daily

The corn-fed horses endured hard work as well as did the oat-fed horses. The corn was not detrimental to the health of the horses nor did it induce laziness, sluggishness, or lack of endurance. With mixed hay (clover and timothy) as the roughage, the ear corn was just as efficient as the oats. Furthermore, it was cheaper.

Seventy or seventy-two big ears of corn will make a bushel of ear corn weighing 70 pounds. Oats weigh 32 pounds a bushel and up. If one is feeding 1 pound of ear corn per hundredweight of horse, a bushel of 70 pound ear corn will last more than twice as long as will a bushel of 32 pound oats.

That is to say, 70 pounds of ear corn fed to a 1,500 pound work horse at 1 pound per hundredweight will last in excess of four days, while a bushel of 32 pound oats will last but a trifle in excess of two days. Hence, ear corn, throughout the years, with very few exceptions has been a cheaper grain ration for horses than oats.

Ohio State University

The following was a daily ration for mares (pulling a manure wagon every day). The weight of the mares was from 1,750 to 1,800 pounds.

> 8 pounds ear corn
> 12 pounds oats
> 2 pounds bran
> 18 pounds mixed (either clover and
> timothy or alfalfa and timothy)

Above ration cut in half on idle days.

Michigan State College

Horses fed this ration weighed from 1,500 to 1,650 pounds and were employed at medium to hard work.

> Ration I: 12 to 18 pounds ear corn
> 16 to 20 pounds alfalfa hay
> Ration II: 8 pounds ear corn
> 10 pounds oats
> 8 pounds alfalfa hay
> 10 pounds timothy hay

This ration was cut in half on idle days. A bran mash with one teaspoonful of saltpeter was fed Saturday nights in place of the regular feed. The saltpeter was a diuretic that stimulated the voiding of urine.

Missouri Station

The following is a ration for work mules.

Lot I: Average weight of mules, 1,268 pounds
    Ration I: 12 pounds shelled corn
           15 pounds hay
Lot II: Average weight of mules, 1,264 pounds
    Ration II: 12 pounds oats
           15 pounds hay

The hay fed was mixed clover and timothy. There was no noticeable difference in the effect of the corn ration as compared with that of the oats. This experiment with mules parallels closely the feeding program devised for work geldings at the Ohio Station at Wooster, Ohio.

More Specific Experimental Data

Feeding Farm Work Horses, with Emphasis on the Utilization of Farm-Grown Feeds

This experiment was carried out by Professor J. L. Edmonds of the University of Illinois, whose work in feeding horses experimentally has been a guide which others have followed in feeding both work horses and pure-bred draft fillies.

FEEDING WORK HORSES   These experiments were conducted to determine the practicability of corn and legume hays for work animals as well as to clear up the skepticism concerning their use, particularly as a feed for work stock. There has always been some skepticism about the use of corn, but experimental data have proved that the troubles resulting have been due either to improper feeding or to the unsuitable character or quality of the corn fed.

There has always been, and is today, skepticism about the use of legume hays for work horses, particularly alfalfa. Many have believed that alfalfa hay will cause digestion disorders and that it reduces the strength and endurance of work horses.

In the first Illinois experiment, the plan was to gather data incident to the feeding of at least two horse teams which were in daily use. The horses averaged 1,445 pounds in the first experiment, 1,578 pounds in the second experiment, 1,621 pounds in the third experiment, and 1,636 pounds in the fourth experiment.

METHOD OF FEEDING   At the beginning, the horses were fed quantities that they would eat readily. Grain was fed three times daily in equal amounts. A quarter of the hay was fed in the morning, a quarter at noon, and the remainder at night.

WATER   The horses were watered five times daily: in the morning, at noon before and after feeding, in the evening before feeding, and at 9 P.M., their last drink. The average daily consumption of water was one hundred pounds, ten to twelve gallons.

SALT   The horses consumed two ounces of salt per head daily.

STABLING FACILITIES   The horses stood in straight stalls on concrete floors and were bedded with shavings. They were kept shod and were exercised in individual lots on idle days.

NATURE OF WORK   The horses did general farm work and teaming.

LENGTH OF TEST   The test ran for 364 days.

Second Experiment

This was the only experiment where the horses lost weight.

FEEDS USED

> Ear corn: two thirds by weight
> Oats: one third by weight
> Clover hay (good quality) limited to
>   1 pound per hundredweight daily.

This ration was satisfactory as to character and kind, but the quantity consumed was insufficient. The average daily grain ration was 16.1 pounds. The average weight of the horses at the beginning was 1,578 pounds; at the close of the experiment it was 1,566 pounds, or an average loss of 12 pounds a head. Hence the quantity of the ration was insufficient to maintain the weight of the horses throughout the trial.

The above ration supplied the minimum requirements of nutrients for horses at medium work, but the horses used in this test were employed at hard work; hence they lost weight during the 140 day trial.

In another trial with work horses at the Illinois Station, the grain fed was corn, two thirds by weight, and oats, one third by weight. One horse in each team was fed alfalfa. His mate was fed alfalfa and timothy. No real difference could be noted in nutritional effect due to the two kinds of hay rations. It was thought that the alfalfa and timothy combined or fed as a mixture, might be more economical because alfalfa is sometimes very high in price.

Instead of timothy, some other carbonaceous roughage, such as corn stover, shredded fodder, or oat straw might be fed with the alfalfa.

The alfalfa, oats, and ear corn made a good ration. Nevertheless, alfalfa, timothy, corn, and oats more nearly met the standard feeding requirements, especially in the case of protein.

Protein in excess of requirements may not be actually injurious to horses, but the cost is usually high. The feeding of excess protein is uneconomical.

In a third trial with work horses at the Illinois Station, the feeds were ear corn and alfalfa. This experiment was probably the most important of the tests. Only two feeds were used in maintaining the horses for a 364 day period; and in many sections these two feeds were—and still are—considered poor or questionable feeds for horses.

Was the ration fed sufficient to maintain weight? The average weight of the horses at the beginning was 1,636 pounds. The average weight of the horses at the close of the experiment was 1,666 pounds—or an average gain of 30 pounds a head.

Did this ration lower the health, spirit, condition, and thrift of the horses? The answer is no.

Did the lack of variety in the feeds influence the appetite? The summer of 1916 was very hot and dry; hence the heat was a real test of any ration for work horses. Some of the horses showed a little decrease in appetite, probably because of the weather rather than because of the ration. Some of the horses were not too sleek in appearance. Yet it should be remembered that there was an average gain in weight of 30 pounds a head.

How much corn was consumed daily? A little under 1 pound per hundredweight of horse.

How much alfalfa hay was consumed daily? About 1.14 pounds per hundredweight of horse.

What kind of alfalfa hay was it? This alfalfa had been in the barn a year. It was well cured, sound, and not so leafy as what is known as "pea-green" hay. *Morrison's Revised Feeding Standard* for 1,600 pound horses at medium to hard work reads as follows:

	Dry Matter (pounds)	Dig. Cr. Protein (pounds)	T.D.N. (pounds)	Nut. Ratio
This ration of corn and alfalfa supplied	24.1–31.6	1.5–1.8	16.6–19.6	1:7.0
	28.4	2.93	20.5	1:6.0

This last experiment shows the advantage of a good, nutritious, leguminous roughage when grain is high in price. This ration, however, supplied more protein than the standard requires. The nutritive ratio is also narrower than necessary.

How could this ration be improved in the feeding of work horses a full year under farm conditions? By providing variety in oats and corn. Moreover, some economy would result from the use of carbonaceous roughage in addition to the alfalfa. Timothy hay, prairie hay, oat hay, oat straw, corn stover might make up one third of the roughage fed.

Summary

Corn and alfalfa hay can and should be used to a large extent in feeding farm work horses and for these reasons: their nutritive values make possible a balanced ration, and their suitability in a crop rotation scheme makes possible the best corn-belt cropping practices.

Feeding Purebred Draft Fillies

The First Experiment

The object of the trial was to determine what part home-grown feeds can play in the raising of purebred draft fillies, as well as the efficiency of corn, oats, and alfalfa hay in growing draft fillies from weaning time until two years of age.

The results of this experiment are included here because the findings are applicable clear across the field of horse production. Within the realm of good judgment and with good management the feeds used, properly supplemented with pasture, can be fed to all kinds of growing horses. Again, the question-and-answer method of presentation is used as an aid in the study of this chapter.

PLAN OF EXPERIMENT   Ten purebred weanling Percheron fillies were used in the trial. The fillies were carried through two winters and one summer.

What feeds were used? The grain feeds were oats and shelled corn, one half of each by weight.

How and when was the grain fed? The grain was fed three times daily, unless the fillies were on grass; then grain was fed twice daily. The oats and corn were ground during the first winter. After that whole oats and shelled corn were fed.

Why was shelled corn used instead of ear corn? To give each filly a chance to get her share of the grains.

When was the hay fed? The hay was fed twice a day unless the fillies were on pasture, during a part of which time no hay was fed. After pasture became short, hay was fed once a day.

Did the rations fed completely satisfy the appetite of the fillies? More grain would have been eaten, but with the alfalfa hay the aim was to feed what would be thoroughly cleaned up. This eliminated waste as well as the necessity of weighing refused food.

Why were alfalfa, corn, and oats the feeds fed? The plan was to attempt to get results with feeds commonly grown on corn-belt farms, thereby eliminating the necessity of purchased feeds.

How were the fillies fed? The ten head were fed as one lot from racks and troughs built along the sides of the box stalls.

How much and what kind of pasture was available? A bluegrass pasture, eight acres in size, with some orchard grass, medium red and white clover.

What were the provisions for salt and water? Salt was regularly added to the grain feed. The allowance of salt per head was about 1.5 ounces. A water tank projected into each box stall; there was thus an ample supply of good water available at all times.

What sort of winter and summer shelter was provided? Two large box stalls, 16 by 20 feet. Doors from these box stalls opened into a cinder exercise lot and into the eight-acre pasture.

Doors were closed only during the stormy nights of winter. This method ensured both protection and exercise. Canvas flappers nailed to overhead joists kept the flies off the backs of the fillies in the summer. Coal-tar disinfectant smeared on the canvas kept them from chewing it or tearing it down.

What sort of bedding was used? Shavings were used to keep the fillies on experiment from eating their bedding.

How often were they groomed? Colts were tied and groomed as occasion demanded. Once every four to six weeks the feet were leveled with a rasp.

What were the age, weight, and height of these fillies when they were placed on experiment? The range in age of the fillies was 159 days (5 months) to 262 days ($8\frac{1}{2}$ months). The average age of the fillies was 214 days (approximately seven months).

The weight of the fillies varied from 685 pounds (159 days) to 970 pounds (227 days). The average weight of the ten fillies was 823 pounds.

The height of the fillies varied from 13–$1\frac{1}{4}$ to 13–$3\frac{3}{4}$. The average height of the fillies was 13–$2\frac{1}{4}$.

How much grain and hay were allowed for the first 28 days? As much hay and grain as the fillies would readily consume, but this proved questionable from the standpoint of profit and safety. Accordingly, the grain ration was restricted to the point necessary to ensure the consumption of a pound or more of alfalfa hay for every 100 pounds of filly. The results show that a well-cured legume hay should be the foundation for feeding young, growing horses. In addition to the roughage consumed, enough grain should be fed to produce good growth.

How much grain is necessary to secure the necessary development of weanling or yearling fillies on pasture? A grain feed of approximately half a pound for every hundredweight of filly ensures good growth on good pasture. If the pasture be poor, however, they may—and probably will—lose weight on such a ration. One to one and one-fourth pounds for every hundredweight of filly during the first four months with legume hay made better gains than one-half pound of grain per hundredweight of filly with pasture and no hay. The figures below represent gains or losses in pounds, plus signs indicating gains, and minus signs indicating losses.

May 25 to June 21: 6.1 pounds of grain, good pasture, no hay
+ 10 + 35 + 60 + 45 + 40 + 75 + 40 + 30 + 50 + 40

June 22 to July 19: 6.2 pounds grain, poor pasture, no hay
(0) − 25 − 40 − 15 + 25 − 5 − 15 − 10 + 15 − 5

July 20 to August 16: 6.4 pounds grain, poor pasture, 6.2 pounds of good legume hay
+ 40 + 40 + 35 + 25 + 30 + 35 + 50 + 55 + 50 + 10

A study of the above figures, which show the amounts of feed consumed by the fillies as well as the resultant gains and losses in weight during parts of the months of May, June, July, and August, plainly reveals that continuous, liberal feeding is necessary if the gains are to be uninterrupted.

At The Ohio State University, liberal feeding of young growing horses has been the practice. As a usual thing we do not have good pasture in Ohio before the middle of May. If yearlings which have been doing well on dry feeds during the winter months are turned into a lush pasture in the middle of May and all grain and legume hay are taken away from them, these yearlings, in spite of the lush pasture in the early spring, usually will lose weight later in the summer, because of the heat and the flies in July and August. This will happen even though the fillies be protected from flies in the daytime and turned to pasture only at night. If it is planned to point any of the yearling colt crop toward the fall shows, grain during the whole period of yearling growth is a necessity if show day is not to be a disappointment.

What was the length of the pasture period in this experiment? May 14 to October 11, five months.

What was the average daily grain and hay consumption for the entire period of the experiment (518 days)? Average daily grain consumption was 9.8 pounds or approximately 10 pounds. Average daily hay consumption was 9.97 pounds or approximately 10 pounds.

What was the average daily gain per head over the whole period (518 days)? The average daily gain was one and a third pounds. The best average daily gain in weight per head was made by one filly from February 2 to March 1, a daily gain of 2.61 pounds. (This was a month on dry feed.)

The greatest loss in weight was recorded between June 22 and July 19, when one filly lost 30 pounds. This was a dry pasture month with grain, poor pasture and no hay.

The best total gain in weight per head for one period was recorded between February 2 and March 1, when one filly gained 75 pounds. She was a very good-doing filly.

The poorest total gain in weight per head for one period in reality was not a gain but a loss of 8.5 pounds. This loss occurred during the period from June 22 to July 19 on 6 pounds of grain, poor pasture, and no hay.

What was the average total gain in weight and height from weaning to two years of age? Average total gain in weight was 690.5 pounds. Average total gain in height was 8 inches or 2 hands. Both gains are very satisfactory increases.

How much more grain and hay per pound of gain were necessary the second winter as compared with the first winter? During the first winter (rising yearlings), it required 5.6 pounds of grain and 4.2 pounds of hay for 1 pound of gain.

During the second winter (rising two-year-olds) it required 9.2 pounds of grain and 12.9 pounds of hay for 1 pound of gain.

These data stress the importance of liberal feeding for the first year. It required approximately twice as much grain and three times as much hay for every pound of gain the second winter as was required to make a pound of gain in the first winter. Thus the growing gains during the first year have a real economic importance.

What was the average weight of the fillies at twelve months and at twenty-four months? The average weight of the ten fillies at twelve months was 1,112 pounds. Average weight of the ten fillies at twenty-four months was 1,548 pounds. Average weight of the eight largest fillies at twelve months was 1,128 pounds. Average weight of the eight largest fillies at twenty-four months was 1,578 pounds.

The largest filly at one year weighed 1,260 pounds. The largest filly at two years weighed 1,775 pounds. The smallest filly at one year weighed 1,035 pounds. The smallest filly at two years weighed 1,430 pounds. Liberal feeding results in a marketable product at two years of age and helps to speed up the turnover in the business. Roughing and stunting them the first year does not pay because it is then that the growing gains are the cheapest.

Are commercial mill feeds absolutely necessary? The results with corn, oats, and alfalfa indicate that there is little or no need to purchase mill feeds if good alfalfa hay is available as the roughage.

Is it necessary to limit the feeding of alfalfa hay to horses? It is not necessary to limit alfalfa hay consumption in the case of young, growing horses, except insofar as their appetite for alfalfa hay would limit the consumption of grain that is necessary to ensure good growth. It is necessary to limit it with older horses, however, particularly work horses doing hard work. Alfalfa speeds up the kidneys and the bowels of horses. Large amounts of it fed to work horses would result in an immediate increase in soiled litter or bedding in the stalls and too much kidney and bowel action.

Feeding alfalfa to colts has several advantages. It furnishes the protein and calcium so essential to good growth and makes possible a liberal use of corn in the ration. Usually corn is a cheaper grain than oats. In 100 pounds of alfalfa there are 10.6 pounds of digestible protein, about 1.4 pounds of calcium and about 0.21 pounds of phosphorus. Alfalfa hay properly cured is also a good source of vitamins A and D. Furthermore, the alfalfa crop fits into a sound program of farm economy because of its place in a good crop rotation scheme.

How much grain and alfalfa hay do draft colts consume from weaning until two years of age? These quantities of feed were consumed by each of the ten Percheron fillies in 518 days:

> 45.3 bushels corn (46 bushels)
> 79.3 bushels oats (80 bushels)
> 2.5 tons alfalfa hay
> 4.5 acres of pasture

This period, it will be remembered, included two winters and one summer, with pasture from May 14 to October 11, five months.

What does it cost to feed a purebred draft colt from weaning until two years of age? The cost of feeding a purebred draft colt from weaning until two years of age, if corn, oats, alfalfa hay, and pasture are to be the feeds consumed, can be determined by first ascertaining what quantities of feed will be necessary, then by figuring this cost at current prices.

In 1933, corn was 12¢ a bushel, oats 9¢ a bushel, alfalfa hay $5.00 a ton. Pasture at that time could be rented for $1.00 per head per month.

In 1948, fifteen years later, The Ohio State University purchased corn at $1.85 a bushel, oats at $1.25 a bushel, and alfalfa hay at $32.00 a ton. Pasture rent was $2.00 per head per month.

Such a wide range in the price of feeds results in a wide range in the costs of growing a draft filly from weaning time until two years of age. Thus to find the answer to the question of cost it is necessary to figure costs at current prices because feed prices fluctuate.

PROBLEM   If it takes 46 bushels of shelled corn, 80 bushels of oats, 2.5 tons of alfalfa hay, and 1 acre per head of good pasture to have draft fillies make satisfactory growth between weaning time and two years of age, a period of 518 days on feed, with five months of pasture, compute the cost of the feed and pasture, at both the 1933 prices quoted above and current prices for these feeds.

Fourth and Fifth Experiment in Feeding Purebred Draft Fillies

The fourth and fifth experiments are of especial significance because of the use made of sheaf oats, soybean hay, and sweetclover pasture in growing yearling draft fillies.

Sheaf oats and alfalfa hay, supplemented with half a ration of oats and bran, proved to be satisfactory feeds for weanling draft fillies during their first winter. The roughage was fed in the proportion of one part of sheaf oats to two parts of alfalfa. Three pounds of oats were fed to 1 pound of bran. During their first winter the fillies ate an average of 4.7 pounds of oats and bran, 10.4 pounds of alfalfa hay, and 4.9 pounds of sheaf oats a day.

Sweetclover during the first part of the grazing season and bluegrass during the latter part made a good pasture combination for yearling draft fillies. They made a good growth on this pasture and remained clean in their legs. While grazing on sweetclover, however, the fillies seemed to crave some other feed. They ate a considerable quantity of their wheat straw bedding during this period, which seemed to indicate that better results would be obtained by giving some additional feed to young fillies on sweetclover pasture. During the latter part of the summer, they were fed some oats and bran and later a light feed of sheaf oats. Their average daily consumption for the summer was 4.2 pounds of oats and bran and 1.2 pounds of sheaf oats.

During most of the second winter sheaf oats and alfalfa were fed in approximately equal amounts without any threshed grain. These feeds produced a good growth in height and frame. These fillies, however, were not so heavy as some other lots previously fed at the Illinois Station, where the fillies received more grain and consequently were in higher condition. During the second winter the average consumption of alfalfa was 12.6 pounds per day and of sheaf oats 13.8 pounds per day. The average weight of these fillies at the end of the experiment was 1,446 pounds, their average height was 15–3.8 hands.

Fifth Experiment in Feeding Purebred Draft Fillies

The results of this experiment indicate that soybean hay, when properly supplemented, is a satisfactory roughage for growing draft fillies. In fact, a comparison with previous experiments indicates that it is equal to alfalfa for this purpose. The combination of sweetclover pasture with bluegrass, gave the fillies the advantage of a longer pasture season.

In summer, June 28 to August 24, the fillies ran on four acres of sweetclover pasture and were fed sheaf oats once daily. Fillies running on succulent sweetclover seem to crave some dry, carbonaceous roughage and it was found that the straw in sheaf oats filled the bill. The light feed of grain was also continued to ensure the consumption of some bone meal, which was fed to experimental fillies for the first time. The sweetclover pasture was a fresh seeding and on account of a very backward spring was quite slow in getting started.

From May 4 until June 23 the fillies were on bluegrass pasture. From June 23 to June 28 they were on bluegrass and sweetclover, which contained a sprinkling of alfalfa plants. They were returned to the bluegrass on August 24 and ran there until December 21. The bluegrass pasture consisted of eight acres.

The sheaf oats, which were fed continuously, served as a balance at all times. They prevented too great a consumption of soybean hay in winter and furnished the dry roughage which the fillies seemed to crave while on sweetclover pasture. The gains made on pasture during the summer were slightly higher than those made in the first winter and considerably higher than those made during the second winter.

As weanlings each of the fillies ate approximately 8 pounds of sheaf oats and soybean hay and 2.3 pounds of grain daily. During the second winter the daily consumption of each filly was over 9 pounds of sheaf oats and soybean hay and 3.4 pounds of grain. These amounts produced good gains in height and frame and kept the fillies in thrifty condition. At no time was there a filly off feed.

The winter ration consisted of equal parts of sheaf oats and soybean hay in addition to a very light feed of grain offered once daily. This consisted of 80 per cent crushed oats and 20 per cent wheat bran with which a small amount of deodorized steamed bone meal was mixed. The fillies were started on 2 pounds of grain and 2 ounces of bone meal daily. This was gradually increased until the end of the experiment, when they were eating 3.6 pounds of grain and 2.4 ounces of bone meal.

The daily consumption of grain in addition to that contained in the sheaf oats was held down to approximately a quarter of a pound per hundredweight. Throughout the test, the fillies ate somewhat less than a pound of each of the roughages per hundredweight daily. Both the grain and the roughage were fed in mangers that were built along the sides of roomy box stalls.

While it is difficult to say just what effect was produced by the small amount of bone meal fed daily, it seemed to be beneficial. The feet on these fillies were exceptional in size and toughness.

At the end of the experiment, the fillies, in medium condition and four of them not yet two years old, averaged 1,484 pounds and stood 15–$3\frac{1}{4}$ hands in height.

Judging from this test, good results in growing young draft fillies may be obtained by moderate, regular feeding of sheaf oats and a legume hay supplemented with a very light feed of crushed oats, bran, and bone meal. Furthermore, the value of using sweetclover pasture along with permanent bluegrass pasture seems to be demonstrated.

Suggestions for Storing Sheaf Oats

In storing sheaf oats in the mow, some precautions should be taken to keep out rats and mice, which not only may eat much of the grain, but may also render a considerable amount of the remainder unpalatable.

Scattering hydrated lime over the successive layers of sheaves as they were put up in the mow during several years of experimental feeding has almost eliminated the damage from this source. One year the hydrated lime was weighed and it was found that 250 pounds had been scattered through the 34 tons of sheaf oats. In feeding, much of the lime is shaken off and the palatability of the feed does not seem to be injured in the least.

Hay or straw should not be piled against the sides of the stack or pile of stored sheaf oats.

Today, in many areas where combines are used, sheaf oats are no longer available as a feed for horses. In California and other western states, however, oats are cut with a mower and cured in the cock, then stored in a mow, loose or baled, and fed in the manger to horses just as loose hay is fed.

The feed chart opposite provides a detailed study of the results of feeding seven different kinds of rations to purebred draft fillies. These same rations, modified as good judgment dictates, can be fed just as satisfactorily to other breeds of horses. The kinds of feed that will produce growth in draft fillies will also produce growth in saddle fillies or Standardbred fillies. We

SUMMARY SHEET

FEEDING PURE BRED DRAFT FILLIES

FIVE EXPERIMENTS

UNIVERSITY OF ILLINOIS

(*in pounds*)

	FIRST	SECOND LOT 1	SECOND LOT 2	THIRD LOT 1	THIRD LOT 2	FOURTH	FIFTH
	Ear Corn ½ Oats ½ Alfalfa Hay Pasture	*Corn 40% Oats 40% Bran 20% Alfalfa Oat Straw Pasture*	*Corn 50% Oats 50% Alfalfa Oat Straw Pasture*	*Cr. Oats 75% Bran 25% Alfalfa Oat Hay Pasture*	*Gr. Corn 75% Bran 25% Alfalfa Oat Hay Pasture*	*Cr. Oats 75% Bran 25% Alfalfa Sheaf Oats Pasture*	*Cr. Oats 80% Bran 20% Soybean Hay Sheaf Oats Pasture*
Length of trial days	518	518	518	490	490	504	504
Number of animals	10	8	8	8	8	10	10
Average age at beginning—days	214	230	220	251	260	218	235
Height—average at beginning	13h-2.3″	13h-3.5″	13h-3.25″	14h-.53″	14h-.53″	14h-.4″	14h-.05″
Average at close	15h-2.3″	15h-3.21″	15h-3.19″	15h-2.88″	15h-3.38″	15h-3.65″	15h-3.4″
Average gain	7.96″	7.68″	7.91″	6.41″	6.84″	7.25″	7.35″
Weight—average at beginning	823	811	818	846	853	874	828
Average at close	1,513	1,544	1,544	1,482	1,490	1,439	1,484
Average gain	690	733	726	636	637	565	655
Average daily gain	1.33	1.41	1.4	1.3	1.3	1.12	1.3
Grain—total eaten	5,079	4,404	4,323	3,115	2,647	1,490	1,483
Average per day	9.8	8.5	8.35	6.36	5.4	2.96	2.94
Average per day per cwt.	.81	.7	.69	.53	.44	.24	.25
Hay—total eaten	5,168	5,762	5,357	3,185	3,225	3,953	3,042
Average per day	9.98	11.12	10.34	6.5	6.58	7.84	6.04
Average per day per cwt.	.82	.91	.86	.54	.54	.65	.51
Other roughage —total eaten		462	460	2,491	2,490	3,607	4,970
Average per day		.89	.89	5.08	5.08	7.16	9.86
Average per day per cwt.		.07	.07	4.26	4.19	.602	.83
Feed per pound gain—grain	7.36	6.01	5.95	4.9	4.16	2.64	2.26
Alfalfa or soybean hay	7.49	7.87	7.38	5.01	5.06	7.00	4.64
Other roughage		.63	.63	3.92	3.91	6.39	7.58

Source: J. L. Edmonds, "Feeding Purebred Draft Fillies," *Bulletin,* University of Illinois Experiment Station.

have proved this statement and we are proving it daily at The Ohio State University.

If a grain feed of 1 to 1¼ pounds per hundredweight of filly produces satisfactory gains the first six months in weanling draft fillies, it should be satisfactory as a feed for saddle and Standardbred fillies. If a grain feed of approximately half a pound per hundredweight of filly on good pasture produces satisfactory growth in draft fillies, the same amount of feed per hundredweight of filly on good pasture will produce satisfactory growth in light-leg fillies. Of course if the pasture is poor, it will take more grain to do the job for both types. The foregoing feed chart should therefore be studied carefully. The data it contains can be helpful, no matter what kind of weanlings or yearlings are being fed.

Other Rations for Purebred Draft Horses

Michigan State College

FEEDING RISING YEARLING DRAFT FILLIES AFTER WEANING

| 2 quarts or 1 pound crushed oats | } | 3 times daily or a total of 6 |
| 2 small ears or 1 pound ear corn | | pounds of grain daily |

As the colts grow, gradually increase the above ration to:

4 quarts or 2 pounds crushed oats	}	
4 small ears or 2 pounds ear corn		3 times daily or a total of 12
10 to 12 pounds alfalfa hay daily		pounds of grain daily
¼ pound linseed oil meal daily		

The Ohio State University

FEEDING RISING YEARLING DRAFT FILLIES AFTER WEANING

Fall and Winter Ration:—

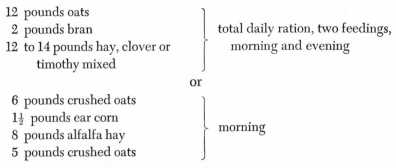

12 pounds oats	}	
2 pounds bran		total daily ration, two feedings,
12 to 14 pounds hay, clover or		morning and evening
timothy mixed		

or

6 pounds crushed oats	}	
1½ pounds ear corn		morning
8 pounds alfalfa hay		
5 pounds crushed oats		

1 pound chopped hay	}	
¼ pound linseed oil meal		night
6 pounds mixed hay		

or

12 pounds crushed oats
2 pounds ear corn
2 pounds bran   } total daily ration, two feedings,
6 pounds alfalfa   morning and evening
6 pounds timothy

ADDITIONAL NOON FEED FOR THESE YEARLINGS WHEN BEING FITTED FOR

Chicago International—

4 pounds crushed oats
1½ pounds bran   } fed as a dampened mixture
½ pound linseed oil meal
4 pounds chopped alfalfa hay

RATION FOR STALLIONS   Below is a maintenance ration given to Hesitation (weight 1,950 pounds) and Gene Tunney (weight 1,850 pounds) to keep these stallions in shape for classroom use.

12 to 14 pounds oats
16 pounds mixed hay, clover,   } total daily ration, two feedings,
        and timothy   morning and evening
2 pounds bran

RATION FOR IDLE PREGNANT DRAFT MARES   This ration kept the mares in rig for classroom inspection. They weighed from 1,700 to 1,850 pounds.

5 ears corn   } morning
8 pounds alfalfa hay

5 pounds oats   } evening
8 pounds timothy hay

RATION FOR PERCHERON MARE CARVILASS, WEIGHT 1,900 POUNDS

Before foaling:

5 pounds crushed oats
1 pound ear corn (2 small ears)   } morning
8 pounds alfalfa hay

12 quart pail damp food mixture { 3 pounds crushed oats
                                   1 pound bran   } evening
                                   1 pound chopped hay
8 pounds loose mixed hay (clover and timothy)

After foaling:

6 pounds crushed oats
2 pounds ear corn   } morning
10 pounds alfalfa hay

12 quart pail dampened mixture $\left\{\begin{array}{l}\text{3 pounds crushed oats} \\ \text{1 pound bran} \\ \text{1 pound chopped hay}\end{array}\right.$

10 pounds loose timothy hay $\left.\right\}$ evening

RATION FOR PERCHERON MARE MISS COLLARD AGAIN, WEIGHT 1,750 POUNDS

Before foaling:

4 pounds oats
1 pound corn $\left.\right\}$ morning
7 pounds alfalfa hay

12 quart pail dampened mixture $\left\{\begin{array}{l}\text{3 pounds crushed oats} \\ \text{1 pound bran} \\ \text{1 pound chopped hay}\end{array}\right.$ evening

6 pounds loose timothy hay

After foaling:

4 pounds crushed oats
1 pound ear corn $\left.\right\}$ morning
8 pounds alfalfa hay

12 quart pail dampened mixture $\left\{\begin{array}{l}\text{3 pounds crushed oats} \\ \text{1 pound bran} \\ \text{1 pound chopped hay}\end{array}\right.$ evening

8 pounds loose timothy hay

NOTE: Miss Collard Again was a free-milking mare. She could not be fed like Carvilass.

Questions

1. What was the price of a bushel of corn at Chicago in 1918? in 1933?

2. What was the price of a bushel of oats at Chicago in 1918? in 1933?

3. What was the price of a bushel of wheat at Chicago in 1918? in 1933?

4. List the items that must be taken into consideration in computing the cost of feeding a work horse for a year.

5. How much more did it cost to feed a Moores and Ross Milk Company horse in 1918 than it did in 1933? (See the figures in this chapter.)

6. Suggest a satisfactory work horse ration, kind, and quantity from farm-grown feeds, for a 1,500 pound work horse that is employed at medium farm work.

7. Compare the value of oats and ear corn as a concentrate for work horses when mixed hay is used, either clover and timothy or alfalfa and timothy.

8. Usually, which is the cheaper grain for horses, ear corn or oats? Why?

9. For years city stables, in feeding work horses, advocated a bran mash and a teaspoonful of saltpeter in place of the regular ration on Saturday nights. Why?

10. Discuss the efficiency of ear corn and alfalfa hay as a feed for work horses.

11. Why should colts be liberally fed from weaning until two years of age?

12. In feeding draft fillies at Illinois, how much more grain and hay were required the second winter than the first winter to make a pound of gain?

13. If corn, oats, and alfalfa are available for feeding young horses, is the use of commercial mill feeds absolutely necessary?

14. Is it necessary to limit the feeding of alfalfa hay to horses?

15. What nutrients necessary for growth are furnished by alfalfa hay?

16. How much grain and alfalfa hay will draft fillies consume from weaning time until two years of age? Figure the cost at current prices of carrying a filly for the time indicated.

17. What use can be made of sweetclover pasture in growing horses?

18. Comment upon soybean hay as a feed for horses.

19. How much grain per hundredweight of filly does it take on good pasture to produce satisfactory growth in fillies from weaning time until two years of age?

20. When weanlings have been carried through the first winter on a liberal dry ration, should the grain be discontinued when the colts are turned to pasture in the spring?

17

Feeding Light-Leg Horses

Feed

The condition of the horse can be regulated by the amounts and kind of hay and grain given. At least two kinds of hay should be in every stable, i.e., choice timothy and alfalfa; where good bright mixed hay (clover and timothy) can be obtained, it is well to have this also. Timothy is fed about half of the time; mixed clover and timothy, if available, about a third of the time; and alfalfa the balance, or a sixth of the time. But the owner must watch his horses and any that need a little more alfalfa should have it. This can be readily determined by watching the urine and the manure. Increased alfalfa will increase urination and give a softer consistency to the bowel movements, so that elimination from both kidneys and the bowels can be regulated absolutely by the amount and frequency of alfalfa feedings.

For grain, there is nothing better than No. 2 white oats thoroughly fanned and cleaned so that they are free from dust and weed seeds, and good yellow corn on the ear, about two ears twice a day. The best plan is to establish contact with a reliable dealer in grain and hays, and give him to understand that you want good, bright, green hays, free from mold or dust and first-class sound, clean grain, and that you are willing to pay a little above the market to get them. He thereupon will save the very best he can get for you. Refuse to accept inferior hays or grain.

360

How Much to Feed

Amounts of feed vary with the type and size of horse and how regularly and how far the animal is ridden, that is, how hard his work is. Generally speaking, a horse should be fed about all the grain he will clean up in half an hour and all the hay he will clean up thoroughly before time for his next feed, until he is up in flesh and condition. From that time on, 1 pound of grain and 1.1 pounds of hay a day for each hundredweight of horse will usually be sufficient to keep him in flesh.

In other words, a thousand pound horse in good flesh and condition should get ten pounds of grain and 11 or 12 pounds of hay a day, and on this stay in good flesh. After horses are in good condition, many owners, drop the feed to 8 pounds of grain a day and increase the hay as much as the grain has been reduced, thus feeding 14 pounds of hay and 8 pounds of grain to a thousand pound horse. Larger mounts must receive more, at the usual rate of 1 pound of grain and 1.1 pounds of hay per hundredweight. An hour on good pasture in the sunshine is valuable in promoting the health and vigor of riding horses, but city owners can seldom provide this.

At all times, however, the eye of the master must regulate the feed. If the horse loses condition, the ration should be increased or varied until a balance is found that will keep the horse in good flesh and condition, sufficiently full of spirit and fire for the amount of riding that is being done. Horses that are "high," that is, are fed enough to possess superabundant energy and vitality, give a more exhilarating ride than those lacking such spirit.

Feeding Equitation Horses at The Ohio State University

The Ohio State University has an equitation unit operated under the joint auspices of the departments of physical education and animal husbandry. The ten head of horses are used four days a week and on these four days are under tack from 9:00 A.M. until 11:30 A.M. and from 1:00 P.M. until 4:00 P.M. These horses will average about 1,000 pounds in weight. They have been kept in good rig on the daily ration listed below:

5 pounds crushed oats
½ pound bran   } morning
6 pounds timothy and clover (light mixed)

2 or 3 ears corn   } noon, when horses
                                                    are working

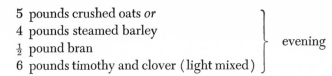

5 pounds crushed oats *or*
4 pounds steamed barley
½ pound bran
6 pounds timothy and clover (light mixed)
           } evening

These horses are watered four or five times daily.

Feeding and Management of Standardbred Stallions, Brood Mares, and Foals at Hanover Shoe Farms

At Hanover Shoe Farms, Paoli, Pennsylvania, Standardbred stallions have access to paddocks daily and are exposed to as much fresh air and sunshine as possible. During the extremely hot weather, when the flies are at their worst, the stallions are turned out about three or four o'clock in the afternoon and are left out all night with a watchman on duty.

The brood mares lead a pretty rugged existence, for they are turned out more, receiving less consideration for the weather than any other type of horse on the place receives. They are turned out permanently earlier in the spring, unless they have foals by their side and they are gotten up later in the fall than any other group on the place, but it seems to agree with them, because they stay fat and healthy. Care is taken not to permit young foals to become chilled during the first few months of their existence; hence mares with young foals are not turned out, except on nice days, until their foals are well started and the weather has definitely settled. This is the last group of horses to be permanently turned out for the summer, usually not before May 15 or 20.

Foals at Hanover Shoe Farms are taught to eat almost immediately and their halter breaking begins about the same time. After they are turned out with their dams, they are fed twice daily in creeps all the rolled oats they will clean up. During the middle of the summer, after the pastures get a little short, a small foal will consume an amazing amount. Only foals and yearlings get rolled oats, which are crushed fresh each day. All other horses when fed grain get their oats whole.

The mares are not fed grain when pastures are good, for the grass seems very nutritious and the mares stay fat, almost too fat, on grass alone, at the same time giving a heavy flow of milk. Occasionally, during this period, a patron who has sent his mare to Hanover Shoe Farms to be bred will complain that his mare is too fat, being hardly able to believe that she is existing on grass alone. This certainly indicates good health and nutritious pastures.

FOALS AND YEARLINGS AT HANOVER SHOE FARMS   Foals and yearlings receive grain, mostly oats, from the time they can eat until they are sold as yearlings, when they are eighteen to twenty-one months old. Good white oats are fed, usually unclipped oats that weight forty to forty-two pounds. The weight of the oats is mentioned because in order to have any control over feeding grain, it is necessary to keep the weight of the oats fairly constant. It is almost impossible to get the average feeder to feed in any way except by measure. He simply refuses to take weight into account and will feed about so many quarts, regardless of whether the oats weigh thirty or fifty pounds to the bushel.

NO HARD AND FAST RULES AT HANOVER SHOE FARMS   Mr. Lawrence Sheppard, manager of Hanover Shoe Farms, a very practical horseman, says that he has never endorsed hard and fast rules governing the quantity of feed to be given to an individual horse: "I am a firm believer in the old adage that feeding should be controlled by the eye of the feeder and not by fixed formula or rule. A pretty good basic rule, however, is to feed as much as a horse will clean up promptly at a feeding and look forward to the next meal. Of course, it goes without saying, that a horse should be kept in fair flesh."

Mr. Sheppard continues with his counsel concerning the feeding of hay: "You are all well acquainted with the food value of hay and why it should be cut early in order to maintain its maximum protein and vitamin content. I do not like timothy hay by itself and never have. I believe I was one of the first to advocate feeding heavily mixed hay (clover and timothy) to horses in training, with the idea of trying to keep my race horses fat instead of poor. Therefore, I like heavily mixed hay with plenty of clean clover in it, and alfalfa, which, incidentally, is hard to obtain in our section. But we feed a slice or two, at least once a day, whenever we can get it, especially to mares in foal and to yearlings. I have heard a great deal of discussion, pro and con, about alfalfa as a feed for horses. I might say in passing that I rather doubt that you can feed too much of it to brood mares, also to foals, and yearlings. But since alfalfa costs more than good mixed hay, we use the mixed hay because of economy."

Feeding Schedules for Thoroughbred Stallions

Listed herewith are the feeding schedules for stallions on three different Thoroughbred farms in Kentucky:

1. December to April: 5 pounds of crushed oats in the morning; 5 pounds of crushed oats at noon; 6 pounds of mash (crushed oats and bran) at night and 20 to 25 pounds of Ohio (light mixed clover and timothy hay) fed either in the manger or on the floor of the box stall. Half a dozen carrots are fed daily during this period. April to December: 16 pounds of crushed oats a day with sufficient timothy and red clover hay. A paddock and long-rein methods of exercise are used.

2. For roughage the stallions are fed timothy and clover hay, the grain ration consisting of 5 pounds of rolled oats in the morning and again at noon, with a bran mash at night depending upon the condition of the stallion. Three cakes of yeast are given the stallion each morning during the breeding season.

For exercise the stallions are allowed two hours a day in paddocks during the breeding season and in addition are worked thirty minutes under saddle each morning.

3. From November 15 to February 15, the stallions get daily 12 quarts of rolled oats, 2 quarts of chopped alfalfa and molasses, also mixed clover and timothy hay. February 15 to July 1, all sweet feed is discontinued after the grass has become plentiful. July 1 to November 15, the sweet feed may again be added to the grain, if the grass is not good.

This farm has three-acre paddocks in which the stallions are turned out during the summer at night and during the winter by day after the frost is off the grass. Horses are groomed daily and front shoes are kept on the year round. They receive only the exercise voluntarily taken in the paddocks.

Feeding Schedule for Saddle-bred Stallions

At one Kentucky saddle-bred nursery, from July 1 to October 1, a saddle stallion is fed a gallon of whole oats three times a day. From October to April, a gallon of grain mixed in the proportion of 3 quarts of oats to 1 quart of bran is fed three times a day. This feed is increased during the breeding season. If the stallion is in poor flesh, corn is added to the ration.

This nursery exercises a saddle stallion by riding or driving if he is in service and is also to be used in the show ring in the fall. After the stallion is withdrawn from the show ring and is used for service only, he receives paddock exercise, being turned out for a couple of hours each day. During hot weather he gets his paddock exercise early in the morning or late in the afternoon or early evening. He is not turned out at night. He is protected from, storms, cold winds, and rains the year round.

Feeding Schedule for Saddle Brood Mares

At a saddle horse nursery in the bluegrass region, Lexington, Kentucky, from October 1 to April 1 foaling mares are fed 1 gallon of a mixture containing corn, oats, and bran at night and the same allowance of grain in the morning. The mixture contains about the following proportions:

2 parts rolled oats
1 part cracked corn
1 part bran

Brood mares and foals in a shaded pasture at Walnut Hall Farm, Donerail, Kentucky, an establishment which has produced many of the most noted trotters and pacers in history. Photograph courtesy Walnut Hall Farm.

To the night feed is added 2 tablespoonfuls of flaxseed meal during November, December, January, and February.

About 16 pounds of clover and timothy hay are allowed each mare daily. Mares are turned into paddocks after the frost is off the grass. In addition to the water available to them in the paddocks the mares are watered at ten o'clock at night.

From March to October during the foaling and the summer season, 2 gallons of a mixture containing oats and bran only are fed daily for about three weeks, at the end of which time the cracked corn is again included and the mares are fed 2 to $2\frac{1}{2}$ gallons of the original mixture daily. Hay is not fed after June 1.

Within a few days after foaling, the mare and the foal are turned out on good days, the time allowed outside being gradually increased. After July 1 they are kept up in the day and are outside at night. Creeps in the pasture for foal feeding are used until about July 1, after which time the feeding is in the stalls inside the barn and the creeps are not used.

Foals are weaned at five and a half to six months of age. Mares are fed grain after the foals are weaned until mid October or November 1 if the pasture continues good.

Salt and Minerals

Minerals are fed best through feeds. Hay, for example, should be bought when possible from farms where the land has been heavily fertilized with lime and phosphate. Some owners make contracts with farmers for a supply of timothy and alfalfa grown on such lands and pay a premium of $2 a ton for hay that has been cut early and cured perfectly so that it is of a bright green color without having been bleached by the sun or leached by the rains. Where rains are frequent, the hay must be cured in cocks under caps, or with forced-draft air dryers.

Green grass, well fertilized and watered as needed, is valuable for riding horses. Where grazing is impractical, feed about 30 pounds of fresh-cut grass daily.

Salt

Salt is needed by horses of all ages. The sodium and chloride which make up salt are necessary for the proper digestion of the ration. Salt may be fed free-choice, given at regular intervals, or fed with the grain. The first method is preferred, since not all horses consume the same amount of salt, and it is difficult for the feeder to know exactly how much is required. As a rule, horses will eat from half to two ounces a day, depending upon their size and age, the work performed, the humidity, the temperature, the nature of the feed, and the character of the soil on which they are kept.

Where goiters occur frequently it is a good practice to feed iodized salt, especially to brood mares, stallions, and colts. Iodized salt should be kept in covered containers, as it is thought that some of the iodine is lost when kept in ordinary sacks or open bins.

Minerals

Calcium and phosphorus are two of the most important minerals that are lacking in common feeds but can be easily and cheaply supplied. Using a variety of feeds lessens the necessity of feeding a mineral mixture.

The following mixture, a simple combination that adds most of the minerals needed to improve the common rations, has been fed to colts and brood mares at Iowa State College with good results:

20 pounds iodized salt
40 pounds finely ground limestone
35 pounds spent bone black
 3 pounds commercial iron oxide
 2 pounds sulfur

The amount horses will consume again depends upon their ages and the character of the feed. Some horses will eat as much as one ounce daily. Horses are particular about eating anything that has a strong odor; hence spent bone black is suggested in place of bone meal.

Water

Water is essential in the ration of horses; yet its functions are often overlooked. Water aids in digestion, carries off waste products from the body, flushes out the system, and cools the horse.

It makes very little difference whether horses are watered before, after, or during a meal. The main thing is to adopt a definite plan of watering and then stick religiously to it. It is seldom that horses will drink too much water under normal conditions. If horses are too hot or if water has been withheld from them for a long time, it is not advisable to allow them to drink all they want; but if they have been handled carefully, they should be allowed to satisfy their thirst.

Automatic watering cups placed in a corner of box stalls are a great convenience. These devices permit horses to get perfectly fresh water whenever they want it, but it is necessary to make sure that the horses are well cooled down before they come into the stable. This is sound practice, however, for all riders should learn that their horses should always be ridden slowly for the last mile so that they will be cooled off when they reach the stable and be cool enough to eat or drink. If, because of special reasons, the rider has to make his entire ride at too rapid a pace to permit the horse to be reasonably cool when he comes in, the groom should be given strict instructions to loosen the girth but leave saddle on and walk him under a "cooling out" sheet for at least twenty minutes so that he will cool out before being put into a stall or allowed any water. Most private owners do not have grooms to do this; hence they must time their ride so that the horses may walk the last mile and be cool enough to eat or drink when they come in. Horses should be rubbed dry with coarse, clean cloths.

Rations for Light-Leg Horses

Numerous rations or combinations of feeds can be used for light-leg horses with good results. A feeder should watch his horses carefully and adjust the ration according to the way they respond to the feeds.

The following rations, which are merely suggestions, can be easily changed to suit the needs of light-leg horses for the kind of work they are doing:

> 7 pounds oats
> 2 pounds wheat bran
> 8 pounds timothy hay
> 4 pounds alfalfa or clover hay

> 7 pounds oats
> 1 pound yellow corn
> $\frac{1}{2}$ pound linseed oil meal
> > *or*
> $\frac{1}{2}$ pound soybean meal
> 10 pounds timothy
> 2 pounds alfalfa or clover hay

> 6 pounds oats
> 8 pounds timothy hay
> pasture

4 pounds rolled oats
4 pounds rolled barley
5 pounds prairie hay
5 pounds alfalfa or clover hay

Fattening Ration

4 pounds oats
4 pounds yellow corn
1 pound wheat bran
$\frac{1}{2}$ pound linseed oil meal
12 pounds timothy and clover
or
12 pounds timothy and alfalfa hay

This grain mixture moistened with $\frac{1}{2}$ pint molasses and 1 quart water

Rations for Stallions in Service

5 pounds oats
2 pounds yellow corn
1 pound ground wheat
2 pounds bran
6 pounds alfalfa
6 pounds timothy or prairie hay

Questions

1. What kind of concentrate heads the preferential list of grains for light-leg horses? Why?

2. If the setup is to be ideal, at least two kinds of hay should be available in light-leg stables. What should these hays be? Why?

3. What is a good horseman's rule for determining the amount of grain and roughage to feed?

4. How much grain and how much roughage are consumed daily by a thousand pound equitation horse at The Ohio State University?

5. Discuss the feeding practices at Hanover Shoe Farms, for Standardbred foals, yearlings, brood mares, and stallions.

6. Discuss the feeding schedules for Thoroughbred stallions as practiced on typical Thoroughbred farms in Kentucky.

7. Comment in some detail upon the feeding and exercise schedules for stallions in some of the most famous saddle horse nurseries in Kentucky.

8. What is the purpose of feeding iodized salt, especially to foals and brood-mares?

9. Suggest a good mineral mixture as a supplement to rations that may be deficient in minerals.

10. Comment upon the importance of a good water supply, the regularity with which horses should be given access to it, and the times at which water should be supplied with caution or withheld completely.

11. Make up two different rations, from farm-grown feeds, for a thousand pound saddle horse that is to be ridden daily.

18

Problems in Stallion and Brood Mare Management

Exercising Stallions: Methods

Traveling the Horse

In the peak days of the work horse business, draft stallions were traveled or stood for service in designated rural districts. Usually the stallion was led behind a cart in which the caretaker carried the needed utensils incident to standing stallions and serving mares. Sometimes the stallion was led beside a lead pony ridden by the caretaker. Prior to the motor era when the work horse population was at its height and large numbers of grade mares were bred, the caretaker walked and led his stallion.

Working the Stallion

At one time, draft stallions worked in harness part time as a unit in a team. Mature stallions were exercised this way frequently and well-grown two- and three-year-old stallions spent part of the day in harness. Young stallions not only got their exercise in this way; in harness they also earned their keep.

371

Box Stall and Paddock Exercise

Box stall and paddock are one of the most common methods of exercising both draft and light-leg stallions. A roomy box stall furnishes a great opportunity for stallions to exercise in all kinds of weather; moreover, box stalls are particularly useful in solving the exercise problem on bad days.

Hand Exercise

Stallions may be exercised regularly in hand with a man on foot or riding a lead pony, but this method of exercising stallions increases the labor bill.

Jogging and Riding Stallions

Standardbred or saddle-bred stallions may be jogged in light harness from two to five miles daily from March to July 1, or during the breeding season. Of course, the saddle-bred stallion may be ridden. The riding of Thoroughbred stallions, thirty minutes to one hour daily, is also a common part of the exercise program.

Longeing Light-Leg Stallions

Exercise at the end of a long lead rein (longeing the stallion) is a common method in the case of Thoroughbred, Standardbred, and saddle-bred stallions and diversifies the exercise program.

Many breeders, however, depend entirely on the exercise taken voluntarily by a stallion in the paddock. The objection to this method is that the exercise cannot be regulated and in bad weather the horse takes very little if any exercise, and on good days may take too much.

The Number of Mares per Stallion per Season

Opinions differ concerning the number of mares a stallion should serve in a season. It depends upon the age of the horse, the fitness of the horse for service, the regularity with which the mares are presented for service, the length of the season, the number of services necessary for each mare. Some of the big breeding farms in the Kentucky bluegrass region state that the average mare requires two services before settling. Others state that three is the usual number. A well-grown two-year-old draft stallion may breed 10 to 20 mares in a season. A three-year-old may breed 35 to 50 mares. An aged stallion may breed 100 to 125 mares.

Miscellaneous Examples

Mr. David M. Fyffe, superintendent of livestock at The Ohio State University for many years, says that Thane of Glamis, a Clydesdale stallion, bred 84 mares one season, settling 79 of them. Mr. Fyffe states that this stallion was unhitched from the plow three times in one afternoon to breed mares although he had bred two mares in the forenoon of the same day. Four of these mares settled to service. This horse's service fee was five pounds sterling per mare, two pounds due at time of service, the remainder due when the mare was seen to be safe in foal.

Mr. Fyffe states also that the Clydesdale stallion General Williams bred seven mares in one day between 4:00 a.m. and 10:00 p.m., the seventh mare settling to service.

Dunure Footprint, possibly the most celebrated Clydesdale stallion in the history of the breed, was the sire of over one hundred foals entered in the Scotch Clydesdale Stud Book in two different years. At the peak of the season this stallion had two caretakers, a day man and a night man. On one occasion the horse which stood at a $600 service fee, bred a mare every two hours for three days and four nights.

Baron's Pride, another famous Clydesdale stallion, stood at The Banks, Netherhall, Scotland. He was owned by William and Andrew Montgomery and earned $225,000 for them in the stud in service fees, plus options on his colts. This stallion stood at a fee of $50, foal or no foal. He died at the age of twenty-two years.

Mr. E. Rittenour in Piketon, Ohio, not a good horse country, had a stallion that bred 149 mares in the season of 1932.

Mr. Prugh Overturf, London, Ohio, reports a cheap stallion, service fee $5 and trucked by his owner, that bred 252 mares in the season of 1932.

Waynedale King, a Belgian stallion, bred 140 mares for Mr. Chat Alexander, Wooster, Ohio, in the season of 1935. He settled 90 of them. In 1936 he bred 209 mares and settled 128 of them.

Woodrow Wilson, a Belgian stallion owned by The Ohio State University, stood for three seasons in the hands of Mr. J. M. Harris at Clifton, Ohio. This stallion bred 127 mares in 1933, 147 mares in 1934, and 172 mares in 1935. In the 1935 season, which ran from March to November, he settled 124 mares. The horse was then seventeen years old.

Mr. Samuel Riddle, owner of Man o' War, limited the services of his famous stallion for years to 25 mares annually.

These figures show how much variation there may be in standing stallions for service.

Handling Stallions at Time of Service

Teasing Mares: Methods

FENCE   Oftentimes a fence has been used as the only barrier between a mare and a stallion at teasing time. A fence does not provide the most satisfactory means of controlling mares and stallions at teasing time; nevertheless a board fence has been used many times as an improvised method of teasing mares.

BARN DOOR   The lower half of a double door on a box stall has been used many times as a method of teasing mares. It is an effective barrier over which the stallion sticks his head when the mare is stood broad-side just outside.

SNORTING POLE   The use of a snorting pole anchored to two posts outside the barn and parallel with the side of the barn, or parallel with the wall of the entry way inside the barn, is a satisfactory way of teasing mares. A snorting pole should be at least nine or ten feet long and it should be elbow and stifle high.

TEASING AND BREEDING STALLS   Where large numbers of mares are bred, a teasing and breeding stall is a most useful piece of equipment. The use of such a stall is sound practice because it ensures the control of both the mare and the stallion at teasing time and at time of service. Complete control of mare and stallion reduces to a minimum the possibility of accident and injury to both.

BRIDLE EQUIPMENT FOR STALLIONS   Some stallions are more rank, noisy, and rough than others at teasing and service time. For most draft and light-leg stallions, the ordinary lead shank with chin chain is an effective control if the man on the end of the shank is experienced.

If a draft stallion shows a tendency to be bad-mannered and unruly, a twisted iron bar beneath his jaw, with hooks at the end of the bar which fasten into the side rings of his halter, will make him easy to control.

Muzzles should be used on all stallions that are too rough with their teeth at time of teasing and service.

Indications of Heat in Mares

Relaxation of external genitals.

Spasmodic winking of lips of the vulva.

Frequent emissions of odorous, discolored urine. If the urine is odorous and discolored, frequently the mares are in heat. If the urine is odorless and clear, the mare is usually not in heat. Some owners who are not clear on this point have trucked mares many miles to be bred in the mistaken belief that they were in heat simply because at the time of trial, they switched their tails and emitted an odorless and normal-colored urine.

Mucous discharge which soils and gums the tail and rear legs.

Obvious desire for company.

Breeding the Mare

The use of a breeding stall has distinct advantages. In a breeding stall the mare and the stallion can both be controlled and the danger of injury greatly minimized.

If the mare proves to be in heat, several precautions should be taken prior to the act of service by the stallion.

First, the mare's tail should be wrapped or tied so that the hair of the tail will not be in the way of the stallion at time of service. A strip of bunting or a sizable cord can be used to tie the tail, or the upper portion can be wrapped with a roller bandage.

The external genitals of the mare should be washed or sponged prior to the act of coition. The materials commonly used for this are castile soap in warm water, or one to two ounces of Therapogen in warm water, or 1 to 2 per cent Coopers' Milk Oil Dip in water.

If a teasing and breeding stall is not available, a twitch and hopples are common methods of controlling the mare at the time of service. A satisfactory twitch can be made from a piece of fork handle, through one end of which a hole has been bored and an eight- or ten-inch loop of window cord has been passed. This loop of cord is placed about the upper lip of the mare and twisted tight as a means of control. The handle of the twitch should be long enough so that the man holding the twitch will be stationed beyond the reach of the mare's front feet.

The breeding hopples most in use loop over the neck of the mare, the main strap running between her front legs, and terminate in a large ring

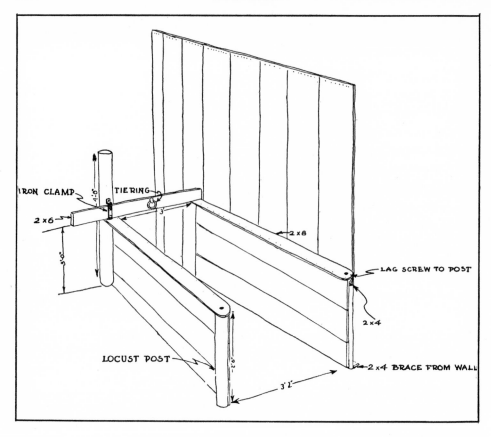

A breeding stall for use at time of teasing and breeding mares. The breeding stall makes it possible to control both the mare and the stallion at time of service and decreases to a minimum the possibility of injury.

from which adjustable straps or ropes with snaps run backward to the hocks and are fastened securely in place. Hopples keep mares from kicking stallions at time of service.

At the time of service a stallion should make his approach from the side, gradually working around to his mounted position at the rear. He should not be permitted to rush the mare from the rear.

The attendant should see to it that the act of coition results in actual ejaculation or a true service rather than a false service. He should also be on guard lest a stallion makes false entrance, getting into the digestive tract instead of into the generative tract. A false entrance may result in a ruptured bowel.

Most stallioners prefer that mares be led for a few minutes following service rather than be permitted to stand and strain and urinate, and possibly eject some of the seminal discharge.

A common practice following the act of coition is to sponge or wash the sheath and the genitals of the stallion in order to guard against infection. Castile soap and warm water, or 1 per cent solution potassium permanganate, or two ounces of Zonite in a gallon of water may be used for this purpose.

Sometimes mares are difficult to catch in heat and refuse to show to a stallion when teased. Such mares have been known to come in heat when stabled in a stall for a few days between two stallions.

Other mares have been forced-bred and then they come in heat naturally. When force-breeding mares, extra precaution should be taken to have both the mare and the stallion under control.

Some maiden mares being bred for the first time have to be opened manually in order that a stallion can serve them properly. The stallioner has to be the judge in such cases. It is important to keep the hands out of the generative tracts of mares if possible in order to minimize the possibility of infection.

In the case of maiden mares the double cover is resorted to as a guarantee that the mare settles to service. One farm in the bluegrass region in Kentucky had thirteen maiden mares one year and all settled to double covers, separated by one day during the heat period.

Trying and Rebreeding Mares

Most mares come in heat between the fifteenth and twenty-fourth days following service. Usually they remain in heat three to five days, sometimes longer. The average length of time between periods is eighteen to twenty-one days. Some of the big breeding nurseries try mares every day, others every other day, beginning the fourteenth day following a breeding date. Some managers of the big farms have their pastures patrolled by a man riding or leading a teasing stallion. All questionable mares are then brought to the barn and tried in the regular way. When mares pass the six weeks' period without coming in heat they are usually in foal. Some mare owners are too indolent to try their mares regularly. High stud fees, however, and part settlement of fees at time of service stimulate attention to such trials.

Rebreeding the Mare after Foaling

A common practice is to rebreed mares on the seventh to the eleventh day after foaling, usually on the ninth day. There are several reasons:

1. There is an unproved horseman's tradition that mares bred on the ninth day after a normal foaling will conceive more readily than at any

A twitch, controlling device used on the upper lip of a horse. This twitch was made from a piece of heavy fork handle and a loop of window cord.

A saddle mare with her tail wrapped, and rigged with hock hopples preparatory to service by a stallion. Hopples furnish a very satisfactory means of controlling mares at time of service.

subsequent period. Breeding farm records, however, indicate that not more than one mare in four conceives on the first cover on the 9th day.

2. The foaling date the following year will be earlier if mares settle to service during foal heat. Many breeders wish to speed up the business as much as possible; hence they rebreed their mares at the earliest opportunity.

3. Sometimes mares nursing foals are hard to settle; therefore breeders wish to avail themselves of every opportunity to settle such mares and will rebreed them in foal heat if possible.

Disadvantages of Rebreeding Mares in Foal Heat

All mares should not be rebred in foal heat. Records show that most new cases of genital infection which develop into cervicitis or metritis occur in foaling mares. At no time is the mare more susceptible to genital infection than during the foaling and for ten days or two weeks following. Results are disappointing when mares with infected genital tracts are presented for service to stallions. Metritis caused by infection may not prevent a mare from getting in foal, but if she does settle to service, the infection may result in abortion, a dead foal, or a diseased foal. Such parturitions are usually followed by a metritis or cervicitis acute enough to render mares permanently barren.

In discussing the rebreeding of mares at foal heat, it may be well to divide all foaling mares into two classes. The first class of foaling mares includes those that have experienced a normal foaling without difficulty or laceration of parts, have dropped healthy foals, and have not retained the afterbirth. A second class of foaling mares consist of those that have experienced dystocia, have aborted, were lacerated, have had dead or diseased foals, or retained afterbirths. Such mares are most likely to be infected. Examination and treatment by a competent veterinarian are indicated before rebreeding. Such mares should not be rebred at foal heat or later until the genital tract has become normal.

Artificial Insemination

Artificial insemination is not generally practiced except as supplemental to stallion service. Some breeding establishments artificially inseminate all barren mares and mares which have failed to settle after two or three natural services. Both the impregnator and gelatine capsules are used. One method is to recover portions of the seminal fluid from the floor of the vagina. Part of the discharge is drawn into the impregnator and then injected into the neck of the uterus. Or a capsule may be filled on the floor of the vagina and then pushed into the neck of the uterus. In either case, the work is done within the generative tract.

Critics of this method of artificial insemination say that there is too great danger of carrying infection into the uterus. They prefer to catch a portion of the seminal discharge from the penis of the stallion as he dismounts. The semen is strained through three or four layers of sterile gauze, then transferred to a capsule or impregnating syringe and then inserted into the uterus. Of course, the hands are clean, the utensils sterilized, and the external genitals thoroughly cleansed.

The semen is a viscid, whitish milky fluid secreted by the testicles, the seminal vesicles, the prostate and Cowper's glands. Normal horse semen is slightly alkaline. It consists of 97.62 per cent water and 2.38 per cent solids. Nitrogen and phosphorus are present in considerable quantities in the solids, more than 60 per cent of which is protein. The stallion at one copulation ejects 50 to 100 cubic centimeters of semen. The sperm cells in semen left in a test tube at 22 degrees centigrade show some loss of movement in two hours; all sperms are dead at the end of six hours on the average. Semen left in an incubator at 38 degrees centigrade, or about animal heat, show loss of movement in less than two hours and total loss in four hours. Such a temperature favors bacterial growth, and putrefaction sets in quickly. Semen to be used for impregnation should be used very quickly (five to thirty minutes after ejaculation) and kept at temperatures a little below body heat. Laboratory light or the darkness of the incubator affect semen very little. Sunlight activates the sperm cells and shortens their life to two hours, whereas in the light of the laboratory or the incubator they live four hours. A 0.045 per cent solution of HCL, HNO_3, or $H_2 SO_4$ is of sufficient strength to kill sperm cells quickly.

Sperm cells are produced in enormous numbers. A single ejaculation of a vigorous stallion may contain more than 200,000,000 spermatozoa.

Stallions whose semen shows only 50 per cent of the sperm cells to be normal in morphology and motility will get very few mares in foal. Five per cent of the normal number indicates sterility or near sterility.

Percentage of Mares Settling to Service

One farm in the bluegrass reported 82 per cent of its mares in foal for the five years from 1925 to 1930. Of course this farm has its mare breeding programs supervised by a skilled veterinarian. Seventy per cent of mares settling to service is very good. In Kentucky at the big breeding nurseries, 60 to 65 per cent of the mares bred produce live foals. Fifty per cent is the average under ordinary corn-belt farm conditions. At The Ohio State University, between 1924 and 1936, 73.2 per cent of the mares bred settled to service; the average of live foals produced based upon the number of mares bred was 64.5 per cent.

Questions

1. Comment upon the various methods of exercising stallions.
2. What factors determine the number of mares that a stallion may serve in a season?
3. Cite a few examples that show the wide range in the number of mares served by one stallion in a single season.

4. List the various methods that have been used for teasing mares prior to service.

5. Discuss standard bridle equipment for handling stallions at time of service.

6. Name four or five indications of heat in mares.

7. Discuss the twitch, breeding hopples, and teasing and breeding stalls as helpful pieces of equipment for handling stallions and mares at time of service.

8. What is meant by a false service?

9. Mention a satisfactory cleansing solution for washing the genitals of mares and stallions at time of service.

10. How would you manage mares that are difficult to catch in heat?

11. Comment upon the practice of force-breeding mares.

12. To guarantee that a mare settles to service is there value in the double cover?

13. What should be the plan for trying and rebreeding mares?

14. Comment upon the rebreeding of mares following foaling.

15. What mares should be rebred in foal heat?

16. What mares should not be rebred in foal heat?

17. Discuss the practice of artificially inseminating mares.

18. Of mares bred, what proportion settles to service?

19

Foaling Season Management

Problems

Foaling Quarters

If the foals do not arrive until warm weather and the sunshiny days of spring, a clean grass paddock is one of the best places for mares to foal. There will be ample room in such foaling quarters and the dangers of infection of the generative tract as well as the danger of navel ill due to extrauterine infection will be greatly reduced.

In cold and inclement weather, foaling stalls furnish the best and most comfortable accommodations for foaling mares. Such stalls should be ample in size. At The Ohio State University, our foaling stalls are 12 by 15 feet and although they have served the purpose admirably, a stall whose dimensions are 15 by 15 feet might be better. Some of the foaling stalls in the bluegrass region of Kentucky are 20 by 20 feet. Such stalls provide plenty of room at foaling time for all cases of dystocia or difficult birth. Furthermore, these big stalls are very useful places in which to run foals at weaning time or a few yearlings during the winter months.

Foaling stalls should be located on the sunny side of the barn. They are warmer in cold weather and they keep more nearly dry and free from

Dope 85577, purebred Percheron mare, pictured here in work horse flesh and nursing a foal a few days old. This picture is included to show a mare that came in heat while pregnant and was served by a stallion six weeks prior to the birth of this foal. Photograph courtesy Cook and Gormley.

dampness. Foals can stretch out and take a sun bath and can be housed under most comfortable conditions.

Clay floors are preferred by the majority of horsemen in breeding barns, not only in the foaling stalls but in all box stalls. Cement floors when wet are too slick for brood mares heavy in foal for they are always more or less awkward and unsure of foot. The pregnant mare is afraid to lie down or attempt to get up on a slick floor. At The Ohio State University we have had pregnant mares that did not lie down day or night for a period of twenty-three days. Such mares always thicken in their legs, and many horsemen feel that pregnant mares will stock in their legs on hard floors more than they do on clay floors.

Stall partitions may be solid or open. The solid partitions are warmer in winter and much hotter in summer. Open partitions are much cooler in summer. Roofing paper, some strips of lath, and a few roofing nails can be used to make open-partition stalls into tight foaling stalls at very little expense.

Straw, everything considered, is the most popular bedding for foaling stalls. It is usually available and, of course, it is the warmest bedding for

Aerial View of the Animal Husbandry Buildings, The Ohio State University. The horse barn is located at the north end of the group. See the detailed floor and mow plans for the horse barn in accompanying cuts. Photograph courtesy Photography Department, The Ohio State University.

foals; moreover, it absorbs urine and moisture readily and keeps the stall dry.

Peat moss, when available and not prohibitive in price, is a fine bedding for box stalls in a breeding barn other than in foaling stalls. It is too mussy a bedding at time of foaling. Before the Second World War, peat moss was used in box stalls in our breeding barn at The Ohio State University for several reasons. It is free of weed seed, it is an absorbent and a deodorant, and it keeps the feet of horses moist. Moreover, peat moss manure always has a good sale value because it is in constant demand by market gardeners and golf course keepers. Peat moss is not practicable to use in single stalls, however, because it is difficult to keep under the horses.

Shavings are popular as bedding in those areas where industrial plants are glad to get rid of them free of charge to anyone who will take them away. Economy and availability often account for the use of shavings.

Prior to the foaling, a box stall should be thoroughly cleaned, all litter removed, and the floor scraped and limed. The sides of the stall should be thoroughly sprayed with a standard disinfectant solution. Cooper's Milk Oil Sheep Dip, in a 5 per cent solution, makes a satisfactory spray for disinfecting stalls.

Signs of Pregnancy

1. The oestrum ceases.

2. A vaginal examination of the uterine seal, forty to sixty days following the last service, is good practice in determining pregnancy. If the mare's generative tract is examined at this time with a speculum and is normal, the cervix is closed with a mucilaginous, grayish-white seal, the *os* is closed and puckered, often deflected to one side against the uterine wall, and the vaginal mucosa is dry and gummy. The speculum may become covered with a sticky, white gum during the examination.

3. The uterine arteries in the fifth month of pregnancy are almost as thick as the little finger.

4. Palpation of the fetus through the rectum, seventy days following the last service, is definite. A gravid uterus is easily determined at this time by an experienced veterinarian.

5. The size of the abdomen increases but this is not always a reliable sign.

6. The mammae (udder, teats) enlarge.

Duration of Pregnancy

The average period of gestation for the brood mare is 340 days. The minimum period of gestation with expectancy that the colt will live is 315 days. Gestation data on 168 Kentucky brood mares ranged from 319 to 379 days. The foal born in 319 days was small and very frail for two weeks. At The Ohio State University mares have carried colts a full year and saved them. They have foaled two weeks early and the colts have been saved. Foals that are long overdue are usually big, helpless, and weak, and mares often have difficulty delivering them.

Weights of Foals

The average range in weight of trotting mare foals is from 100 to 120 pounds. The weights of 39 Thoroughbred foals in Kentucky varied from 92

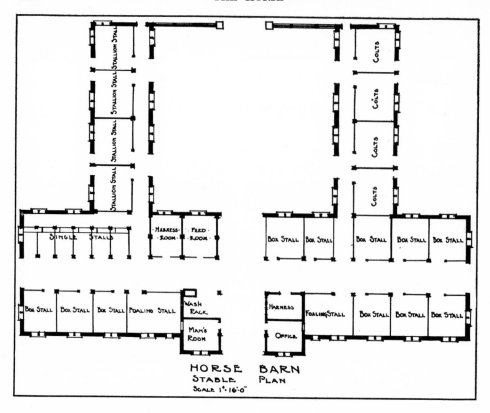

Floor plan of the horse barn at The Ohio State University. This barn features cross drive-ways wide enough to admit a truck or manure spreader, twenty-one box stalls with open partitions, six single-tie stalls, two large foaling stalls, a stallion wing, a brood mare wing, a tack stall, a wash rack, a feed room, an office, four water hydrants, dirt floors, and exercise paddocks immediately adjacent to the barn. In this barn are housed the equitation horses and all purebred saddle horses owned at the university.

to 162 pounds, with an average of 124 pounds. Weights of draft foals at the University of Illinois have averaged about 150 pounds. Weights of Percheron foals at the farm of Mr. William B. Murray, Wellington, Ohio, have ranged from 140 pounds to 185 pounds, with an average of about 150 pounds. The average daily gain of such draft foals for the first three months is about 3.2 pounds. At one year, the best-grown draft colts should weigh between 1,000 and 1,200 pounds.

Signs of Approaching Parturition

1. The sacrosciatic ligaments sink, resulting in depression of the croup muscles on each side of the tailhead.

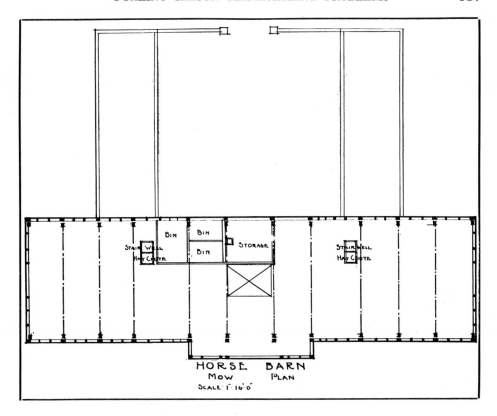

BIN BIN

STAIR WELL
HAY CHUTE

BIN

STORAGE

STAIR WELL
HAY CHUTE

HORSE BARN
Mow Plan
SCALE 1"-16'-0"

Overhead grain bins, two hay chutes, and ample space for hay and straw storage are features of the mow plan in this barn.

2. The lips of the vulva enlarge and relax.

3. The udder becomes full. This usually starts a month or six weeks before foaling. The udder enlarges at night, decreasing in size as the mare exercises during the day.

4. The belly becomes pendulous. Sometimes there are edematous swellings on the ventral surface of the abdomen due to the oozing of watery fluid through capillary walls into the intercellular spaces of the connective tissues.

5. Sometimes the mucous secretions of the external genitals increase and are discharged, soiling the tail and hocks.

6. Beads of wax appear on the teats.

7. Milk starts to run (sometimes for ten days or two weeks).

Immediate Signs of Foaling: Indications of Labor Pain

1. Restlessness.
2. Pawing the litter of the stall.
3. Stall walking.

4. Straining.

5. Sweating, noticeable in the flanks.

6. Frequent urination (in some mares).

7. Appearance and rupture of the water bag (the outer fetal membrane).

Reasons Why an Attendant Should Be Present When Mares Are Foaling

1. High investment.

2. Element of risk.

3. Slow turnover in the horse business.

4. The low birth rate in horse breeding.

5. The high mortality among foals.

6. The danger that the mare may get cast in the stall or lie down too close to a partition.

7. The necessity of treating the navel cord to prevent navel ill or joint ill.

8. The possibility of saving weak foals which otherwise might chill to death or die of neglect, especially if the weather is cold.

9. Slow, difficult deliveries which require assistance or which need the services of a veterinarian.

10. The problem of starting the foal to nurse. In the case of young mares especially, the udder may be swollen and tender and the teats partially inverted. In such cases, immediate care may be the difference between profit and loss in the business.

11. Administration of injections if needed to start the digestive apparatus of the foal. The colostrum milk is supposed to act as an agent in starting the bowels but it has failed to do this so often with mares at The Ohio State University, that injections to start the bowels are a part of good management. Some foals, because of the pain in their digestive tract, refuse to nurse until the black, rubbery, fecal material has been expelled from their bowels.

12. The possibility that nervous, high-strung mares may injure a foal.

The Act of Parturition

In normal foalings, shortly after labor pains start, the first indication of delivery is the rupture of the water bag (the outer fetal membrane) with the escape of considerable fluid. The front feet and nose of the foal are forced into the pelvic canal and appear at the vulva. They can be distinguished through the inner fetal membrane, which may not rupture until the head of the foal arrives at the vulvar opening. If the inner sac does not rupture promptly, the attendant should rupture it to keep the foal from suffocating. If the foal is presented normally, the back will be up against the top of the pelvic canal, with the head and the chin outstretched in the groove between the front legs. It is a good plan to push back the upper part of the vulva to keep it from tearing. It is poor policy to attempt assistance by pulling on the front legs too soon. If conditions are normal, let the mare labor until the withers and the elbow of the foal have passed the pelvic orifice. The body of the foal should then deliver nicely. Sometimes the fetus lodges at the hips. In such cases, pulling downward on the legs of the fetus toward the hocks or rear feet of the mare may be helpful. Do not grasp the front legs of the foal and pull straight outward. Pull downward. Following delivery of the foal, the mare should have a bran mash and a drink of water with the chill off. In normal foalings, the afterbirth usually comes away within two hours, often within less time. If a mare has not cleaned in four to six hours following foaling, a veterinarian should be called and the afterbirth removed by hand. Cows and ewes can carry the afterbirth longer than mares with much less risk of toxic conditions along the generative tract. Horses, like human beings, are very susceptible to infections, and a retained afterbirth or the retention of a portion of the afterbirth may set up toxic conditions that will result in a case of "foal founder." Sometimes the laminae of only the front feet of the mare may be affected. In severe cases of foal founder all four feet of the mare may be involved.

Following delivery of the foal, the hind quarters and tail of the mare should be washed and disinfected. All soiled litter should be removed and the stall rebedded. After a mare has foaled some breeding nurseries give her a bran mash once daily for two or three days, gradually increasing grain and roughage.

Navel Ill

Caring for the Newborn Foal: Treating the Navel

The handling and care of a colt should be started at foaling time. With all kinds of foals, one of the first duties of the caretaker is to treat the navel cord to prevent joint ill. Navel cords are $2\frac{1}{2}$ to $3\frac{1}{2}$ feet in length and $2\frac{1}{2}$ to $3\frac{1}{2}$ inches in circumference. The cord is usually about as long as the fetus is tall. The umbilical cord is long enough so that during parturition, with the mare lying down, the cord remains unbroken but ruptures when she arises and turns toward the foal or starts to move away from it. Sometimes the foal ruptures the cord by its own sprawling efforts in its first attempts to rise.

A cross section of the navel cord reveals the umbilical arteries, the two umbilical veins (sometimes fused), the urachus, and the Whartonian jelly. The urachus is a canal connecting the bladder with the umbilicus (the allantoic cavity). The Whartonian jelly is an embryonic connective tissue cementing all parts together. Sometimes a navel cord has to be broken by the attendant. It should be grasped between the thumbs and fingers of each hand about two inches from the umbilicus and broken or torn apart. If this fails it should be scraped with a knife. It should not be cut off squarely for hemorrhage may result. Both the hands and the utensils should have been cleansed with antiseptic solution. After the cord is broken, the umbilical arteries and the urachus retract into the abdomen, but the umbilical veins remain open for a time and may serve as an avenue for infection. The retraction of the arteries accomplishes two important purposes: it draws their wounded ends away from the exterior, thereby preventing the entrance of infectious germs; and the inverted connective tissue drawn back with them prevents hemorrhage. Two methods are used to combat navel infection, although one is considered poor practice by the best caretakers. The cord is tied about half an inch from the body and is then severed just beneath the string that encircles it. Gradually this method is being discarded, since it has been shown that navel ill is an acute infectious disease of newborn foals, developing as a result of umbilical infection which may be prenatal or postnatal in origin. Tying the cord is useless as a preventive measure if germs have already entered. Navel cord infection occurs from two sources, intrauterine and extrauterine causes.

Facts in Support of Intrauterine Navel Infection

1. Some mares year after year produce foals dying of navel ill.

2. The disease appears so early that postnatal infection could not have had time to develop.

3. Even when the navel cord has been treated immediately and with great care, joint ill has set in.

4. The same bacillus is found in the uterus of the mare that is found in the tissues of the foal.

Comment upon the Practice of Tying Navel Cords

1. This practice may prevent the retraction of the umbilical arteries and the urachus.

2. Tying the cord may impede drainage, thus preventing the escape of the jelly and venous contents, and so favoring necrosis.

3. Presence of prenatal infection in the umbilicus, if the cord be ligated, is sure to cause serious trouble.

4. Untied cords, if treated at once, seldom become infected.

5. Usually there is very little danger of fatal hemorrhage from untied cords.

6. A normal cord under proper treatment soon dries, hardens, and forms a seal which keeps out infection.

Treating the Navel Cord with an Antiseptic

The other method and the best method of treating the navel cord where the cord breaks naturally is to apply some antiseptic solution to the stub of the cord. Some squeeze out the contents of the cord before treating; some swab the cord with cotton or cheesecloth moistened with the antiseptic solution; others, by means of a wide-mouthed bottle, dip the cord right into the solution. Tincture of iodine (10% strength) has wide use in treating navel cords. Twenty per cent (20%) formalin solution, which is used at The Ohio State University, has a rapid drying and withering effect upon the tissues and is a little nicer to handle than the iodine because it is colorless and does not stain the hands or the tissues.

Some breeding farms in Kentucky use this mixture:

1 part alcohol
9 parts carbolic acid
25 parts camphor

This gives a clear oily solution that can be used freely with practically no danger of cauterizing the parts.

Antiseptic Powders for Navels

Any of the preceding navel treatments are followed by the application of a drying powder. A drying powder recommended by Dr. R. R. Dykstra is composed of equal parts of starch, alum, and powdered gum camphor.

H. H. Mulford Co. recommends a good drying powder, the active agents of which are as follows:

alum	50%
zinc oxide	35%
boric acid	13%
phenol	1%
camphor	1%

The Veterinary College at The Ohio State University recommends the following drying powder called Pheno-Camph. Its active agents are camphor, phenol, alum, boric acid. It is good for use on all cuts and wounds.

Prevention the Best Precaution against Navel Ill

1. Cleanliness and sanitation in the foaling stall before, during, and after parturition.
2. Prompt treatment and care of the navel cord until it is desiccated.
3. The breeding of mares whose genital tracts are free from infection.
4. The isolation of affected foals and the disinfection of contaminated premises.

Miscellaneous Comments upon Treatment of Navel Ill or Pyosepticemia

Pyosepticemia has been recognized as due to the presence of

> streptococci
> diplococci
> colon bacilli
> bacillus abortive equinus
> bacterium viscosum equi

Bacterium viscosum equi was first isolated and identified in the Pathology Laboratory, Kentucky Experiment Station, April 27, 1922. Prior to the year 1926, the Kentucky Laboratory had posted 36 foals. Bacterium viscosum equi caused the death of 29 of them.

In studying 314 cases of navel ill, Magnusson found that the organisms responsible were grouped as follows:

streptococci	31.8%
bacterium viscosum equi	30.9%
colon bacilli	27.1%
diplococci	5.1%
other bacteria	5.1%

Dr. Adseren definitely diagnosed these causative agents in 87 cases of navel ill.

streptococci	62.0%
bacterium viscosum equi	33.3%
colon bacilli	4.6%

Dr. W. W. Dimock of the University of Kentucky, states that in the majority of cases, the source of navel infection is intrauterine. In many cases of bacterium viscosum infection, the evidence of prenatal infection is un-mistakable. In foals having symptoms of the disease at birth, the organism has been recovered in the uterus and in the lesions of the diseased foal and its fetal membranes. Dr. Dimock states further that the subsequent history of mares with streptococcic infection is that they have a cervicitis or metritis fol-lowing a delivery of a diseased foal.

How Is Prenatal Infection Accomplished?

1. Infection may be present in the endometrium at the time of con-ception.

2. Infection may be introduced at time of service and gain entrance to the fetal body through the fetal membranes and thence to the fetal circu-lation.

3. The bacterium viscosum infection may be transmitted from the ma-ternal circulation to the fetal circulation through the placentae.

Symptoms of navel ill usually appear twenty-four to forty-eight hours after birth; however, the disease may occur later or the foal may be born af-fected with it. Acute cases of navel ill succumb usually in three or four weeks. Chronic cases may persist for several months.

Lutze says that bacterium viscosum is not the cause of navel ill between the ages of eight days and three months, and that 54 out of 58 cases of navel ill caused by bacterium viscosum died within four days.

Streptococcic navel ill usually develops more slowly than that caused by bacterium viscosum equi, which is the more virulent form.

Treatment with Dam's Blood

Dr. M. G. Fincher, of Himyar and Shoshone studs in Kentucky, treated eight foals with the dam's blood. All foals were treated at the age of one to two days, some repeatedly. The total amount of dam's blood varied from 100 to 500 cubic centimeters. The blood was drawn directly from the vein and transferred to the foal by subcutaneous injection. Four foals died and four lived. One died at 2 days, one at 6, one at 10, and one at 165. All four showed bacterium viscosum.

Dr. Dimock is doubtful about the effectiveness of dam's blood. He states that it may help somewhat in cases where navel ill is of intrauterine origin. This technique seems to have had more satisfactory results in Europe than in America.

The use of 1 per cent aqueous solution of Mercurochrome intravenously has been tried in a number of cases, given in doses of 20 cubic centimeters every three to five days. Navel ill caused by a streptococcus may respond to this treatment but it has no value when the causative organism is bacterium viscosum equi.

Some breeders vaccinate colts in the first twenty-four hours against joint diseases and repeat the vaccination every twenty-four hours for two or three days. Vaccine or serum is used. Dr. John Baird, a veterinarian who practiced in Kentucky, used an antistreptococcic serum and started the preventive treatment thirty days before the mares were due to foal. He used red iodide of mercury, two drams, potassium iodide, two ounces, and water sufficient to make eighteen ounces. He gave half an ounce to the mare each evening mixed in cooked food for thirty days before foaling and continued it for seven days after foaling.

Feeding Potassium Iodide to Mares at Minnesota

From 1910 to 1925, at the University of Minnesota, only 60 per cent of the foals were raised. Feeding of potassium iodide to mares in foal at Minnesota was started in 1925 and following that date, 73 per cent of the foals were raised annually. It is thought that the iodine stimulated the metabolic processes and a stronger fetus resulted that was more resistant to infections. One gram of potassium iodide crystals was fed in a bran mash Saturday nights to each brood mare during pregnancy.

Feeding Iodine and Minerals to Mares at Purdue

During the years 1922 to 1928 Purdue was losing large numbers of foals, some years as many as half of them. Navel ill accounted for 55 per cent of the losses. After iodine and minerals were given to the brood mares the losses decreased annually until 1934, when there were no losses. One ounce of potassium iodide crystals was added to one gallon of water, four ounces of this solution being fed on the grain to each mare per week. The following mineral mixture was also fed to the mares during winter months.

        500 pounds finely ground deodorized steamed bone meal
         15 pounds iron oxide
        300 pounds powdered limestone
          5 pounds powdered anise seed

One and a half pounds of this mixture were added to each hundred pounds of grain, which was usually dampened to make the minerals stick to the grain.

Constipation in Foals

As noted above, it is usually necessary to give an injection to draft foals and light-leg foals at birth in order to start the digestive apparatus working. The colostrum milk is supposed to perform this function. In the great majority of cases, however, injections are indicated. A bulb syringe with a rubber nozzle 8 or 10 inches long should constitute part of the foaling equipment. Need for injections to clear the digestive tract of the accumulated fecal material (called the meconium) is indicated by such symptoms as laying back the ears, switching the tail, lifting the hind legs, or straining. Usually the symptoms appear three to six hours after birth. One or two ounces of mineral oil or glycerine in a quart of warm water produce very satisfactory results. Castile soap suds and warm water may be used. In fact, any mild soap answers the purpose, but oil and glycerin are a little less irritating to the membranes of the digestive tract. The hard lumps of meconium may be removed with the index finger. Oftentimes, as a result of injections, a large handful of black fecal pellets are eliminated. These enemas should be continued until the caretaker is sure that all the lumpy, rubbery pellets have been expelled and in their place appears a soft, pasty fecal mass.

Diarrhea

The mare usually experiences foal heat between the seventh and the ninth day (usually about the ninth day) following parturition. At this time the foal may scour. A dose of castor oil, two ounces or a soda pop bottle filled about one fifth to one fourth with the oil, generally takes care of such cases. Give the oil as a drench, warming the bottle and oil sufficiently so that the oil runs from the bottle readily. Cut down the feed of the mare and milk out her udder. It is particularly important to do this if the mare be a free milker. Sometimes a colt two or three months old may experience diarrhea or scours when the dam comes in heat, or when permitted to nurse her when she is overheated. Foals of this age may have four ounces of castor oil. Feed the mare dry feed, milk her partially, or, if the foal is too weak to nurse with its normal appetite destroyed, milk her several times a day to keep the udder from caking and secure the services of a competent veterinarian to prescribe for the foal.

The Orphan Foal

Orphan foals, if left orphans at birth or a few days later, are a real problem in management, oftentimes a tragedy. Some big nurseries breed an occasional mare that is a good milk producer, but whose foal is expected to be of little value and use her as a stepmother to substitute for mares who have too little milk to grow a well-bred foal properly, to mother an orphaned but valuable foal, or, in rare cases, to help feed twin foals. The foal of the stepmother may be destroyed or raised on the bottle, which is always a real task. To make the mare accept the foal rub it with oil of aniseed or whisky. If foals have had a start of four to six weeks before they are orphaned the situation is much easier to handle. Carthela, twice grand champion Percheron mare at Chicago, was left an orphan at about six weeks of age. She was owned by Mr. William B. Murray of Wellington, Ohio, and he brought her through, winning with her as a yearling, a two-year-old, and a three-year-old.

A mixture of two ounces of milk, two ounces of water, and one teaspoonful of sugar has been used to feed the very young orphan foal. It is fed every two or three hours, the amount gradually increasing until the foal is three or four weeks old, when it is given straight Holstein milk. The appetite of the foal, the condition or thrift of the foal, and the judgment of the feeder are all factors which will determine whether or not a particular foal can be raised. All new foals need their dams to start them on their way. Some attendants may have better success with orphan foals than other attendants have, but no one relishes the job, which is a very difficult and oftentimes a disappointing assignment.

Biological Test for Pregnancy in Mares

For several years Dr. T. S. Sutton of The Ohio State University conducted a pregnancy test service for mare owners in Ohio. This service was a laboratory service incident to the diagnosis of pregnancy in brood mares, the test to be conducted in brood mares from 42 to 120 days after the last date of their service.

The blood serum of mares pregnant from 42 to 120 days contains one or more hormones which will stimulate sexual maturity in an immature female.

Consequently, if some of the blood serum from a pregnant mare is injected into an immature female laboratory animal (the white rat is used), pregnancy in the mare can be diagnosed on the basis of the response of the rat to the serum injected.

White female rats (18 to 24 days of age) are used in this pregnancy test. Following the subcutaneous injection of the test rat, with 5 cubic centi‑ meters of the blood serum from a pregnant mare, the generative tract of the rat becomes greatly activated. The female rat for such tests is slaughtered, usually about ninety-six hours following the injection. By that time, the ovaries of the rat are greatly enlarged, and other tissues of the rat are gorged with blood, indicative that one or more hormones in the serum of the pregnant mare have stimulated sexual maturity in the immature female rat. The uterus of the test rat will be enlarged and frequently filled with secretion.

This pregnancy test is as reliable as any of the pregnancy tests and is more reliable than the manual test unless the diagnostician making the manual test has had a great deal of experience.

Hormone activity in mare's serum is usually at its height about 80 days after pregnancy begins. The optimum time to kill the immature test rat is about ninety-six hours after it was injected with mare's serum.

Horsemen should be interested in availing themselves of the pregnancy test for mares and for these reasons:

1. This test is extremely accurate when carried out on blood serum obtained between 42 and 120 days following the last breeding date.

2. Not all veterinarians are competent to diagnose pregnancy by man‑ ual exploration.

3. Forty to sixty days is the early limit for diagnosis of pregnancy through examination by hand.

4. Many owners prefer not to have valuable mares exposed to the haz‑ ards of unskillful manual manipulation, whereas any practitioner should be able to draw blood samples without hazard.

5. When heavy transportation costs and expensive board bills are in‑ volved, it is most important to know definitely and as soon as possible whether or not the mare is in foal.

6. A great deal, and possibly a sale, may depend on the ability to guar‑ antee a mare in foal.

Curative Hormones from the Urine of Pregnant Mares

At one time in this country there were only four business concerns whose research laboratories made a special business of processing the urine from pregnant mares. The hormone which at that time was being extracted from the urine was called estrogen, a hormone with remarkable curative properties. Twenty-five thousand gallons of raw urine are required to make one pound of estrogen powder. The estrogen is given with a hypodermic needle and in some instances in powder form in a capsule.

Shortly after its discovery, estrogen was heralded so widely as an effective medicinal agent for human beings that numerous business concerns started to exploit it. It was in great demand and the concerns that processed and sold it multiplied several times over. But when estrogen was placed upon President Franklin Roosevelt's Reciprocal Trade Agreement list, the product in this country came into sharp trade competition with the estrogen produced in Argentina and which came into the United States duty-free.

In the spring of 1946, Argentina sent 3 pounds of estrogen powder to the United States, a shipment of which sold for $120,000. Such a sale was without precedent in this country, and concerns in the United States and in Argentina immediately started to expand production. In the spring of 1947, the Argentine manufacturers dumped 310 pounds of the product onto the market in this country, but this great quantity brought only $70,000. This drop in the price for a pound of estrogen powder resulted in a great decrease in the manufacture of the product in the country, but the business continued on a reduced scale.

The common practice is to start testing a pregnant mare's urine 120 days after breeding. The test used is known as the Cuboni test. All tests will be negative or positive in results. If mares which have been bred do not show positive in 140 days, they are regarded as open mares. If the test shows positive, then urine collections are started immediately. The peak period of hormone potency in the urine of pregnant mares is from 160 to 250 days after breeding.

Light-leg mares do not produce as much urine as draft mares but their urine is fully as potent as, if not more potent than, that of draft mares. In twenty-four hours' time, the average mare under normal circumstances will produce three gallons of urine.

In recent years, another hormone has been discovered in the urine of pregnant mares, a hormone sold under the name of Kutrol which was 89 per cent successful in treating more than 1,800 cases of stomach ulcers. Kutrol is taken per orem in powder form in a capsule.

The farm of Mr. Glenn S. Sonner, Delaware, Ohio, is the collection headquarters for the urine of pregnant mares in the Ohio area. All the raw urine from this collection center is shipped in big tank trucks at six- or seven-day intervals to the Ben Venue Laboratories at Bedford, Ohio, a little town near Cleveland. Here, the raw urine is processed and the hormone products extracted. These products are sold commercially by Parke, Davis & Co. under the trade names Estrogen and Kutrol.

The Delaware Collection Center in the winter 1950–1951 handled 196,-451 gallons of pregnant mares' urine. The best week was one week in December, 1950, when more than 11,000 gallons were delivered to the Collection Center. The urine of 704 pregnant mares was brought to the Delaware Collection Center in 1950. All consignors to the Center have their check from the Ben Venue Laboratories within thirty days following receipt of their shipment. In 1950 and 1951, these consignors received 60 cents a gallon for pregnant mares' urine.

Mr. Sonner reports that his pregnant mares earned for him $225 a head in 1950. To avoid too wide a variation in the pregnancy periods of mares, he prefers to breed them between June 1 and July 15. If the mares prove pregnant 120 days after breeding, urine collections start immediately and are continued for 130 days.

The urine is caught in a rubber pouch, usually a slit inner tube of an auto tire, with fasteners attached to the tube in such fashion as to suspend the tube between the hind legs of the mare in proper position to catch the urine when voided and make impossible the admixture of any manure. If any manure is caught in the pouch, the contents of the pouch are discarded. The pouches are emptied into fifty-five gallon metal drums which are delivered to the local collection center.

At the Sonner farm, both day- and nightmen are employed to handle the mares. In addition to being fed in the daytime the mares are fed at midnight. The nightman empties the urine pouches, cleans the barn, and thus gives the dayman a running start at his job. Mr. Sonner states that he feeds but little grain to his mares. He depends largely on pasture and an ample supply of hay of good quality.

Questions

1. Discuss in detail the foaling quarters for mares, stressing the advantages and disadvantages of foaling stalls vs. the grass paddock.
2. Discuss the foaling stall: location in the barn, size, floors, partitions, bedding, preparation for foaling, cleaning after foaling.
3. Mention a half dozen of the most common signs of pregnancy.
4. What is the average period of pregnancy in mares?
5. Discuss the weights of Percheron foals as compared to Thoroughbred foals.
6. Mention six or seven signs of approaching parturition.
7. List six or seven of the immediate signs of foaling.

8. Mention ten or a dozen reasons why an attendant should be present when a mare foals.

9. Discuss the act of normal parturition with comment concerning the duties of the attendant.

10. Discuss the immediate care of a newborn foal, including the treatment of the navel.

11. List a few facts in support of intrauterine navel infection.

12. Comment upon the practice of tying navel cords.

13. What antiseptic solutions and drying powders would you recommend for treating navel cords?

14. What precautions under the head of prevention may reduce the cases of navel ill?

15. How is prenatal infection accomplished?

16. Comment upon the practice of injections to prevent constipation in newborn foals. What injection solutions are used?

17. Discuss diarrhea as a management problem in young foals.

18. Discuss the orphan foal problem in horse production.

19. Discuss the biological test for pregnancy in mares.

20. Comment concerning the curative hormones in the urine of pregnant mares.

20

Horse Parasites

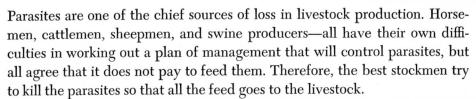

Parasites are one of the chief sources of loss in livestock production. Horse-men, cattlemen, sheepmen, and swine producers—all have their own diffi-culties in working out a plan of management that will control parasites, but all agree that it does not pay to feed them. Therefore, the best stockmen try to kill the parasites so that all the feed goes to the livestock.

More than a hundred different kinds of parasites infest horses. Para-sites, both external and internal, sap the energy, reduce the strength, and decrease the efficiency of a horse, no matter what his job may be. Not only does parasitic infestation result in unthrifty appearance; it may cause indigestion, colic, or stoppage of blood vessels or embolism. The following brief discussion of parasites is not meant to be all-inclusive; it is intended to summarize some useful facts concerning some of the most common and troublesome parasites infesting horses.

External Parasites

Horse lice and mites are the most common external parasites to be found on horses. Unlike some of the internal parasites, they spend their entire lives on their hosts. Horse lice do not infest animals other than horses, asses, and mules.

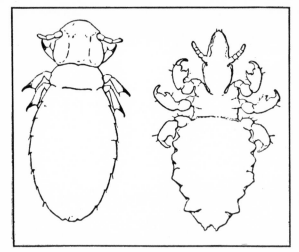

Two species of lice that infest horses. Left: *Biting louse.* Right: *Sucking louse. Lice do their greatest damage to horses and colts in winter, when the animals are confined in close quarters and the parasites can spread easily.* Courtesy Frank Thorp, Jr., Dr. Robert Graham, and C. O. Mohr.

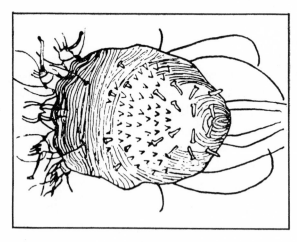

Sarcoptic mange mite. This parasite burrows into the skin, and soreness and wrinkling result. Mange is communicable to other animals and to man by direct contact. Courtesy Dr. Robert Graham.

Horse Lice

Two kinds of lice infest horses, the sucking louse (Haematopinus) and the biting louse (Trichodectes). Sucking lice, which are thought to do the most harm, are a little more difficult to eradicate. These two kinds of lice have similar life histories.

LIFE HISTORY   Lice can live only a few days when removed from their natural host. Their eggs, commonly called nits, are laid on the hair, to which they are firmly attached. Ten to twenty days are required before the nits hatch. The newly hatched nits reach sexual maturity and lay eggs when they are about eleven or twelve days old. Long hair, commonly found on horses in winter, favors the development and spread of lice. Lice spread most easily through direct contacts and through hair carried on grooming utensils. Tufts of infested hair removed while rubbing or grooming animals, as well as harness, blankets, and other stable equipment, can, through contact, infest horses free from lice.

SYMPTOMS OF LICE INFESTATION   Biting lice live by feeding on the external layers of the skin, hair, and exudates. Sucking lice actually puncture the skin of the host and suck blood. When not feeding, lice move about on the skin and annoy the host. The itching sensation causes the lousy animals to rub, bite, and kick in an endeavor to dislodge the pests. If lice are present in great numbers, the hair coat becomes rough, and patches of skin are stripped of hair by frequent rubbing.

Lice can be detected with little difficulty by pulling a tuft of hair and holding it against direct sunlight. The regions of the horse's body usually inhabited by lice are the sides of the neck, croup, flanks, and under the jaws. A heavily infested horse, however, may have lice on all parts of its body.

TREATMENT FOR HORSE LICE   One treatment will kill all live lice but will not destroy the eggs. Therefore, for permanent relief, a second treatment should be given seven to fourteen days later.

Dipping in a special tank is the best means of control if the weather is suitable. A coal-tar product is effective as a dipping agent, although both nicotine or tobacco solutions are used. Dry treatments or dusting powders may hold lice in check, but are not so effective as dipping. Sodium fluoride dusted into infested areas will control the spread of biting lice, but is of no value for treating sucking lice. This drug is very poisonous and should be used only under the direction of a veterinarian.

Oils and greases commonly used as insecticides on hogs will destroy horse lice, but are not recommended for horses because they remove hair and injure the skin.

Mites (Sarcoptes, Psoroptes, Chorioptes)

Mange or scabies of horses is a specific skin disease caused by small mites which live on or in the skin. The mites, about a fortieth of an inch in diameter, are so small that a microscope must be used to identify the species. The general contour of the body of a mite is oval and the mature parasite has four pairs of legs. Mites spend their entire lives on the host.

LIFE HISTORY OF MITES (SARCOPTES, PSOROPTES, CHORIOPTES)   The life cycles of the three types of mites are virtually the same, varying only in detail. The female mite lays her eggs in the channel she makes in the skin. From ten to twenty-five eggs are laid in approximately two weeks. Soon after this the female mite dies. Incubation of the egg takes from three to ten days, and the young mites develop to maturity in ten to twelve days.

SYMPTOMS OF MANGE MITE   The sarcoptic mite is the one most commonly found in horses. This parasite burrows into the upper layer of the skin and forms channels in which it mates and reproduces. In the early stage of sarcoptic mange the only symptoms noticeable are areas of irritation or inflammation. Although any portion of the body may become affected, the withers, sides of the neck, shoulders, and head are the most common regions. The burrowing of the mites causes an intense pruritis or itching of the skin. An infested horse tries to get relief by rubbing against objects, by biting the itching areas, and by constantly twitching its skin. It is not uncommon to have scales form over infested areas.

Treatment of all three types of horse mange is the same, the object being to put some noxious agent on the troublesome parasite. Dips such as lime sulfur, nicotine, and coal-tar products are recommended. Frequent and thorough applications are necessary. In generalized cases, dipping in an especially constructed tank is necessary. Four to six dippings at intervals of one week usually eradicate the mites. The job is one for a veterinarian.

Internal Parasites: Gastrophilus or Botflies

Bots

There are three species of botflies: the chin or throat fly, the common botfly, and the nose botfly. The throat and common botflies are the most widely distributed of the three species.

LIFE HISTORY   All three species lay their eggs on the hair of horses from July to September. The eggs are glued to the hair on parts of the body indicated by the names of the different species. After larvae of the common botfly hatch, they enter the mouth and burrow into the mucous membrane of the tongue. After molting, these larvae become attached to the pharynx and later enter the stomach. They require about one month to travel from the mouth to the stomach, where they are attached during the fall and winter months. It is not unusual to find two hundred to six hundred bots firmly attached to the stomach lining. The throat and common bots leave the body directly with the manure, but the nose bot reattaches to the rectum and the anus before it finally passes out. The bots pupate in the ground and emerge as adult flies during the summer months to lay their eggs on the hair of the horse; thus the cycle is repeated.

SYMPTOMS OF BOT INFESTATION   Horses that have large numbers of bots in their stomach may suffer from digestive disturbances and colic. The hooks of the bots imbedded in the wall of the stomach, as well as their spines on the body surface, cause irritation. Large numbers of bots result in unthriftiness

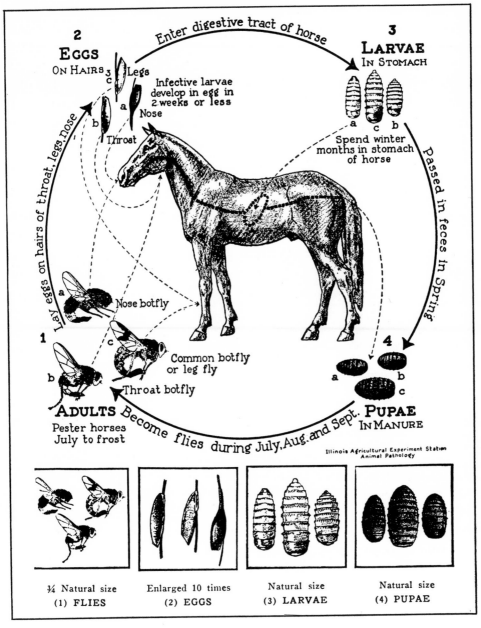

2
EGGS
ON HAIRS

Enter digestive tract of horse

3
LARVAE
IN STOMACH

Infective larvae
develop in egg in
2 weeks or less

Legs
Nose
Throat

Lay eggs on hairs of throat, legs, nose

Spend winter
months in stomach
of horse

Passed in feces in Spring

Nose botfly

Common botfly
or leg fly

Throat botfly

1

ADULTS Become flies during July, Aug. and Sept.
Pester horses
July to frost

4
PUPAE
IN MANURE

Illinois Agricultural Experiment Station
Animal Pathology

¾ Natural size	Enlarged 10 times	Natural size	Natural size
(1) FLIES	(2) EGGS	(3) LARVAE	(4) PUPAE

Life History of Botflies. (1) Flies pester horses from July till frost, laying their eggs on the hairs of the nose, throat, jaws, breast and legs. (2) Larvae develop in the eggs in two weeks or less and enter the digestive tract. (3) Larvae spend the winter months in the stomach, where they are a drain on the animal. In the spring they pass out in the manure. (4) In the ground, pupae develop from the larvae. During July and until September, these pupae become flies which start the life cycle all over again. Courtesy Dr. Robert Graham.

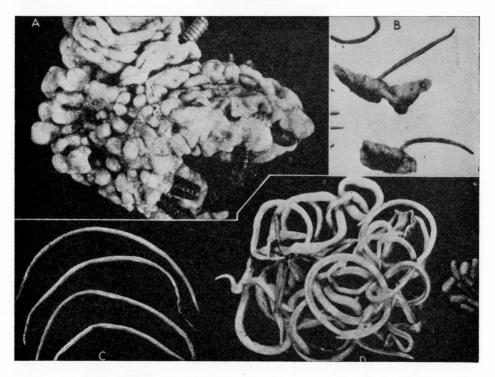

Three common internal parasites of horses. (A) Bots attached to the inner wall of a horse's stomach. Note nodules and tumors caused by these parasites. The tumors are the result of bots of several years' standing. Chronic thickening of the stomach wall interferes with normal digestion. (B) Palisade worms of the strongylus species. These and other palisade worms bury their heads in the lining of the intestines and cause extensive inflammation. (C) Large intestinal roundworms (ascarids) live unattached in the intestines and cause intestinal catarrh, indigestion, and unthriftiness. (D) Large intestinal roundworms and bots expelled by the same treatment. These parasites were passed by one horse a few hours after treatment. Many more were passed on successive days. Photographs courtesy Dr. Robert Graham.

and may even obstruct the opening at the junction of the stomach and the small intestine. While nose bots are attached to its rectum, a horse may show signs of pain and itching and rub itself against the stall in an effort to get rid of the parasites.

TREATMENT FOR BOTS   Horses to be treated may be allowed water but no feed of any kind, grain or roughage, for twenty-four hours prior to treatment. Water and all feed should be withheld for five hours after treatment.

According to findings of the Bureau of Animal Industry, Washington, D. C., the time to treat for bots annually is thirty days after the first freezing temperature of twenty-four hours' duration. The treatment should be administered in December, January, and February, before the parasites start to migrate from the stomach.

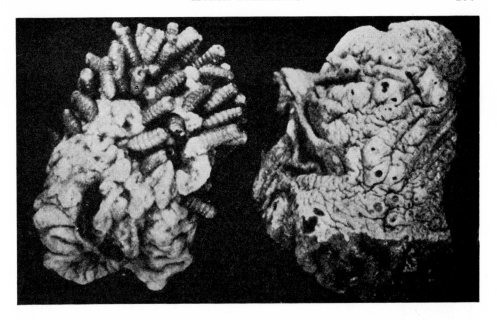

Injury to wall of stomach from Bots. Bots attached to the stomach may puncture the lining and cause thickened folds to develop as a result of chronic inflammation. Courtesy Dr. Robert Graham.

Carbon disulfide has proved the best treatment for bots. The proper dose is six fluid ounces (twenty-four cubic centimeters) for each thousand pounds of live weight. Caution is needed in giving carbon disulfide, as it causes a local inflammation where it comes in contact with mucous membranes. If carbon disulfide gets into the lungs, it may cause a mechanical pneumonia. Therefore, a skilled veterinarian and not a layman should administer this drug.

Large Intestinal Roundworms (Ascaris equorum)

Large intestinal roundworms are more common and do much more damage to young horses than to mature horses.

The mature roundworms or (ascarids) are yellowish white in color, cylindrical in shape, and six to twelve inches long, tapering toward both ends. In the horse this worm is found chiefly in the upper part of the small intestine and less frequently in the stomach and other parts of the intestinal tract. A single horse may be host to hundreds of large intestinal roundworms. The ascarid of the horse does not infest other animals.

LIFE HISTORY The female ascarid lays large numbers of eggs in the intestine of the host. These eggs, which cannot be seen with the naked eye, pass out in the manure, each covered with a thick shell which protects it.

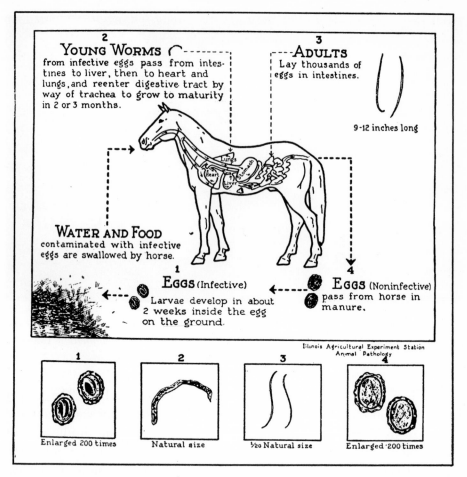

2
YOUNG WORMS
from infective eggs pass from intestines to liver, then to heart and
lungs, and reenter digestive tract by
way of trachea to grow to maturity
in 2 or 3 months.

3
ADULTS
Lay thousands of
eggs in intestines.

9-12 inches long

WATER AND FOOD
contaminated with infective
eggs are swallowed by horse.

1
EGGS (Infective)
Larvae develop in about
2 weeks inside the egg
on the ground.

4
EGGS (Noninfective)
pass from horse in
manure.

Illinois Agricultural Experiment Station
Animal Pathology

1   2   3   4

Enlarged 200 times   Natural size   1/20 Natural size   Enlarged 200 times

*Life History of Large Roundworms of Horses. (1) Infective eggs, with larvae developed
inside each one, are swallowed by the horse in feed and water. (2) The young worms
that hatch from the eggs pass from the intestines to the liver, then to the heart and lungs,
and re-enter the digestive tract by way of the windpipe to grow to maturity. (3) Adult
worms in the intestines lay thousands of eggs. (4) Noninfective eggs pass from the horse
in the manure. Within a few weeks, larvae develop within the eggs. When the horse
swallows them the cycle starts all over again. Courtesy Dr. Robert Graham.*

Under favorable conditions of temperature and moisture, the eggs on the
ground or in the manure undergo certain changes before they become infective. They must spend two weeks or more outside the host before they
become infective to susceptible animals. The appearance of the embryo or
tiny worm in the eggs marks the infective stage, but the infective egg remains
dormant until swallowed by the host. The infective eggs hatch in the intestinal tract and the live embryos leave the shells. The young worms then burrow into the walls of the intestines to enter the blood stream and migrate
to the liver, the heart, and the lungs, where they undergo further changes.

About one week elapses from the time the young worms are liberated in the intestinal tract until they are present in the lungs in great numbers. The young worms move up the windpipe and are swallowed. Upon reaching the intestine for the second time, the young worms develop into mature worms in about two or three months.

SYMPTOMS OF ROUNDWORMS Ascarids in the intestinal tracts of foals and yearlings may cause digestive disturbances such as colic. As a result of irritation to the walls of the intestines, a catarrh accompanied by a diarrhea alternates with the passage of hard, dry feces coated with mucus. Toxins or poisons may kill horses that are heavily infested with roundworms. Heavily parasitized horses often have harsh, dry, dull hair coats and every action suggests a lack of vitality. The treatment for ascarids is the same as for bots.

Strongyles or Palisade Worms

Palisade worms (strongyles) of horses and mules are small roundworms, commonly called red worms, palisades, or bloodworms. They are probably as deadly in their attacks as any parasites that infest horses.

Colts are more susceptible to attacks by strongyles than are older horses. These parasites are much smaller than the large roundworms, varying in length from a third of an inch to two and a half inches. They also differ from the former in that the adult worms are usually attached to the mucous membrane lining of the intestine by means of a mouth (supplied with suckers and sometimes with teeth) which is connected to the body of the parasite by a threadlike neck. Some bloodworms are free, however, in the fecal content.

LIFE HISTORY OF STRONGYLES Eggs of the strongyle are laid in the intestinal tract of the host and pass out with the manure. When conditions are favorable the eggs hatch in a day or so in the manure on the ground. The liberated larvae feed on the manure to which they have access, undergo two changes, and reach the infective stage in a short time. It takes the young worms about a week to reach the infective stage under favorable conditions, but a much longer period is necessary during the cold months, or during weather which is not conducive to their development. Moisture must be present for their development and enough is ordinarily found in horse manure. Although direct sunlight is injurious to the hatching larvae, in the infective stage, the young worms are resistant to adverse weather conditions such as cold, heat, and dryness, and can remain viable in pastures for a long time.

After reaching the infective stage, the larvae, when there is enough moisture supplied by dew or rain, migrate up the stems of grasses and remain there. Grazing horses pick them up, and they pass into the large intes-

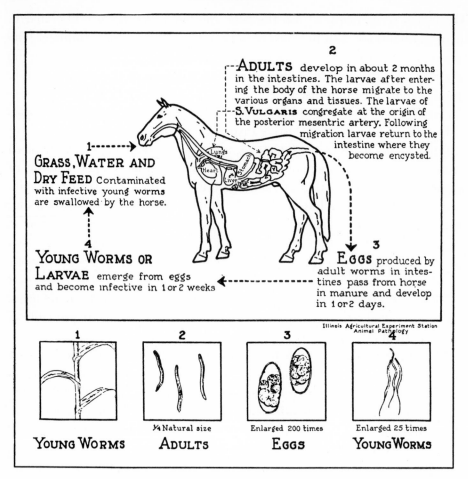

2

r--ADULTS develop in about 2 months in the intestines. The larvae after entering the body of the horse migrate to the various organs and tissues. The larvae of S. VULGARIS congregate at the origin of the posterior mesentric artery. Following migration larvae return to the intestine where they become encysted.

1------▶
GRASS, WATER AND DRY FEED Contaminated with infective young worms are swallowed by the horse.

4
YOUNG WORMS OR LARVAE emerge from eggs and become infective in 1 or 2 weeks

3
EGGS produced by adult worms in intestines pass from horse in manure and develop in 1 or 2 days.

Illinois Agricultural Experiment Station Animal Pathology

1   2   3   4
¼ Natural size   Enlarged 200 times   Enlarged 25 times
YOUNG WORMS   ADULTS   EGGS   YOUNG WORMS

Life History of Palisade Worms of Horses. (1) Young worms (larvae) are swallowed by the horse in feed and water. They travel to the various body tissues and organs, such as the liver, pancreas, spleen, lungs, and kidneys, and return to the intestines to develop into mature red worms. (2) Adult worms lay eggs which pass out in the manure. (3) Within one to two weeks, eggs develop into young worms, and when they are swallowed by the horse they start the life cycle all over again. Courtesy Dr. Robert Graham.

tine, where they may develop into mature parasites. This part of the life cycle is not definitely known, as many of the larvae are known to migrate through the internal organs and tissues and have been found in practically every organ of the body. It is an established fact, however, that in the mature or adult stage they are found attached to the mucous membrane lining of the large intestine of horses, mules, and foals, where they lay eggs and begin their life cycle over again.

SYMPTOMS   Horses mildly infested with strongyles may not show diagnostic symptoms. Anemia, weakness, emaciation, and general unthriftiness mark advanced cases. In heavy infestations, animals may suffer intermittent or persistent diarrhea or constipation, the hard, dry feces being covered with slimy mucus. The diarrhea is the result of the chronic irritation of the intestine.

Strongyles injure the walls of the intestine, to which they are firmly attached as they suck blood and tissue juices. They attach themselves by sucking a portion of the intestine into their mouth. Like ascarids, strongyles also produce primary toxins or poisons which may prove fatal.

The migration of strongyles to body tissues brings about serious conditions. It is not uncommon for one type of strongyle to lodge in the mesenteric arteries, causing a stoppage of the circulation which results in death.

TREATMENT FOR STRONGYLES   At one time oil of Chenopodium was used effectively against strongyles, but today phenothiazine is the drug commonly used. Oftentimes a combination treatment is given simultaneously, carbon disulfide for bots and roundworms with the phenothiazine added to get the bloodworms.

Dr. Vernon L. Tharp of The Ohio State University gives the following directions incident to dosage of saddle foals, yearlings, and two-year-olds.

> phenothiazine suspension: 12 grams to each fluid ounce
> 9 grams to each 250 pounds of body weight
> 36 grams to 1,000 pounds for adult horse

In the combination treatment with carbon disulfide, Dr. Tharp does not give a larger dosage than 36 grams, regardless of weight.

Carbon disulfide, 6 cubic centimeters for every 250 pounds of body weight up to 1,000 pounds. Do not go over 30 cubic centimeters regardless of weight.

Phenothiazine gets the strongyles. Carbon disulfide destroys the bots and the ascarids.

Keep horses off feed for twelve to eighteen hours before treating. Administer the dose through a stomach tube. Three to four hours after treatment give light feed of soft, laxative feed, and give a light feed of hay the following evening. Sample dosage for saddle horses at The Ohio State University in the early spring of 1952 was as follows:

Adults (1,000 pounds): 36 grams of phenothiazine, and 24 cubic centimeters of carbon disulfide

Two years (800 to 850 pounds): 27–30 grams of phenothiazine and 20–22 cubic centimeters of carbon disulfide

Yearlings (650–700 pounds): 20–27 grams phenothiazine; 18–20 cubic centimeters of carbon disulfide

Weanlings (500–550 pounds): 18 grams of phenothiazine; 12 cubic centimeters of carbon disulfide

Pinworms (Oxyuris equi)

Pinworms are relatively long, whitish worms with a very long, slender tail. They occur in the large intestine of the horse. The males are very small and are seldom found. The female may attain a length of three to six inches.

LIFE HISTORY   The adult worm passes from the horse in the manure and deposits the eggs in the manure or becomes attached near the anal opening and deposits the eggs in this region. The eggs are seen as a yellowish external incrustation. In either case the eggs develop outside the body and under favorable conditions become infective in one to three days. Eggs are capable of producing infection from one to four months after development. Infective eggs may be taken into the body of the horse through infected water, pasture, grain, or hay. The young worms reach the large intestine and become adults in three or four months.

SYMPTOMS   The attachment of the pinworms in the region of the anus and the egg incrustation produce an intense itching that causes the infected animal to rub its posterior parts against any object available. This may cause an eczematous inflammation. Pinworms may cause digestive disturbances, emaciation, and, in rare cases, anemia.

TREATMENT   Phenothiazine administered as for strongyles is effective in ridding horses of pinworms. Oil of turpentine, 1 to 2 fluid ounces, 30 to 60 cubic centimeters for every thousand pounds of live weight, given with one quart of raw linseed oil is also effective.

Preventive measures are the same as those recommended for the large intestinal roundworms and strongyles: regular, systematic treatment of horses to control parasites, particularly in the case of foals, yearlings, and two year olds.

Furthermore, sanitation must be stressed constantly under the head of management. Filthy stables, poorly drained barnyards and paddocks, low swampy pastures with slews and stagnant surface ponds—all of these are common causes of parasitic infestation of horses. The water supply should be clean.

The continuous feeding of horses on the same ground or in filthy paddocks and the overstocking of pastures year after year may increase intestinal parasites in horses and be chiefly responsible for disappointing results.

Students will have a much clearer conception of parasites as a management problem in horse production if they will carefully study the cuts in this chapter. For these illustrations I am indebted to Dr. Robert Graham of the University of Illinois.

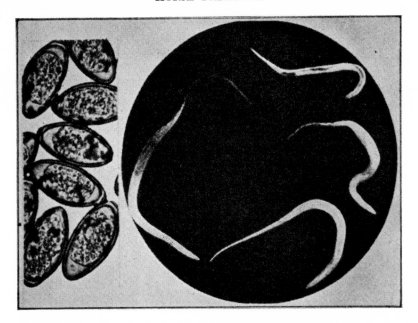

Pinworms (Oxyuris equi and eggs). The female worms are found in the large intestine of the horse. Passing out with the manure, they deposit their eggs with it or on the ground. Under favorable conditions the eggs become infective in a few days. Females attached to the anus may deposit eggs around the external anal region, causing intense pruritis. Horses will rub on any object available to relieve the itching sensation. Courtesy Dr. Robert Graham.

Questions

1. How does parasitic infestation affect horses?
2. What are the most common external parasites of horses?
3. Name two kinds of lice which infest horses.
4. Discuss the symptoms of lice infestation.
5. How many treatments are required to destroy horse lice? Why?
6. Name a few dipping agents that are effective in destroying lice.
7. Name some of the most common symptoms of infestation by the mange mite.
8. What treatment is effective in combating the mange mite?
9. Name three different species of botflies affecting horses.
10. Discuss the life history of bots, explaining how these parasites make entrance to the stomach of a horse.
11. What are common symptoms of bot infestation?
12. What is the common treatment for bots?
13. What is the common name for ascarids?

14. In what portion of the digestive tract are ascarids usually found?

15. Discuss the life history of intestinal roundworms.

16. What are some of the symptoms of ascarid infestation?

17. What is the common treatment for intestinal roundworms?

18. Mention two synonyms for bloodworms in horses.

19. Describe typical bloodworms.

20. Discuss the life history of bloodworms.

21. What are common symptoms of bloodworm infestation?

22. Why are bloodworms more deadly in their attack than bots or round-worms?

23. What drug is commonly used in combating bloodworms in horses?

21

Equitation

A horse's usefulness is in proportion to the completeness of his control. The more we know of his mental capacity, the more completely may we accomplish his control.

Our whole system of breaking, schooling, and driving is fundamentally deceptive. We aim to give a horse an exalted notion of those of his powers which are useful to us and at the same time create the idea that certain others which might prove detrimental to our purpose are hardly worthy of the horse's consideration.

The all too common notion that the primary essential in riding or driving is to "hold him" leads one wide of the mark in the rudiments of real horsemanship. Such a misconception is responsible for many of the disasters in which runaway horses are conspicuous. Indeed, the most convincing proof of the absurdity of such an idea is the faultless performance of a pair of horses in a class for ladies to drive, while the same pair, under identical conditions, had proved unmanageable for some heavy-handed, strong-armed driver in a preceding class. Control, or at least the only system which renders horses serviceably safe, is of the mental and not the muscular activities of the horse; therefore, the proper method is control by suggestion rather than by force.

Let us take the horse that has been educated and driven by the strong-arm method, that requires a flogging to make him go, a man's weight to stop him, and two hands to pull or turn him round a corner, always handled as if he might conceive and carry out at any time some fool notion beyond the physical power of man to check, and compare that creature with the thor-

415

oughly schooled horse responding to the light yet firm and strongly suggestive hand of the master reinsman, who is able to stop, back, start, and drive any place, without a word or even a perceptible twist of the wrist.

Transmitting the Impulse to Act

Now that the principle has been exposed, the system may be outlined. It may be summarized under these headings: hands and mouths. These are the two essentials in the system of control, serving alternately as transmitters and receivers. By means of the former, either the instructions or the demands in the mind of the driver are conveyed through the medium of the reins to the sensitive structures constituting the mouth of the horse, to be forwarded after being received through the sensory nerve trunks to the brain of the horse, thence the motor nerves convey the authorized instructions, as it were, to the proper parts for execution. What is here described at length and in detail is accomplished in a flash, but it is well to follow the actual transmission of an impulse in order to appreciate good horsemanship.

Hands of the right sort are capable of such delicate manipulation as to constantly feel, and to be felt by, the mouth, without maintaining a drag which destroys all sensibility in both. Such hands convey to the mouth graduated pressure, from the lightest touch to the most compelling pull, if occasion demands, and all with a convincing firmness.

Relation of Hands and Mouth

Mouths are the product of hands and therefore are complementary in every respect. The heavy, rough hand produces a hard, unresponsive mouth and destroys any other kind; in contrast, the light, impressionable hand can be relied upon to create or preserve a most sensitive mouth. There are features of this relationship between hands and mouth which can neither be described nor prescribed. They are best learned by contact, the one with the other; only one who has experienced the intimacy of such a fine system of communication has any conception of all that it means. With many, good hands are instinctive; they cannot tell why or how they do as they do; others are heavy-handed in spite of themselves, and are fully conscious of their offense and its attendant bad result. Of course, practice has much to do with this; one accustomed to driving trotters may find himself in trouble with the lighter mouth and different bitting arrangement of an actor and high-goer; whereas he who has had his schooling with the latter class of horses may

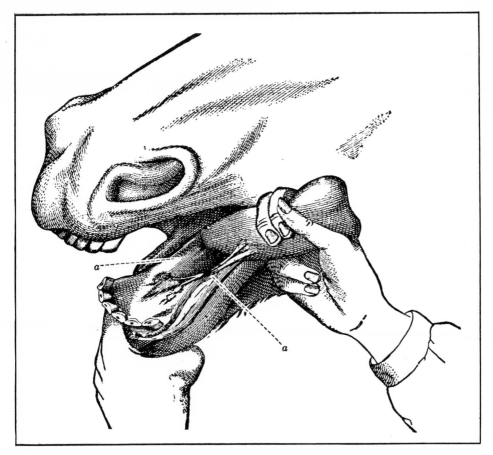

Tongue held back to show the bars (a) *of the mouth upon which the bit bears.* From Gay,
Productive Horse Husbandry, courtesy J. B. Lippincott Company.

be incapable of taking a strong enough hold to steady and support a pulling
trotter at speed.

The bit is the instrument by means of which communication between
the hands of the driver and the mouth of the horse is carried on. A decision
in the mind of the driver is represented in a manipulation of the reins so as to
bring the pressure of the bit on the structures of the mouth with which it is
in contact, and in such a manner as to suggest a corresponding notion in the
mind of the horse, which, if he be well schooled, he immediately responds
to or executes. In the reverse order, the horse may conceive the idea of taking
some steps on his own initiative. What the horse is about to do will be felt by
the driver and if not in order, he flashes back counterinstructions. This is the
advantage of keeping the horse always in hand.

Intelligent use of the bit requires some knowledge of the structures of
the mouth involved and the methods by which the bit operates.

Following are the structures with which the bit is more or less in contact, the extent and nature of their importance depending upon the style of the bit:

1. The bars of the mouth, that region of the lower jaw between the incisor and molar teeth in mares, between the canines and the molar teeth in stallions and geldings.

2. The tongue.

3. The angles of the lips.

4. The groove of the lower jaw into which a curb chain or a chin strap fits.

5. Sometimes the lower premolar teeth in the case of a horse that takes hold.

Proper Fit and Adjustment of Bit

The fit and adjustment of the bit are as essential to the preservation of a good mouth as is the type of bit itself. It should just hang easily in the mouth, wide enough not to pinch the cheeks and low enough so that it will not stretch the angles of the mouth or draw the cheeks in against the teeth. Curb bits should be lower in the mouth, as a rule, than the snaffle. In fact, some bits are constructed so that the bar or mouthpiece has play up and down on the shank in order that the position of the bit may be automatically adjusted to a certain extent. The curb chain should be loose enough to admit at least two fingers when the bit hangs naturally with no pressure upon it. Then the bit should be so adjusted as to bring the curb chain into its proper groove. If too high, its pressure comes on the sharp margins of the lower jaw with injurious effect.

Classification of Bits

Bits may be classified as snaffle, curb, and special or miscellaneous. Snaffle bits may have a straight or a jointed mouthpiece in which the principle involved is a direct pull on the mouth. The jointed snaffle is more severe because it puts the pressure chiefly on the bars of the mouth, while the plain bar mouthpiece bears also on the tongue, which has a cushioning effect. The four-ring snaffle is doubly severe because the rings at the ends of the cheek pieces are drawn into the mouth.

Curb bits consist of a plain or port mouthpiece (bar) with a cheek lever or shank at each end of the mouthpiece.

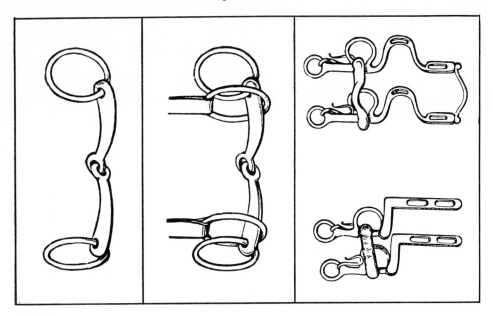

Bridle Bits, left to right: *The plain jointed snaffle. The four-ring snaffle. The elbow bit and the Buxton bit.*

Three standard types of curb bits are used on heavy harness horses and ponies. These heavy harness bits are the Liverpool, the elbow, and the Buxton bits. The Liverpool has a mouthpiece that is usually smooth but is sometimes smooth on one side and corrugated on the other. Such bits can be reversed so that the smooth side of the mouthpiece is against the bars of the normal mouth and the corrugated side of the mouthpiece is against the bars of the mouth of a horse that takes hold.

The elbow bit resembles the Liverpool bit but has an angle in its lower shank to prevent a horse from catching it with his lips and interfering with or preventing the operation of the bit.

The Buxton (named after Lord Buxton) is known as the full-dress heavy harness horse bit and is used commonly in appointment classes for heavy harness horses. This bit has long S-shaped shanks, the lower extremities of which are joined by a light crossbar which adds to the elaborateness of the design and also prevents the lower shanks of the bit from catching in other parts of the harness.

Riding Bridles and Bits

There are two common types of riding bridles and two common types of riding curb bits: the Weymouth riding bridle, which has two bits, a light

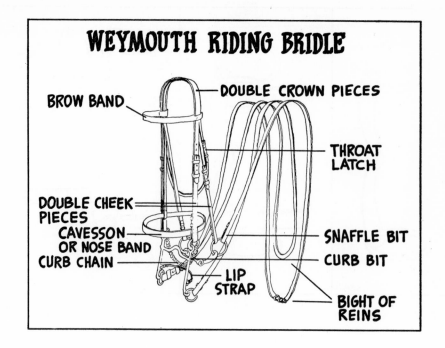

WEYMOUTH RIDING BRIDLE

BROW BAND

DOUBLE CROWN PIECES

THROAT LATCH

DOUBLE CHEEK PIECES

CAVESSON OR NOSE BAND

CURB CHAIN

SNAFFLE BIT

CURB BIT

LIP STRAP

BIGHT OF REINS

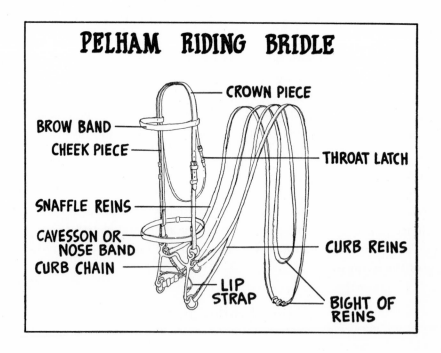

PELHAM RIDING BRIDLE

CROWN PIECE

BROW BAND

CHEEK PIECE

THROAT LATCH

SNAFFLE REINS

CAVESSON OR NOSE BAND

CURB CHAIN

CURB REINS

LIP STRAP

BIGHT OF REINS

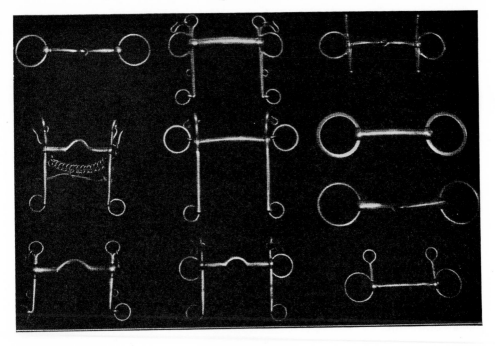

BRIDLE BITS

Snaffle	*Pelham, half-moon with*	*Snaffle with cheek bars*
Curb with chain and lip	*sliding bar*	*Snaffle, straight*
strap	*Pelham, half-moon*	*Snaffle, hunting*
Curb, Tom Thumb type	*Pelham, straight bar with*	*Snaffle, Baucher with*
	port	*straight bar.*

Photograph courtesy Horse and Mule Association of America.

jointed snaffle and a Weymouth curb bit; and the Pelham riding bridle, which has only one bit, a Pelham curb bit.

The Weymouth riding bridle is most commonly seen in show ring competitions. The Pelham riding bridle is used more for everyday purposes on bridle trail and cross-country rides.

The Weymouth bridle also differs from the Pelham in that it is provided with double crownpieces and double cheekpieces. One set of cheekpieces fastens into the rings of the snaffle bit; the other set fastens into the rings of the curb bit. In addition a complete Weymouth bridle has a noseband, curb chain and hooks, throat latch, and a lip strap or curb chain strap. There are also two sets of riding reins, one set fastening into the rings of the snaffle, the other set into the rings of the curb.

The Pelham bridle is an attempt to combine in a single bit the features provided by the two bits of the Weymouth bridle. The Pelham bridle has a single crownpiece, single cheekpieces, and a single bit, a curb. The Pelham curb bit differs from a Weymouth curb bit because it has a set of rings at

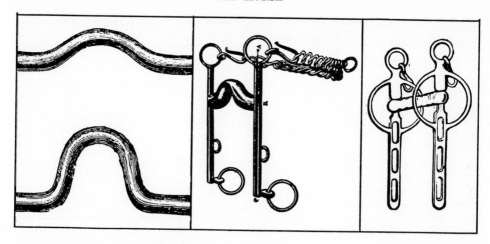

Left to right: *Low and high ports. A Weymouth curb bit. A Liverpool bit.*

the end of the mouthpiece of the bit into which one set of riding reins fastens. The other set of reins fastens into the rings at the lower end of the cheek-pieces of the bit.

Accessories

MARTINGALES   Martingales are useful features of both saddle horse and harness horse equipment and assist in the proper bitting and rigging of many horses. A martingale is a strap, one end of which is looped for the passage of the saddle girth or the belly band of the harness. The other end of the martingale is brought forward between the horse's fore legs and terminates in two divisions at the end of which are rings for passage of the reins. In another type of martingale is a single piece which continues up to the head, where it fastens into the noseband or cavesson. The first martingale described is known as the ring or running martingale. The second type described is known as the standing martingale.

The running martingale is in most common use on either harness or saddle horses of the "star-gazing" variety that get their heads so high as to interfere with the bearing of the bit. A running martingale should be long enough to leave the reins in a straight line from bit to turret ring on the back pad or from the bit to the hands of the rider. Running martingales are supposed to aid in setting a horse's chin and holding his nose down in position; they should not pull the head down out of position.

When Weymouth riding bridles are used on saddlers, the snaffle reins only are passed through the rings of the running martingale. For this reason the reins of the snaffle bit in a Weymouth riding bridle have a buckle so that

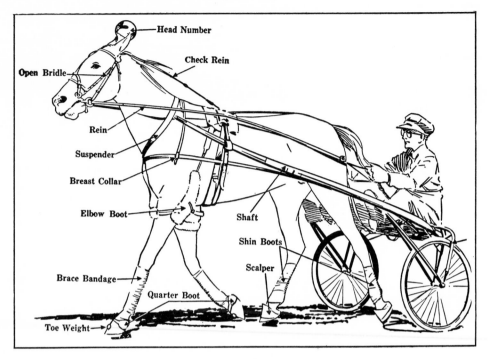

Race horse tack, Trotter.

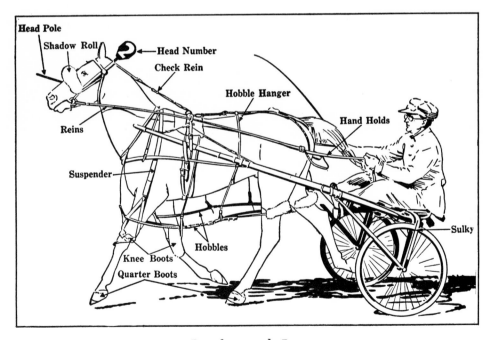

Race horse tack, Pacer.

Drawings courtesy United States Trotting Association.

they may be unfastened and passed through the rings of the martingale. The reins of the curb bit on a Weymouth bridle do not have a buckle because they are not used with the martingale. The effect of the curb bit and its chain would not be further augmented by passing the curb reins through the rings of the martingale. Hence the curb reins on a Weymouth riding bridle are sewed together.

Standing martingales are used on horses that fail to respond satisfactorily to a running martingale. The standing martingale permits much less head freedom than does the running martingale. Standing martingales are in common use on polo ponies to overcome their tendency to throw their heads back when pulled up sharply. Standing martingales may thus keep a rider from being struck in the face by the head of his pony as his pony turns sharply and maneuvers for position in playing the game. They are used on trotters or pacers that have a tendency to carry their heads so high that they appear to be trotting or pacing up into the air. Standing martingales are also used on horses that display a tendency to rear on the slightest provocation.

In addition to its use on saddle horses, the running martingale is used on light harness horses, trotters and pacers at speed, and on roadsters at the shows. Running martingales are also in common use in the exhibition of fine harness horses because they help set a horse's chin and get him to go in form.

CURB CHAINS   Curb chains consist of a series of links of steel of different shapes and sizes, usually single-linked, sometimes double. The links gradually increase in size from the extremities of the chain to the middle, where in riding curb bits a plain round pendant ring is suspended at right angles to the chain proper. Through this pendant ring the lip strap runs. To function properly, a curb chain should lie flat in the groove of the chin. The greater the number of links, the more smoothly the chain will hug the jaw. A curb chain is not a device of cruelty to inflict pain. Its function is to provide purchase for the bit against the jaw and to subject the head and the neck, and hence the whole body to the control of the hand. Pressure on the lower jaw pulls the lower jaw and chin inward toward the body. This causes a horse to arch his neck, get his legs beneath him, pull himself together, and be set for command.

THE DUMB JOCKEY   The snaffle bit is used to guide a horse and to lift or raise his head. The curb bit is useful in setting the chin and collecting the horse so that he may go in balanced and collected form. Horses have to be taught to go up against a curb bit. To save time in working horses on the curb, some trainers resort to the use of the "dumb jockey," a bitting device by which the horse is taught to tuck or pull in his chin and arch his neck through the use of side lines which extend from the cross arms of a surcingle or pad on the back to the rings of the bit in the horse's mouth. This "contraption" can be worn in the box stall or paddock a short time each day. The horse is turned loose and allowed to drill himself in setting his chin and arching his neck in response to gradually increased pressure on the reins.

THE LIP STRAP   The strap running through the pendant ring on the curb chain and fastening into eyelets on the lower cheekpieces of the bit functions in two ways: it helps to regulate and maintain the position of the curb chain with reference to the lower jaw; it also prevents a horse from grabbing the lower cheekpieces of the bit with his lips.

THE CHIN STRAP   The chin strap (not to be confused with the lip strap of a saddle horse bit) is a strap that passes under the chin of driving horses, either in front of or through the bit especially designed for it, and serves to place the bearing of the check rein under the chin instead of on the upper jaw. Chin straps help to keep the mouth shut and to prevent the lateral pulling of the bit through the horse's mouth. Chin straps are also used on saddle bridles instead of curb chains.

THE BRISTLE BUR   A round leather disc, fitted around the bit inside the ring or shank, against the cheek and often applied to one side only, is called the bristle bur. It is used on horses which either side-rein or bolt to one side in order to keep them off that side of the bit.

THE NOSEBAND   The noseband (cavesson) is a strap which encircles the jaws and keeps them closed. It also aids in helping to keep the bit properly placed in a horse's mouth, making it almost impossible for him to open his mouth and shift the bit from the bars of his mouth to his teeth. It prevents lugging as well as opening the mouth (yawing). The noseband also furnishes a point of attachment for a standing martingale.

The Horse's Mouth

The kind of mouth that a horse has and its condition depend primarily upon two things: the hands of the man that rides or drives, and the bits that are used.

The Kinds of Mouths

"Normal mouth" is the mouth of the horse who carries the bit freely and responds promptly and readily to a pull on the reins. "Tender mouth" is the mouth of the horse who responds very quickly to only a slight pull on the reins. "Spoiled mouth" describes the mouth that fails to react properly to the signals from the reins. Mouths that have become hardened, calloused, and dead because of bad bitting or poor riding or driving as well as very tender mouths come in this class.

The Word

Well-schooled horses in competent hands may be either started, pulled up, backed, turned, or changed in their gait without a word being spoken. Only a few words, such as "Whoa," "Back," or "Steady," are justifiable under any circumstances and they should be spoken distinctly and always for the same purpose. It is more the tone and the modulation of the voice than the word itself which the horse understands. The objection to a careless and indiscriminate use of words in either driving or riding is that they not only may confuse the horse for which they are intended but may disturb all other horses within hearing. Every horse should be taught and compelled to heed the command "Whoa," which should always mean a full stop.

Accessories Used with the Harness Horse

Check Reins, Bearing Reins, and Coupling Reins

All of the reins are accessories where road horses, race horses, or heavy harness horses are shown singly or in pairs.

The overdraw check and jointed snaffle bit are standard equipment for roadsters, trotters and pacers, and fine harness horses. The overdraw check, usually attached to a small check bit, a chin strap, or some modification of either or both, takes the bearing directly over the poll of the head and has the effect of extending the nose and at least suggesting if not favoring an extension of stride. The overdraw check runs from the small check bit in the mouth of the horse upward between the ears, over the poll of the head, and backward to a hook on the back pad of the harness. Such a check rein prevents the compression of the larynx and the interference with breathing which come from sharp flexion of the neck under a pull. The overdraw check is always used with the snaffle bit, never with the curb. The check rein billets should not be fastened to the snaffle bit itself, for the bearing of the check rein would displace the snaffle bit in the horse's mouth, thereby preventing it from resting on the bars of the mouth where it is supposed to rest.

Check reins of the overdraw type are out of place on horses that have to do continuous road work, that have to pull a heavy load, especially uphill, or that have to stand hitched for any length of time. Ignorant or thoughtless

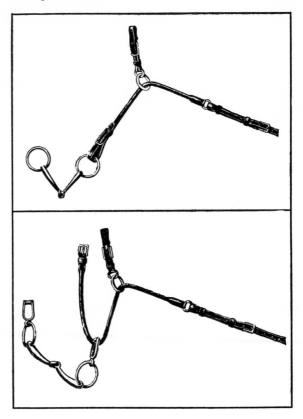

Side bearing reins. Above: *The side check or bearing rein with bridoon bit.* Below: *The pulley bridoon bearing rein.* From Gay, *Productive Horse Husbandry,* courtesy J. B. Lippincott Company.

misuse of the overdraw check is one of the most common and severe abuses which horses are called upon to endure.

The side rein or bearing rein is commonly seen on work horses, on heavy harness horses, and on ponies. A side or bearing rein on a draft horse's bridle is usually attached directly to the bridoon or snaffle bit in the horse's mouth. It places the bearing at the side of a horse's head and has the effect of drawing the chin in and arching the neck without necessarily raising the head very much. This rein is an adjunct to the Liverpool, elbow, or Buxton bits for heavy harness horses, enhancing the function of such bits in suggesting a shorter but higher stride and a more collected way of going. Its use is especially indicated for horses which yield to the curb with the entire neck, instead of with the head only, a response which brings the chin to a position almost against the breast. Severe reining of this character, especially in short, thick-necked horses, may seriously compress the larynx in addition to causing extreme discomfort and muscular cramp.

In hitching pairs of horses, the reins used are the draft or outside reins and the inside or coupling reins, one of which is attached to each draft rein and passes to the inside of the bit of the opposite horse. A pull to the right, for instance, is thus communicated to the off side of each horse's mouth and in equal degree provided the coupling reins have been properly adjusted.

Coupling, in fact, is the most important part of putting a pair of horses together and determines whether they are to drive "like one horse" or whether the driver is to be constantly conscious of the presence of two horses in his team. In order to exert equal pressure on both sides of each mouth, the relative carriage of heads, the promptness of action, the disposition of the two horses, and similar factors, must be taken into consideration. With a pair of horses closely matched in every way, the coupling reins should be from four to six inches longer than the draft reins, since they are the hypotenuses of triangles. If one horse carries his head higher than the other, his coupling rein should be on top in order not to be borne down upon by that of the lower-headed horse. If one horse sets his head and neck in a flexed position, his rein should be shortened to take up the slack so produced. If one horse drives more freely than the other, his rein must be shorter to keep him under restraint without pulling the other horse. In order, however, to keep the heads of the horses an equal distance apart, and their bodies straight behind their bridles and parallel with the pole of the rig, whatever is taken up in one rein must be let out in the other. Having the coupling reins too short draws the heads of the horses together and throws their bodies too far away from the pole so that their thighs rub against the outside traces. Coupling reins that are too long turn the heads of the horses out too far and force their bodies in against the pole of the vehicle.

Hitching Roadster Pairs

In the old days, when roadster pairs were used on country roads, it was customary to put the nervous horse on the right side so as to bring the other horse between him and any object to be passed on the road, it being the American rule of the road to keep to the right. The practice also brings the nervous horse closer to the hands of the driver, who sits on the right side of the rig. The larger horse is customarily put on the right or off side because in turning to the right on crowded roads, and in the old days narrow roads, the off side horse was called upon to pull more after the passing was complete and the load had to be returned to the center of the road.

Blinds or Winkers

Many horses are rendered much more serviceable by having their field of vision restricted to the direction in which they are supposed to go. Nervous horses, which will jump at any sudden movement of those behind them, and lazy horses, which are disposed to loaf, usually drive much more steadily and promptly with winkers. Careful adjustment of the winker, both as to height and as to length of the winker-stay, should be made so as to prevent the horse from looking over it, but allowing him full vision forward. A sudden change from a blind to an open bridle or the reverse may be most disconcerting to a horse. Appointments require winkers on heavy harness. With light harness horses they are optional but are generally used.

Whips

Whips with harness horses and riding crops with saddle horses should be used more for discipline and punishment than for constant persuasion. Continued tapping by a whip or continued light slapping by the reins will make a loafer of any horse. Horses differ widely in temperament and disposition; hence the whip and the crop should be used with discretion. With some horses the whip and the riding crop are carried only as a threat.

Saddles

All saddles are built on the same general principle. The framework of the saddle, consisting of the side bars and the arch, is known as the saddle tree. The side bars, usually made of ash, rest on the ribs of the horse on each side of the spine. They are connected by front and rear arches. To be of sufficient strength, these arches are made of steel, or else wood reinforced with steel. The front arch or pommel must be strong enough to prevent spreading, wide enough to prevent pinching, and high enough to clear the withers. The rear arch must be strong enough to maintain the weight in the saddle clear of the horse's spinal column. The lining or panel of the saddle which is in contact with the horse's back is usually of felt or leather. Leather is easier to keep clean and does not absorb the sweat. Felt panels or linings can be dried after use and then brushed clean. Applications of a weak ammonia solution will remove cakes of grease or dandruff.

Saddle girths are made of leather, twisted cord, or webbing. Leather girths are the strongest and have been popular on military saddles. If kept clean and soft by frequent greasing, they give good service under conditions of hard usage. Such girths commonly have longitudinal slits to provide ventilation and to prevent slipping. White webbing girths on show saddles can be cleaned by rinsing with warm water and then whitened with applications of pipe clay. Sponges are sometimes sewed to webbing girths to prevent their slipping.

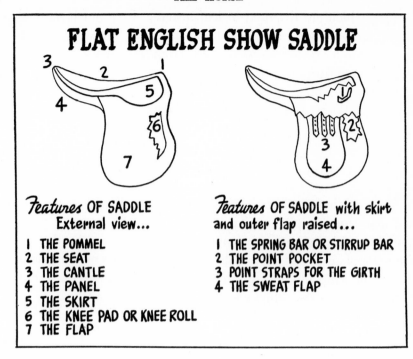

FLAT ENGLISH SHOW SADDLE

Features OF SADDLE
External view...

1 THE POMMEL
2 THE SEAT
3 THE CANTLE
4 THE PANEL
5 THE SKIRT
6 THE KNEE PAD OR KNEE ROLL
7 THE FLAP

Features OF SADDLE with skirt
and outer flap raised...

1 THE SPRING BAR OR STIRRUP BAR
2 THE POINT POCKET
3 POINT STRAPS FOR THE GIRTH
4 THE SWEAT FLAP

Types of Saddles

The saddle in most common use is the flat, English pigskin saddle seen in show competitions and used almost altogether for pleasure riding, in academy or school riding, and in hunting and polo.

The cowboy saddle or western stock saddle is generally used in the western cattle country. A strong, steel tree, high pommel and cantle, deep seat, and bucking girth or cinch adapt it to the work of roping and rough riding.

The McClellan, the regulation army saddle, provides a deep seat and long stirrups which favor a thigh grip, also sidebars designed to prevent sore backs even though the saddle is loaded with army impediments.

Equitation Goals

Two ends are sought by good horsemanship: the safety and comfort of the individual who is riding or driving, and the ease with which this is accomplished.

Form may be defined as the manner in which a thing is done. So much importance is attached to form in some instances that results are all form and nothing else. Form usually marks the "handmade" equestrian whose real ability as a horseman still lacks something because intuitive competence and resourcefulness are so apparently lacking in the pinches. On the other hand, the naturally good rider or driver will number form with his other accomplishments.

Good form consists in doing a thing in the right way. "Right," in this sense, does not mean according to the dictates of fashion, but in that manner which assures its being done with the greatest efficiency, readiness, and ease.

We should accept what has been established as the correct manner of riding and driving as that which contributes most to the safety, comfort, and appearance of those directly concerned. If beginners in horsemanship could be induced to take advice from someone who really knows, ultimate results would be much more satisfactory both to themselves and to their horses. One frequently sees accidents narrowly averted or the most flagrant cruelties practiced simply because of the ignorance of the perpetrators, who would be as much embarrassed and distressed as anyone if they fully realized the seriousness of their mistakes.

Rudiments of Driving

The rudiments of the proper way to drive heavy harness horses are as follows: Under ordinary conditions drive with the left hand, with the right hand free for either take-up or whip; hold the near rein over the forefinger, the off rein between the middle and ring fingers, thus leaving the reins separated by two fingers. This arrangement allows sufficient space to introduce the fingers of the right hand quickly, to make use, if necessary, of what horsemen call the "take-back." This is done by dropping the thumb and forefinger of the right hand over the near rein and slipping the other fingers between the two reins at such distance in advance of the left hand as may be required. The reins should be gripped by their edges rather than by their flat sides. Either rein may be taken up by the right hand as in the case of a turn, and the off rein may be released by the left hand, passing it through the right hand and over the thumb in case a two-hand grip is desired.

The left hand should have the knuckles turned forward and perpendicular, the forearm horizontal and at very near right angles with the reins. This position ensures the greatest freedom of wrist and fingers, is conducive to a light hand, and renders almost impossible a continuous dragging pull on a horse's mouth.

Holding the Reins When Riding

The usual method of holding the reins of a curb and snaffle riding bridle is to take the near snaffle rein over the little finger of the left hand, the near curb rein between the little and ring fingers, then passing the off curb rein between the ring and middle fingers and the off snaffle rein between the middle and index fingers, the ends of all four reins coming out of the hand over the index finger and clasped by the thumb. Either curb or snaffle reins can be taken up independently by the right hand in back of the left, or the right hand may be dropped in front of the left, the little finger between the off curb and snaffle reins in case a two-hand grip is desired. The hands may be separated and their position on the reins changed by running the reins through the fingers as the hands are drawn apart.

The single rein from the plain snaffle bridle is usually simply crossed through the hands.

The trooper commonly holds his single curb reins in the left hand, the two separated by the little finger, then passed through the hand and over the index finger, where they are clasped by the thumb.

The cowpuncher uses an open, unbuckled rein which falls to the ground the moment it is released from the hand, serving to hold his pony as though it were anchored securely. He usually holds the reins loosely, separated by the forefinger, or he may grip both reins between thumb and forefinger.

The trooper, mounted officer, or cowboy rides with one hand in order to have a free hand for saber, gun, stick, or rope, but the rider in the park or cross country should use both hands. Continued one-hand riding with the other hand dangling disengaged has a tendency to produce an unsymmetrical development and carriage of shoulders. Since the trooper and the cowpuncher guide their horses exclusively by neck-reining, using the bit only for restraint, their fingering of the reins is quite different from that of the rider of a gaited saddle horse.

Some Fundamental Rules for Beginners

A knowledge of good form in riding contributes to riding ability, comfort, and grace. Furthermore, it increases interest in horseback riding on the part of everyone who participates, the person who knows that he is riding in good form gets more pleasure from his ride than one who is inexperienced on the back of a horse.

Opinions among the accepted authorities on equitation vary so widely on certain points that it is difficult for the novice or the youthful rider to know what practice to follow. Many books have been written upon the subject of equitation, but most of them take for granted an elementary knowledge which the youthful rider does not possess.

In order, therefore, to have some basis for coaching beginners, a few simple and explicit rules are listed in this section. These rules are by no means

Golden Butterfly 42254, a champion gaited mare working at the trot. This picture is included not only because it shows a beautiful mare with flaxen mane and tail, but because it sets up an equitation goal in seat and hands. Note that the rider has his feet directly beneath his haunches. He is not sitting braced in his saddle. He is riding on the balls of his feet, with heel lower than the toe. He has a natural posture in the saddle and is riding with light hands held fairly close to the pommel of the saddle. He has the snaffle reins on the outside where they should be. He is riding his saddle in perfect balance, with no evidence of a duel between his hands and the mare's mouth. Welsh Grenwell of Shelbina, Missouri, up. Photograph courtesy J. A. McClasky.

the last word in finished equitation; they are simply some suggestions which have been found useful in coaching beginners. In formulating these rules I have not attempted to exhaust the subject of equitation, but to list, step by step, some of the points most essential to safety, grace, and skill in riding horseback.

The Seat and the Position of the Feet and Legs

One of the most important requirements of a good rider is a good seat. It gives both horse and rider the greatest amount of security and ease with the least amount of effort, and it is a prerequisite to confidence, to safety, to grace and balance, and, finally, to good hands.

The seat differs according to the object for which one rides horses, whether it be for hacking, show riding, hunting, polo, flat racing, or steeple-chasing. We are considering now the seat for hacking or park riding, a seat which should be acquired and mastered as the foundation for horse train-ing, and for all other more difficult or hazardous forms of riding.

The good seat is a natural seat, comfortable, strong, and erect without rigidity. It depends on balance and grip. Balance is paramount, although it is grip that preserves balance and strengthens and reinforces the seat when necessity arises.

The rider should sit squarely to the front, and comfortably, with the muscles relaxed so as to grip with the flat of the thigh, the knee, and the inner calf. His feet should hang in a natural position as in walking, nearly parallel to the sides of the horse and with the ball of the foot resting lightly on the stirrup and the heels slightly depressed. By keeping the heels down, the inner calf muscles are brought into play, and it is by these muscles that the aids are given.

For hacking, a properly adjusted stirrup should be of medium length. Sit in the saddle with the legs hanging loose, then adjust the leather until the bottom of the stirrup is level with the inside ankle bone. When riding a difficult horse or doing a difficult thing on a horse the stirrup may be slightly shortened. Riding "home," that is, with the stirrup under the arch of the foot, is not done when hacking and never for show riding except in riding hunters and jumpers. Care should be taken to keep the feet back so that the stirrup leathers always hang perpendicularly. When they hang per-pendicularly the feet cannot be thrust forward almost on the horse's shoul-ders, which is so common a fault and which at once puts a rider off balance. One should not sit braced in the saddle. Such a posture gives the impression that the horse is taking hold of the bit.

Hands

The body above the hips should be supple, so that it may sway easily with the movements of the horse, but suppleness should never degenerate into sloppiness. The upper arms should be held naturally at the sides and parallel to the body, not with the elbows bowed at right angles, or flapping up and down with each motion of the horse. The hands should come just above the front of the saddle about at the waistline, with the backs of the hands toward the horse's mouth, the knuckles nearly vertical, and the wrists slightly rounded so that the reins may be manipulated by a slight turn of the wrist.

While there are several ways of carrying the reins, all considered correct, a common way is to carry the four reins in the left hand, with the right hand lightly feeling the horse's mouth and thereby anticipating his movements.

This method allows for the greatest delicacy of touch, since it gives opportunity for the play of the little and fourth fingers on the reins and it is through these fingers that one gets the most sensitive and sympathetic action on the horse's mouth.

> *Left Hand:* Left snaffle outside the little finger.
> Left curb between the little and fourth fingers.
> Right curb between the fourth and middle fingers.
> Right snaffle between the middle and index fingers.

All four reins should then be brought through the hand, over the second joint of the index finger, where they must be held flat and in place by the thumb.

> *Right Hand:* The right hand rests slightly in advance of but beside the left on the reins.
> Right snaffle outside the little finger.
> Right curb between the little and fourth fingers.

If only the curb or only the snaffle is wanted, the middle and index fingers are free to take up those reins from the left hand. When a whip is carried, it rests between thumb and first finger of the right hand and far enough above the center to balance easily in the hand. If it must be used, and this should seldom happen, the right hand must always be taken from the reins to avoid jerking the horse's mouth.

The Reins

When this method of carrying the reins is used, the play on the horse's mouth comes from the fingers and wrists and not from the shoulders, as is too frequently the case. There is rarely a need for shifting and changing the position of the reins, but should a rein slip through the fingers of the left hand the right hand can readily draw it back into position.

Except in necessity, both hands should always be kept on the reins. The reins should be of medium length. Constant pressure or "dead lug" between the horse's mouth and the rider's hands should never be allowed, but the reins should be short enough to maintain contact with the horse's mouth and keep up an almost imperceptible play with the fingers so that the horse will always "feel the bit." There should be an increasing and decreasing pres-

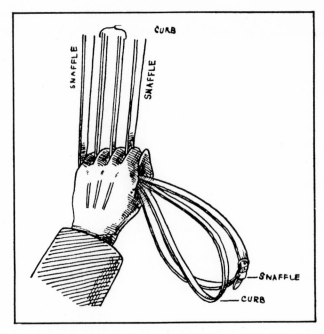

One-hand grip when riding with a Weymouth riding bridle equipped with both a snaffle and curb bit. Snaffle reins outside. Curb reins inside. Courtesy Arts Service, Ohio State University.

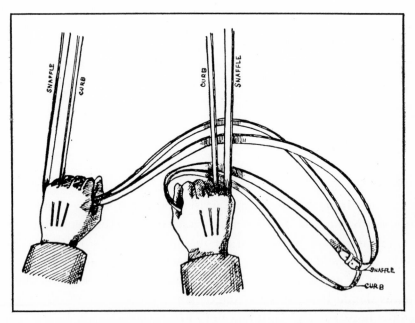

Two-hand grip when riding with a Weymouth riding bridle equipped with both a snaffle and curb bit. Snaffle reins outside. Curb reins inside. Courtesy Arts Service, Ohio State University.

sure on the reins, but never a constant pressure. All horses should have good mouths; if they have not, it is the fault of some rider with bad hands.

Long reins do not make good hands; it is the delicate give-and-take between the rider's hands and the bit, produced by the subtleties of fingers, wrists, and forearms, together with the leg aids and a perfect balance between horse and rider, that exemplifies good hands.

Very young riders find it difficult to carry the four reins in one small hand. These youngsters and the inexperienced rider who still lacks full confidence in the horse should carry the reins in both hands. Indeed, it is quite correct but inconvenient to carry them thus for hacking, but it is very likely to produce heavy hands because there is less opportunity for the play of the fingers. Unyielding hands are the invariable result of not realizing the need of gentle manipulation of a horse's mouth. When the reins are carried in both hands, the hands should be close together with the thumbs uppermost but always held on the reins to prevent slipping. The reins are separated by the little fingers: the snaffle reins outside the little fingers, the curb reins between the little and fourth fingers, with both pairs drawn over the first fingers and held in place by the thumbs. The right reins may quickly be placed in the left hand by putting the middle finger of the left hand between them without displacing the others.

The Aids

The expression "Use the aids" seems to frighten new riders, and experienced ones find difficulty in explaining its meaning without a wealth of detail. Too much detail obscures rather than clears the explanation to the inexperienced. "Using the aids" simply means the use of both the hands and the legs to indicate the rider's desires to the horse.

The hands, through the reins, control the horse's front legs; the feet and inner calf muscles pressed against the horse's sides control the hind legs. By using both hands and legs, all four of the horse's legs come under control.

The Walk

For example, to make a standing horse walk, take up the reins lightly and at the same time press both legs against his sides behind the girth. The leg pressure signals to the hind legs, which provide the motive power to push the front legs forward. When he responds, release the pressure. Let him walk with a free head but do not let him shuffle or jiggle. If he lags or loafs increase the leg pressure. Stop him by gripping him with the legs so as to bring his hind legs under his body, at the same time exerting pressure on the reins and keeping the weight of your body back in the saddle.

The Trot

The same procedure is used at the trot as at the walk, except that the reins are shortened a little and more pressure is exerted with the legs. Sit close to the saddle and do not attempt to rise or post until the horse is trotting squarely. Keep him "collected," a term used to indicate that the horse's weight is distributed as nearly as possible on all four legs, and that he has his chin set and a light hold on the bit.

To make a horse carry his head correctly, use the legs to bring his hindquarters well under him and send him up into his bridle, at the same time restraining him so as to permit him to go with a balanced stride, to move collectedly, and to go in form.

Understanding the Diagonals

The trot is a diagonal two-beat gait done at moderate speed in the case of three-gaited saddlers. Left fore leg and diagonal right rear leg work as one pair while the right fore leg and diagonal left rear leg work as the other pair.

When the left shoulder and fore leg are forward as you post, you are said to be posting the left diagonal. If you are out of the saddle when the right fore leg is forward, you are posting the right diagonal.

There is some confusion over the meaning of the two expressions "riding a diagonal" and "posting a diagonal." If you are out of the saddle posting the right diagonal, you will have to be in the saddle riding the left diagonal.

To keep from tiring a horse at the trot one should not post the same diagonal all the time. In riding in an oval ring, the rider should post the right diagonal or outside diagonal when going to the left and he should post the left or outside diagonal when going to the right. Posting the outside diagonal helps a horse to maintain his balance at the trot when making the turns.

The Canter

On the canter, a well-balanced horse must be just as handy on the left lead as on the right, and a good rider equally comfortable on either lead. Always break from a standing position or walk to a canter, never from a trot. When cantering in a circle to the right, the horse must lead on the right fore foot. If cantering to the left, he must lead on the left fore foot. To break on the right lead, collect the horse, bend his head slightly to the left, and at the same time press both legs against his sides, touching him at the point of the right elbow with the right foot, thereby urging and helping him to lead with the right fore leg, as well as helping him to maintain his balance when working in an oval arena. To canter on the left lead, bend the horse's head to the right, pressing both legs against his sides, and touch the left elbow with the left forefoot. The rider must measure the amount of the leg pressure by the flexibility and the responsiveness of the horse. Given an experienced rider and a properly trained horse, it is not necessary to bend the horse's head but slightly when breaking to a canter. The merest touch with hand and heel is sufficient, but as one cannot and does not always ride perfectly trained horses, the detailed procedure is given above.

Mounting and Dismounting

Some horsemen mount with their backs toward the horse's head and facing his hindquarters, some with the front of the bodies toward the horse's body. Either method is correct. The rider should use whichever one gives him the most confidence.

The reins and whip should be held in the left hand and the hand placed on the horse's withers.

Care must be taken to stand close to the horse. Place the left toe in the stirrup, place the right hand on the cantle (back) of the saddle, and spring from the right foot so that the right leg will just clear the saddle, using care in so doing not to touch the horse on the quarters. Sit well into the saddle. To dismount, keep the reins and whip in hand on the withers, as was done in mounting, slip the foot from the right stirrup, and pass it over the saddle. Keep the toe of the left foot in the iron until the right foot has fairly touched the ground.

Mounting and dismounting in this way, the rider faces toward the horse's side and can see both ends of the horse. Thus he is able to anticipate any movement and to act accordingly. The reins should *always* be kept in hand until the rider is on the ground.

Backing

To back a horse, shorten the reins and take the weight off the quarters by leaning slightly forward. Grip his sides with your legs. If he is standing on all four feet, as he should be, or if he shows resistance, ride him forward a step to relax his muscles or to "unfreeze" him. Do not ask him to back from a frozen position. He may rear up and go over backward. Keep the hands low, and starting on the side where the fore foot is most advanced, gently pull the reins, first on one side and then on the other. This alternating pressure on the reins helps to keep his quarters on a straight line and also dispels the inclination to rear.

Confidence

Learn to like your horse and to make him like you. Each horse has a different temperament, as has each rider. Study your horse so that you will sense the difference between playfulness, fearfulness, and willful disobedience in him. There should be a reciprocal relationship between the horse and rider so far as understanding each other is concerned.

Horses are very responsive to the voice. Speak to your horse when you want him to change his gait; tell him to walk, trot, or canter, as the case may be, and when you want him to stop say "Whoa." If he is nervous and worried, "Steady" will work wonders. A sharp command will often control him. A gentle word and a pat on the neck may reassure and quiet him. Be prepared for the unexpected. Anyone can ride well enough on a quiet horse if nothing happens. Be a rider, not a passenger. Learn to hack and handle and then you will be prepared for the added joys of schooling, polo, hunting, and jumping.

The essence of good horsemanship is confidence. Understanding your horse leads to confidence. With confidence comes relaxed muscles and with relaxed muscles a rider sits comfortably in the saddle and attains the balance which is the basis of good horsemanship.

Riding is a matter first of confidence and courage, then study and knowledge. There is no easy road to finished horsemanship. It must be acquired by constant attention to form and through experience with many horses.

There is no one authority as to what is right and wrong in riding; some like one style and some another. The object in offering these suggestions is not to propound new theories, but to present the methods which have been helpful in teaching youngsters to ride.

To aid understanding, use simple terminology, such as left and right, as well as near and off; curb and snaffle, as well as bit and bridoon; front leg and hind leg, as well as forehand and hindquarter; and similarly with many other expressions.

Horsemanship Competitions

We question whether show committees and many judges quite realize how much thought and effort the boys and girls who enter riding competitions put into trying to improve their horsemanship. Show managements send all over the country for competent judges of horseflesh; yet they will often ask someone who chances to be standing at the rail to judge the efforts of the children in equitation classes.

Riding is an art, and only a careful student of equitation is competent to judge it. More than half of the art of riding is in the use of the leg; yet in horsemanship contests, many judges give it absolutely no consideration. They have no fixed standards in mind when appraising the performance of the entries in equitation classes. They glance superficially at the young riders and their decisions are influenced by whether or not a child is "cute" or manages to stick on regardless of the form with which he rides.

Win or lose, the competitors have the greatest respect for the judge who really knows and can tell them their faults or their good points. For the benefit of boys and girls who have shown so much interest and enthusiasm in improving their horsemanship, and such splendid sporting spirit in competition, the following suggestions are offered for the equitation classes.

In the first place, dress neatly, as attention is irresistibly drawn to the well-appointed rider. Workmanlike clothes give the impression of experience. Never wear jockey caps or fancy hats, sleeveless coats, or gay, colored suits.

There is as little difference between the clothes for a boy or a girl on a horse, as between those of a well-appointed man or woman rider. The difference is not in color and material but in cut. Stick to tans, grays, and browns. Tweeds are always smart, with breeches or jodhpurs of Bedford cord or cavalry twill in some shade of tan. Entire suits of the same material are not used except black for very formal occasions, with a silk hat. Although there is a vogue for this type of suit at present, it is to be hoped that it will be but a fad, and that smarter and more workmanlike clothes, such as are used in hunting classes, will become the style in saddle classes as well. With a derby wear light tan breeches and black boots, and a coat of Oxford or very dark blue. Wear mannish hats and shirts, with collar and tie, or stock. One-button gloves in doeskin or chamois are best. Carry only a natural wood or leather-covered riding stick, without handle or trimming. It must not have leather loops.

Equitation Classes

Always let your horse walk out with a good free walk on a light rein. If he walks fast enough to pass a competitor let him do so. The walk is the greatest pleasure gait of all.

Regardless of what any other horse does, ride your own horse. Pass any horse you care to but do not race or let your horse become unbalanced and sprawly in his stride. Keep him collected and ride in form.

Never allow yourself to be blanketed or ridden into pockets by another horse and never play the same trick on anyone else. Any time that you get into a pocket or are blanketed, turn your horse across the ring to the opposite rail and get away from the crowd.

Help your horse by anticipating the next gait and by having him prepared before starting each gait. During the walking period between the trot and the canter, keep close to the rail and when the command to canter is given break him promptly and canter slowly. Learn to feel and to know when your horse is on the correct lead, but do not lean over to see. If his lead is wrong, or mixed, stop him immediately and start again. The walk is known as the foundation gait because it is the only gait from which any of the other gaits may be requested.

When you are called on to line up, stand your horse squarely on all four feet. Do not let him stretch too much. Remember that you are sitting on a horse and being judged, so do not watch the other riders or have a chat with your neighbor, but watch your own position and your horse's position.

If the judge asks for a rail performance, that is, to show your horse up and down near the rail to demonstrate your knowledge of the right and left leads and your use of the aids, be sure that you understand the directions, then go to the rail quietly and do as directed. When turning at the ends always turn the horse's head toward the rail, never away, so that he will not run out from the rail and so that he will be in a position to break readily.

You may be required to change horses. If so, be sure that the stirrup leathers are the correct length; otherwise you cannot do yourself justice. If you want to change the length of the stirrup when you are in the saddle, do not take your foot from the stirrup iron. Hold the knee away from the saddle and keep the reins in one hand so that you will be prepared should your mount start unexpectedly.

Be careful when asked to ride a strange horse. Take the reins up gently and should the horse make a move do not jerk him but restrain him quietly. Start him slowly, first at the walk to get the feel of his mouth, then on the trot and the canter. Ride your saddle; do not ride your horse's mouth. Remember that one of the most sensitive parts of a horse is his mouth. Remember also that a horse's gaits are in his mouth and that your handling of his mouth will be one of the tests of your horsemanship.

Oftentimes it is one of these seemingly unimportant details that influence the decision of a well-informed, observant, and thoroughly qualified judge.

Questions

1. Cite an example to show that a horse's usefulness is dependent upon the control which a rider or driver has over him.

2. Explain the reciprocal relationship which always exists between a horse's mouth and the hands of rider or driver.

3. What are the bars of the mouth?

4. Describe a jointed snaffle bit.

5. Describe a Weymouth curb bit.

6. Describe a Pelham curb bit.

7. Describe a Liverpool bit.

8. Describe an elbow bit.

9. Describe a Buxton bit.

10. Describe a Pelham riding bridle.

11. Describe a Weymouth riding bridle.

12. What is the purpose of the port in a curb bit?

13. What is the function of a curb chain?

14. What is the purpose of a lip strap?

15. What are the chief functions of the snaffle bit in a Weymouth riding bridle? of the curb bit?

16. What is a standing martingale?

17. What is a running martingale?

18. Explain the use of both types of martingales.

19. What is the difference between a chin strap and a lip strap?

20. What is a bristle bur and how does it function?

21. What is the purpose of the noseband or cavesson?

22. What is the meaning of the term "yawing"?

23. Define these terms: normal mouth, tender mouth, spoiled mouth.

24. Discuss the holding of the reins when riding with both snaffle and curb reins.

25. Why should the snaffle reins be held on the outside?

26. Define these terms: check reins, bearing reins, and coupling reins.

27. Winkers constitute what part of the harness and serve what purpose?

28. Name the parts of a flat English saddle.

29. Name the parts of a Weymouth riding bridle.

30. In teaching equitation, what two goals should be kept constantly in mind?

31. Discuss the importance of a good seat as a prerequisite to good riding.

32. Discuss the importance of good hands as a requirement in good riding.

33. Define the trot as a saddle horse gait.

34. Explain the term "diagonals."

35. How can you be sure that you are posting the right diagonal? the left diagonal?

36. Distinguish between the expressions "posting a diagonal" and "riding a diagonal."

37. Define the term "canter."

38. What is meant by the "left lead" or the "right lead"?

39. What are the objections to a cross-legged canter?

40. Discuss mounting and dismounting as equitation assignments.

41. Why is it best to ride a horse forward a step or two from standing position before asking him to back?

42. When riding along the rail in equitation competitions, why is it good policy when turning your horse to turn toward the rail?

22

Horseshoes and Horseshoeing

The ideal foot for any horse or pony should be big in proportion to body weight or bulk, full and rounding at toe and quarters, wide and deep at the heel, with enough arch of sole and strength of hoof wall to guarantee long tenure of service in whatever area of activity the horse or pony is used.

During the heyday of the work horse business, flatness was the prevailing foot ailment of work horses whose job it was to earn their living on city streets. It was important therefore that the feet of these horses have sufficient concavity of sole and toughness of hoof wall to oppose flatness.

The feet of light-leg horses, unlike the feet of draft horses, are seldom troubled with flatness. Nevertheless, the feet of light-leg horses do have their prevailing ailments, the most common of which are contraction and navicular disease. Feet with narrow heels are predisposed to contraction. Hence light-leg horses of all kinds should stand on feet that are wide at the heels. Width of heel in the make-up of a horse's foot opposes contraction.

Of course, the wide-heeled horse is comparatively easy to shoe, because the inside and outside walls of his feet have sufficient flare to them to permit the driving of the nails with ease and safety. The narrow-heeled horse, on the other hand, with his upright hoof walls is one whose feet are very difficult to shoe and shoe properly.

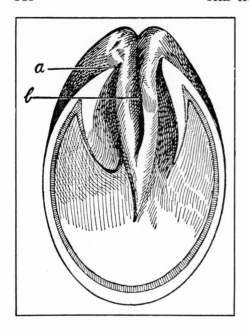

A narrow fore hoof with bilateral contraction of the rear quarters: a, spur of hoof wall which compresses the frog; b, very narrow cleft of frog due to compression. From Lungwitz and Adams, *Horse Shoeing,* courtesy J. B. Lippincott Company.

The Shoe and the Hoof Wall of the Foot

A primary aim in shoeing horses of all kinds is to shape the shoe to fit the foot, rather than to whittle and rasp the foot to fit the shoe. It is not good practice to nail into place a shoe which is really too small for a horse's foot; then take the rasp and rasp away all of the protruding hoof wall about the exterior of the shoe. This may give the appearance of a more finished job, but in reality the practice results in cutting away the thickest portion of the hoof wall, which should be saved as a bearing surface to support weight. Not only does the hoof wall function in protecting the inner, more tender tissues of the foot; one of its primary purposes is to support the weight of the body. Hence the shoe should be shaped to fit the foot and the hoof wall should be saved for the weight-bearing function.

Factors Determining the Kind of Shoe

The kind of shoe that a horse should wear depends upon the set or position of a horse's legs, the shape and position of his feet, the kind of service demanded of him, and the kind of ground or surface upon which he works.

In the old days, when work horses were employed in numbers on city streets, the kind of service of which a city horse was capable depended a great deal upon the paving materials used in the construction of city streets and the kind of shoes with which a horse was rigged. The farm work horse has always worked barefooted at many of his jobs in the field. The same horse on a teaming job over gravel roads would need to have his feet protected with shoes. Such a work horse could get along with the ordinary three-calk work shoe with a toe clip. The calks could be blunt when weather conditions were mild and the roads free from snow and ice. During the winter months, when ice and snow and sleet interfered, the same work horse would have to be shod with sharp calks or with never-slip calks which screwed into the web of the shoe and could be replaced when they became too worn and blunt to give a horse secure footing.

The shoes for trotters and pacers differ much more in design than do the shoes for any kind of work horse. Trotters and pacers work at speed and of course over all kinds of tracks. I have known of trotters rigged with smooth shoes in front that would scalp themselves worse on a track when the cushion was deep and soft and loose than they would when rigged with a rim or a three-calk shoe on their front feet. I have known of horses that were completely cured of the scalping and speedy-cutting faults by the use of shoes with low, sharp grab calks on them. Some horses can't go a step with a calk on the front shoe; others can't go their best without them. A trotter that glides along in front, making two distinct impressions with his front foot on the track every time he lands, will not do well wearing a calked shoe. The wide-webbed, thin, plain shoe suits him better. A calk will stop his slide, shorten his stride, interfere with his front action, throw him completely out of balance, and oftentimes make him so sore in his muscles that he will appear to have been foundered. These examples are cited to show why various designs in shoes are essential to meet the needs of horses that are required to do altogether different jobs.

Specific Features of the Shoe

The front feet of a horse are more nearly circular or rounding at the toe and quarters than are the hind feet. Usually the front feet are wider at the heels than are the hind feet. The hind feet are more pointed at toe and quarters and are commonly more narrow at the heels than are the front feet. Hence the difference between a front shoe and a hind shoe is sharply defined and easily distinguishable. Since the outside wing or web of a hind shoe is always longer than the inside web, it is easy to distinguish the difference between left and right rear shoes.

The hoof wall is thicker at the toe than at the heels of the foot; hence the web of the shoe is usually wider at the toe than at the heels. The shoe should be so placed upon the foot as to permit the hoof wall to function as a weight-bearing agency from toe to heel.

The wings of the front shoe should be long enough to reach the bulbs of the heel and provide support for the hoof wall, but not so long that a hind foot can come in contact with them and pull them off. Usually the wings of the hind shoes are a little longer than the wings of the front shoes. Especially is this true of the outside wing of the hind shoe, on which a low heel calk is sometimes used. This extra length of the outside wing of a hind shoe gives a little more support to a hind foot; the low heel calk raises the outside of the foot a little and tends to throw the hocks closer together to produce more collected action.

That part of the shoe which is in contact with the hoof wall should be horizontal. The web of the shoe should be wide enough to cover the hoof wall, the white line, and a small fringe of the outer edge of the sole. Shoes for large hoofs require a broader bearing surface than do shoes for small hoofs. The hoof surface of the shoe has to be concave or seated to relieve pressure on the sole of the foot, the degree of seating depending upon the shape of the sole of the foot. Shoes have to be seated but slightly if they are to be used on feet whose soles are strongly arched and very concave. The object of making a shoe concave is to prevent pressure upon the horny sole except at the outside margin of the sole. Undue pressure of a shoe upon the horny sole might result in bruises which could develop into corns.

The inner borders of a shoe should be fitted snugly. If his shoes are so fitted, it is more difficult for a horse, in shifting the position of his front feet, to catch the inner edge of a shoe on a supporting foot with the shoe of a shifting foot and literally tramp off his own shoes. This could happen in the case of hind feet also if the shoes are not snugly fitted along the inside borders of the feet. Moreover, interference, either slight or severe, is not so likely if the inside borders of shoes are snugly fitted. And if the inside borders of shoes are moderately rounded, open wounds are not so likely to result if interference occurs.

Fullering or creasing the ground surface of the wings of a shoe is not absolutely necessary, but it has several advantages: the crease in the wings of the shoe from toe to heels makes a shoe lighter in proportion to its size; it makes easier the uniform placement of the nail holes; and it roughens the ground surface of the shoe, thereby giving a better purchase upon any surface with which the shoe is in contact.

In every job of shoeing, the number, the depth, and the distribution or placement of the nail holes are very important. The nail holes must be so placed that nails can be driven into the hoof without being driven into the

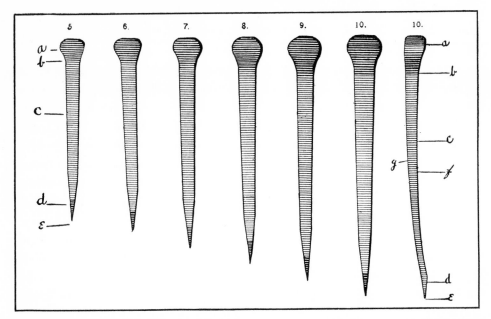

Machine-made horseshoe nails (natural size) with a low, wide head for a fullered shoe. Nail 10 is shown from one border, the others from the inner face of the nail: a, head; b, neck; c, shank; d, bevel; e, point; f, inner face; g, outer face. From Lungwitz and Adams, *Horse Shoeing*, courtesy J. B. Lippincott Company.

sensitive tissues of the feet, called driving the nails "too green." The nails should be driven in such a manner as to avoid the splitting of the hoof wall. The nail holes should be so punched as to permit the driving of the nails without interference with the expansive mechanisms of the feet. Finally, the nails should taper from the ground to the hoof surface, all of them driven at about the same angle so that when they are clinched none of them will have been driven too green and cause blood poison, nor will any of them have been drawn so tight as to cause painful compression.

In the case of shoes of medium weight, six nail holes are sufficient. With heavier shoes, especially those with toe and heel calks, eight nails may be necessary. The rear nail holes in front shoes are driven just slightly rearward of the center of the wings of the shoes. In hind shoes, the nail holes should be driven in the anterior two thirds of the wings of the shoes. A common rule is to drive the rear nails but slightly rearward of the middle of the wings of the shoes. The heels of the foot must have opportunity to expand as the foot touches the ground. If the nails are driven too far rearward, the heels are held too rigidly in place, there is no opportunity for the heels to expand, and the supporting structures are unduly abused because of maximum concussions. Nails should not be driven inside the white line of the foot, which is the junction between the hoof wall and the sole.

Clips are semicircular or semitriangular features of a shoe and anchor a shoe more securely on a horse's foot. Clips reduce to a minimum the chances of a shoe's shifting position after it has been nailed to the foot. Both toe clips and side clips are in common use. It is common practice to place a side clip on that branch of the shoe which first meets the ground in locomotion. So placed, a clip helps the nails to keep the shoe firmly anchored in correct position.

Some clips are made by heating the web of the shoe at the toe or on the side and drawing a portion of the web upward from the outer edge of the shoe. Such clips are called drawn clips. Other clips are braised on or welded into position. There is a rule among blacksmiths that the height of a clip on flat shoes should at least equal the thickness of the shoe. On shoes that have toe and heel calks, the clips should be higher and stronger. Drawn clips make a neater, more finished job of shoeing than do welded clips.

Shoes with Toe and Heel Calks

Shoes with toe and heel calks should be of uniform thickness from toe to heel. Usually such a shoe requires longer and stronger heel calks than the heel calks on shoes that do not have any toe calks at all. In the three-calk shoe, the toe calk should not be higher than the heel calks.

Horseshoes use three common kinds of toe calks. One of these, the sharp toe calk, may be made by hand from a bar of toe steel of proper width and thickness from which toe calks of the desired length are cut for any shoe. The back face of a sharp toe calk should be set perpendicular to the ground surface of the shoe. Machine-made toe calks—sharp, half sharp, and blunt, or featuring a sharp spud at one or both ends—are in common use by blacksmiths. The toe of the shoe is heated, the toe calk is placed in position, and the spuds of the toe calk are driven into the molten webbing of the shoe. The use of such calks may require two heats. Moreover, the sharp calk may be slightly blunted in the welding.

The blunt toe calk is a rather long, rectangular piece of toe steel. When this calk is placed on the web of the shoe, it can be set straight across the toe of the shoe, that is, at right angles to the toe of the foot, or it may be curved to conform to the toe or the rim of the shoe. In either instance, these calks are welded into position, oftentimes with a single heating.

The semiblunt or half-sharp toe calk, also sometimes called the "coffin lid" toe calk, resembles the blunt toe calk except at the point of attachment to the shoe. The base of the half-sharp toe calk, where it is attached to the shoe, is wider, thereby increasing the area of attachment and making it possible to weld the calk more firmly into place. Usually one heating is all that is necessary to weld the semiblunt calk into position.

Three-calk shoes should be so made that when they are nailed to a horse's foot they disturb the levelness of the foot and the normal setting down of the foot as little as possible. The aim of the blacksmith is to trim the foot and place the shoe in such a fashion that wear on the shoe is uniform. Another purpose in using the three-calk shoe is to reduce to a minimum the possibility of slipping, and to give the horse maximum stability on his feet.

Since heel and toe calks raise the hoof from the ground and prevent all frog pressure, such shoes diminish the elasticity of the hoof because there is less expansion at the heels. Nevertheless, such shoes are indispensable where the footing is rough or slippery.

Selecting the Shoes

There are a number of factors to consider in selecting the shoes with which a given horse should be rigged. The weight of the horse, the shape of the hoofs, the set of his legs, the nature of his work, the footing over which he works, the gaits required, the texture of his feet—these are some of the factors upon which the selection of the shoes is based.

The length of the shoe in relationship to the length of the foot is very important. The usual practice is to choose a shoe that is ample in length, because, as the hoof wall grows, the shoe is carried forward with it. Furthermore, the rear quarters of the feet are gradually lowered because of the rubbing and wear of the rear hoof wall upon the wings of the shoe. As the foot grows and the shoe is carried forward, it is important that the tips of the wings of the shoe be sufficiently spread so as to prevent too much shoe contact with the sole of the foot and the resultant bruises of the sole which develop into corns.

In the case of work horses shod with the common three-calk work shoe, the wings of the shoe should extend backward far enough to furnish ample support to the bulbs of the heels.

In the case of light-leg horses whose job it is to work at speed, shoes should be fitted snugly. This is especially important for the front shoes. If the wings of his front shoes are too long, any horse may be thrown off balance, mix his gaits, and catch his shoes and pull them off. The loss of a shoe may mean the loss of a race or the loss of an important class at a show. Furthermore, when a horse pulls a shoe, there is always the possibility that a large portion of the foot will be broken off and the horse will be temporarily unusable.

There is a wide range in the weight requirements of shoes for horses and ponies of various types. There is so much difference in the size and the action of horses that inevitably there is a wide range in the weight of the shoes they wear. A racing plate for a Thoroughbred may weigh only three or four ounces. The Scotch-bottom show shoe for a drafter may weigh from three to three and a half pounds.

Many front shoes have some roll to the toe of the shoe at which point a horse's foot breaks over. The rolled toe results from a more or less pronounced upward turn of the toe of the shoe. The rolled toe or rolling motion shoe in front guarantees more nearly even wear on the shoe and also hastens the breaking over of the forefoot, thereby reducing the possibility of the defect in gait known as forging. If the front foot breaks over readily, a horse is less likely to strike the toe of a hind shoe against the extremities of a front shoe.

The White Line a Guide to the Blacksmith

The white line of a horse's foot is the guide which the blacksmith follows in driving the nails into the hoof wall. This line is the boundary line between the hoof wall and the sole of the foot. It corresponds to the quick of a fingernail or a toenail in man.

If nails are driven inside the white line, blood poison may result. Therefore the nail holes of the shoe should cover the white line of the foot; then the blacksmith can drive the nails as they should be driven and with comparative ease.

Usually, the last nail holes are driven slightly rearward of the center of the wings of the shoe. From the last nail holes rearward to the distal extremities of the shoe the wings of the shoe should widen gradually until at their extremities they project at each quarter slightly beyond the outside rim of the hoof wall. This extra width between the wings of the shoe will furnish the hoof wall at the heels with a supporting base upon which the hoof walls may expand as the foot comes in contact with the ground. Of course, the inner wing of the shoe, both front and hind, should fit the hoof wall more snugly to prevent interference and to keep a horse from tramping off his own shoes.

Shoes for Trotters and Pacers

The purpose in shoeing all horses is to protect their feet and to make it possible for them to go in a balanced, coordinated fashion. In the case of trotters and pacers, as well as in the case of all show horses who work at speed and in form, the shoes may augment or retard performance.

If a trotting colt stands squarely on his legs and can go straight at the trot barefooted, his first shoes are usually absolutely plain, with the edges and heels well leveled off. The hind shoes can be smooth, plain, and without calks of any kind. But if a colt has a strong, bold way of going, with a tendency to go wide-gaited at the hocks, a very light swedged shoe can be used to good advantage, for the slight hold he will get with it will have a tendency to pull him together, to help him collect himself, and to give him confidence. Also, he will not tire so quickly, for it is in his hind legs that he gets his propelling power and it is there he will tire first.

The weight of the shoes for a trotting colt is simply a matter of judgment after having watched the colt move barefooted. If the colt is a high, natural, gaited colt in front, folds his knees satisfactorily, and strikes the ground lightly, shoe him with light, plain shoes chiefly to protect his feet. Square the toe of his front shoes slightly and bevel them off a little so as to reduce to a minimum the friction or resistance at the point where the breakover comes. By a light shoe is meant a shoe weighing four to six ounces. In preparing the foot do not dress it too close. Leave him enough hoof wall to take away the sting of the blow when the foot hits the ground. It is better to do this than to cut the hoof wall close and then use a leather or fiber pad to make up for the lack of natural horn.

If a colt's action is low, if he stubs his toes and is lacking in knee action, a heavy bar shoe made of half round iron or steel may help him. Have the nail holes well countersunk so that there will be no projections of any kind, for the heavier shoe in front may cause him to scalp or speedy-cut himself or both.

A good plan, where considerable weight is necessary to make a colt "break loose" and go to trotting, is to use a rubber pad and a half round tip shoe, squared at the toe. A colt can carry more weight in rubber with less effort than he can in metal and there is a rebound to rubber that helps him to a full, round stroke or revolution.

When the object for which it is put on is attained, the weight should be taken off. In some cases it is necessary to reduce the weight gradually and carefully. But this does not always apply to colt trotters, for once the youngster discovers he can trot, that is, "finds his gait," so to speak, taking off a good portion of the weight at one time may not bother him. If he does miss it and shows you that he misses it by mixing and shuffling when he starts out, a heavier quarter boot or a light toe weight put on when you are about to step him up may be all that is needed to square him away.

I knew of a three-year-old trotting filly that for a period of two weeks carried twenty-six ounces on each front foot. After two weeks she had learned to break or fold her knees and was a good, gaited trotter. The weight of her front shoes was reduced to ten ounces and she never missed the additional weight. She had learned to use her feet, had gotten the trotting gait fixed in her head, and went on to race successfully the next season in six-ounce shoes.

I also knew of an over-two walk, trot gelding that wore shoes weighing forty-six ounces on each front foot when in competition in the ring. When he was returned to his stall, the heavy shoes were removed, not to be replaced until time for the three gaited stake the last of the week. This horse was shown successfully and won the three-gaited stake at the Kentucky State Fair. He carried more weight on his feet than any saddle horse I have ever known. Removing the heavy shoes between shows was a precaution against bowed tendons. I mention this particular case because it shows what a great range there is in the weights of shoes worn by horses.

If the trotting colt's hind toes are full and rounding in shape, shoe him with a round-toed shoe. If his toes are narrow and a little pointed, make the toe of the shoe square, but in order to get it square do not sacrifice the toe of a foot which may be already too short. If this be the case, let the shoe project on each side of the toe a little, for it will do no harm. Colts with sharp, pointed hind feet are predisposed to knuckle over. Knuckling is also attributed to long toes and weak ankles, but in many cases it is caused by the fact that foot and ankle rock sideways when breaking over, for a horse's leg pivots on the point of a narrow rear toe. A hind shoe squared at the toe gives a horse a good base to break over on and may help the colt that is predisposed to knuckling.

If the prospective race colt is a pacer, he can be shod with a light, swedged shoe in front. Fit the shoe snug at the heels, especially the inside heel, and bevel it off well so that it really looks like a part of the foot. This is a precaution against the colt's hitting his rear shins or his hocks in passing or grabbing the shoe with the opposite hind foot if he cross-fires.

In shoeing the average pacing colt behind, lower the foot a trifle on the inside and use a half-swedged shoe, swedged on the outside, half round or plain on the inside. Set the shoe full on the outside, leaving on the outside wing at the heel a trail of half an inch turned slightly out, and fit the inside close and short.

Many young colt pacers are started with about five-ounce shoes in front and four ounces behind. As they improve and make speed, many times pacing colts gather speed more rapidly than do trotters. To steady them it may then be necessary to add a little toe weight or a pad in front, or use a heavier shoe. Sometimes it may be necessary to reduce the weight of their hind shoes slightly, but it is not a good plan to make any radical changes in dressing their feet.

Every ten days to two weeks, if in training, a colt's shoes should be removed and his feet leveled and dressed. If the feet must be cut down considerably and their angle changed, it is not safe to give the colt any fast work for a few days until ligaments and joints have become adjusted to the new conditions. It is possible to bow a tendon by cutting the feet down one day and giving a colt a stiff workout on the next.

Thin Hoof Walls a Problem in Shoeing

Particular care should be exercised in the treatment of feet with a thin, delicate wall. Small nails should always be used; although it may be necessary to use the coarse rasp on the bottom of the foot, it should never be used in finishing off the clinches. A fine, flat file will do the work much better without disfiguring the wall of the foot and without destroying its glazed surface to any extent and so making possible the evaporation of the moisture from the hoof wall. Dry hoof walls lose their toughness because dry tissues are brittle and break readily.

If the colt's foot is low at the heels and the wall is thin and weak, the proper shoe is the bar shoe. The frog in a foot of that kind is usually very prominent and if the colt happens to be the big, bold-gaited sort that hits the earth a hard blow at every stride, the frog should be protected with a bar, for there is always danger that a foot of that kind will spread enough under pressure to cause acute pain. This characteristic is more prevalent, however, among Thoroughbreds than among trotters and pacers, for the texture of the wall of the Thoroughbred's foot is finer than that of most harness horses. If the wall of a colt's foot is very thin at the heels and if, after being shod a few days, the foot begins to creep or expand over the edges of the shoe which has been fitted flush, it is a good idea to draw a clip up on each side of the shoe, back pretty well toward the heel. Every time the shoe is removed draw the bar a little if the heels of the foot seem the least bit pinched or cramped. There is a very little danger, however, of a foot of this kind becoming contracted.

Types of Shoes for Trotters and Pacers

The shoes shown in the cuts on pages 456 and 457 are types of race shoes in common use on standardbred horses, both trotters and pacers. These shoes

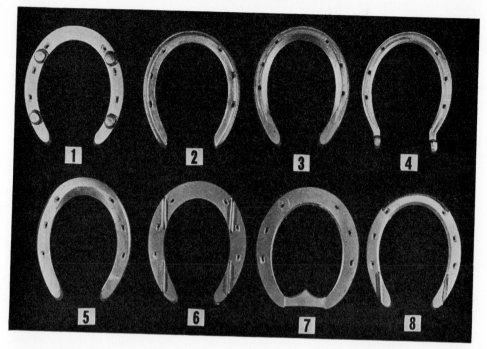

Types of Shoes for Pacers and Trotters. 1, *Memphis nub shoe;* 2, *rim shoe (front or hind);* 3, *swedged shoe (front);* 4, *swedged shoe (hind);* 5, *scooped, rolled toe shoe;* 6, *four-calk shoe (front);* 7, *plain toe, bar shoe (front);* 8, *three-calk pacing shoe.*

were made for me to use in animal husbandry classrooms by Mr. Al Yuenger, a blacksmith who for years has operated a shop at the race track at the Ohio State Fairgrounds in Columbus. The patterns for these shoes were copied from shoes that were made years ago by Dr. Jack Seiter, a veterinarian who was also one of the most skilled blacksmiths who ever worked at the profession.

Dr. Seiter always believed that horseshoes should be as simple in design as possible, that they were worn primarily for purposes of protection, and that careful workmanship, rather than freaky shoes, was the answer to the problem of balancing trotters or pacers and correcting defects in gait.

In the following paragraphs describing the shoes pictured on pages 456 and 457 I have summarized comments of Dr. Seiter and of many other competent horsemen:

1. *The Memphis Nub Shoe*

A modified form of the Memphis bar shoe, this has practically replaced the latter as a shoe for the gaiting of trotting-bred colts. It is used where a

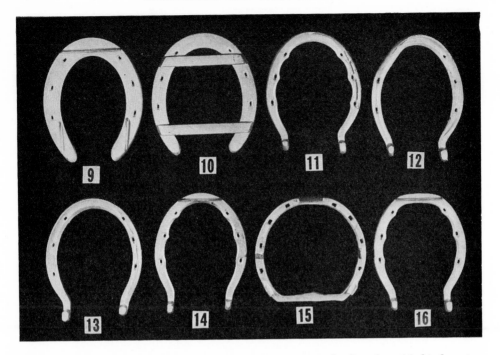

Types of Shoes for Pacers and Trotters (cont'd). 10, *Memphis bar shoe;* 11, *hind pacing shoe;* 12, *half-swedged oblique toe shoe;* 13, *half-swedged cross-firing shoe;* 14, *hind trotting shoe, full and rounding at the toe;* 15, *ice racing shoe* (*front*); 16, *hind trotting shoe, squared at the toe.*

rolling motion is needed. An eight-ounce shoe of this kind gives practically the same amount of rolling effect that formerly required a shoe of twice the weight. The weight of the Memphis nub shoe in the photograph is nine and a half ounces.

2. Rim Shoe

This is an ideal pacing shoe where a horse needs a good foothold. Unlike the calked shoe, it requires no effort or a minimum of effort in breaking over at the toe. Rim shoes are in common use on both front and hind feet. The weight of the rim shoe in the photograph is six ounces.

3. Swedged Shoe, Front

This is an ideal type of shoe for trotters because it is easily fitted and furnishes a good, flat, bearing surface, together with a firm grip or foothold on either a hard or a soft track. It does away with the toe grab and its diffi-

Mr. George Stephenson of West Jefferson, Ohio, and Mr. Jack McAllan, Michigan State College, East Lansing, Michigan, a pair of blacksmiths who are rated tops in their profession. These two men have shod so many Percheron and Belgian futurity winners and so many draft horse champions at the Ohio State Fair that each of them is regarded as a master in his field. Photograph courtesy Cook and Gormley.

cult breakover. It usually works better when fitted with a pair of heel or jar calks to break the concussion on a hard track. It also makes a good foundation for a bar shoe.

4. *Swedged Shoe, Hind*

The swedged shoe also works well behind. It gives the horse a perfect toe grab without any elevation of the toe and with no danger of a badly cut quarter, which is often caused by the ordinary toe grab. A swedged shoe is considerably lighter in weight than a plain grab shoe and at the same time furnishes a better contact surface for the foot. The opponents of the swedged shoe, however, say that the swedge fills up with dirt, but as someone else has asked, What gives a better foothold than dirt itself? In the photograph the weight of the front swedged shoe is seven and a half ounces, and that of the rear swedged shoe is four and a half ounces.

5. Scooped, Rolled Toe Shoe

This is an excellent type of shoe for trotters because it allows a free breakover, while the ridge which separates the roll and the scoop, when properly made, furnishes a fair grab or hold to prevent slipping back. The scooped, rolled toe shoe in the photograph weighs eight and a half ounces.

6. Four-Calk Shoe

This form of shoe has not been in great demand in recent years, but at one time it was used to correct knee knocking. The four sharp longitudinal calks were supposed to keep the feet from making a twist when about to leave the ground. The four-calk shoe in the illustration weighs seven and a half ounces.

7. Plain Toe, Bar Shoe

This shoe is as plain in design as a bar shoe can be. It is used for purposes of protecting a foot that is thin and shallow at the heel. With such a shoe the breakover is accomplished easily. The bar furnishes frog pressure and strengthens the wings of the shoe. The weight of the plain toe, bar shoe in the photograph is eight ounces.

8. Three-Calk Pacing Shoe

This is a good form of shoe for a bold, high-going pacer. The calks minimize the concussion and the toe rim furnishes a firm foothold on the track. The three-calk pacing shoe in the illustration weighs six ounces.

9. Three-Calk Trotting Shoe

This is a style of racing shoe that has wide use. The calks break the concussion on hard tracks and the grab gives a good foothold. The grab is set back from the toe so as to give an easy breakover. The three-calk trotting shoe in the photograph weighs seven and a half ounces.

10. Memphis Bar Shoe

This shoe was very popular several years ago, but it caused too many bad tendons. The hind bar is set ahead too far from the point of the heels and so lets the rear of the foot drop too low. The strain of getting up and over this bar caused much injury to tendons. The forward bar supplied what little virtue the shoe possessed as it furnished a good roll and easy breakover. The Memphis bar shoe in the illustration weighs ten ounces.

11. *Hind Pacing Shoe*

This hind shoe, like the front shoe (Style 8), is for use on bold, high-going pacers. The toe grab runs down the outside pretty well and if the foot is properly dressed, the grab prevents a horse from going over diagonally to the opposite front quarter and cross-firing. This type of shoe was worn by Dan Patch in his trials against time.

12. *Half-Swedged Oblique Toe Shoe*

This shoe is used for pacers. The swedged part furnishes a firm foot-hold and prevents the foot from being carried in too far. The hoof is left projecting over the oblique toe, the sharp edge of the hoof being rounded off to prevent cutting the quarter. This shoe may be used without heel calks, especially where the inside cannot be cut low enough to put the foot in proper shape. The hoof of a cross-firing horse must be cut low along the inside, especially the inside toe. The half-swedged oblique toe shoe in the photograph weighs four and a half ounces.

When a horse has a long, sloping pastern and the low heel which usually goes with it, a long, high, side calk on the outside heel should be used or the toe grab should be permitted to follow the outer edge of the shoe all the way to the heel. The hind pacing shoe in the photograph weighs five ounces.

13. *Half-Swedged Cross-Firing Shoe*

This shoe is of the same general design as Style 11, except that the toe is not oblique. It is the type of shoe generally used on pacers. The swedged part furnishes a firm foothold and prevents the foot from being carried in too far, while the inside wing of the shoe is half rounded to reduce the probability of hitting a diagonal fore foot. The half-swedged cross-firing shoe in the accompanying photograph weighs four ounces.

14. *Hind Trotting Shoe; Full and Rounding at the Toe*

This style of shoe is used more than any other on the hind feet of trotters, in many instances without a toe calk. Where a grab or toe calk is used, the calk should be set well back so as not to be dangerous in case a quarter is struck. The hind trotting shoes in the accompanying chart weigh four and a half and five ounces, respectively.

15. *Ice Racing Shoe, Front*

Note the toe calk, side calks, and heel calks to prevent slipping.

16. *Hind Trotting Shoe with "Dubbed" or Squared Toe*

This shoe weighs five ounces.

Shoes for Saddle Horses

The shoes for three-gaited and five-gaited saddlers vary a great deal in design to suit the needs of horses whose natural aptitudes at the several gaits differ so widely. If a saddle horse can work his legs barefooted, the shoes he wears are generally plain in design and are worn mostly for protection. Usually shoes for saddle horses are comparatively light, short, and fitted snug to prevent forging, interfering, and pulling of the shoes.

The hoof surface of the shoes should be wide enough to support the hoof wall and to cover the white line and a small margin of the sole. Usually both front and hind shoes are fullered and concaved on the ground surface.

The wings of the front shoes should be long enough to give good support to the buttresses of the feet, yet snug enough at the heels to reduce the danger of being caught and torn off by a hind foot. Usually, the outer border of the shoe is beveled. This contributes to neatness of workmanship and gives a dressier appearance to the feet.

If heel calks are used, it is general practice to bevel them strongly downward and forward under the foot. This helps to prevent forging. The ground surface of the shoe at the toe may be plain and flat or it may be spoon-shaped, giving a horse's front foot a little better purchase on the ground and providing a kind of uphill point of turnover which forces a horse to use his knees. Also, the toe of a saddle horse shoe may be oval in design, providing a "roller" motion type of action in front in order to aid a horse in breaking over quickly at the toe. Some front shoes for saddle horses have additional weight in the web of the shoe at the toe. This helps a horse to lengthen his stride. Others have additional weight in the web at the rear extremities of the wings in order to help a saddle horse to break or lift his knees and thus add height to his stride.

Hind shoes for saddlers may have wings that project rearward of the heels one fourth to three eighths of an inch. The toe of a hind shoe should be blunt and either fairly well rounded or squared, with the rim of the hoof wall extending slightly beyond the rim of the shoe. The branches of hind shoes are usually of equal thickness. The height of the calks on hind shoes equals the thickness of the shoe. To prevent interference, the inside calk may be omitted and the inner wing of the shoe thickened, beveled, and fitted snug. Clips may be placed on the inner and outer toes. In the case of narrow feet, clips may be used on both front and hind shoes. Six or seven nails may be used.

The shoes for hunters that are ridden to hounds or in steeplechase events are not widely different from shoes worn on any good saddle hack or pleasure horse. The shoes for a hunter are usually lighter than most shoes for saddle horses because the hunter does not have so many different gait assignments. The hunter is a galloper and his shoes should be chosen accordingly. They should fit the feet snugly to prevent injury from interference and to guard against being pulled off by his treading or by his galloping through soft going, over boggy ground, or even through stiff mire.

Common features of a hunter's front shoes are a narrow web, roller motion toe, and a central toe clip. Heel calks designed to prevent forging are advisable. The hind shoes, usually set back a little at the toe, may have both inner and outer toe clips and a low outside heel calk, with the inner branch of the shoe snugly fitted. Seven nails are commonly used in nailing the rear shoes.

Shoes for Racing Thoroughbreds

Runners are usually shod with light racing plates primarily to protect the hoof wall and to give them a good foothold on the ground. The shoes are made of steel so that they will not break and yet be as light as possible. The web of the shoe is wide enough to support the hoof wall all around and to cover the white line and a narrow portion or fringe of the outer sole. The ground surface of the shoe features clean, deep fullering all the way around the shoe. Otherwise the ground surface of the shoe is plain because calks are of no advantage. Front and hind shoes have six nail holes. The rear nails are located pretty well rearward in the wings of the shoe to prevent the bending or spreading of the light shoe. Front shoes have a central toe clip. Hind shoes may have both inner and outer toe clips and are fitted snug, sometimes with the toe of the hoof wall extending slightly beyond the toe of the shoe. Many shoes for race horses do not weigh more than three or four ounces.

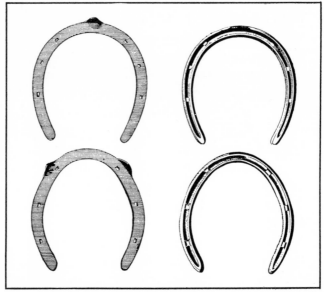

Shoes for Thoroughbreds. Above, left to right: A fore running plate: hoof surface, and ground surface. Below, left to right: A hind running plate: hoof surface and ground surface.

Rubber Pads

The use of asphalt and other slippery materials for surfacing streets and highways has made the going dangerous for horses shod with plain plates or even three-calk shoes. Therefore, rubber pads are in common use to give a horse's feet a better grip on all smooth, hard pavements. A pad of rubber, wide enough to cover the branches of the frog and the buttresses of the hoof, is firmly cemented to a leather sole. The wings of the short shoe with which the pad is used reach the middle of the quarters. The upper surface of the branches of the shoe should be beveled to conform to the pad and to hold it firmly against the frog and the buttresses of the feet. The thickness of the shoe should equal two thirds of the thickness of the pad, so that when fitted, one third of the thickness of the pad will project below the ground surface of the shoe. The shoe should have a strong toe clip to help anchor it in position. With the heavy, thick pads sometimes seen on draft horses, a low toe calk may be used, but heel calks are not used on short shoes. Pads are not often necessary on rear feet. Pads help to prevent slipping, diminish concussion, and relieve feet with sore heels. They are also a distinct aid for feet that have corns or bruised soles. In addition, rubber pads furnish frog pressure and help to retain the moisture in the feet and so prevent contraction.

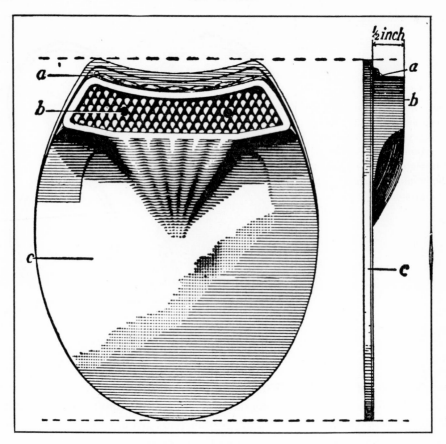

A light driving pad, gummed and stitched to a leather sole, seen from the ground surface and in profile. Used with a seven- to ten-ounce short shoe: a, stitching; b, rubber bar under buttress of foot and frog; c, leather sole. From Lungwitz and Adams, *Horse Shoeing,* courtesy J. B. Lippincott Company.

Shoeing the Drafter for Show

Scotch-bottom shoes are the show shoes most commonly seen on drafters. Both front and rear Scotch-bottom shoes are beveled at the rim all the way around in such a fashion as to permit the edges of the shoe to continue the slope of the hoof wall to the ground. The Scotch-bottom shoe, therefore, makes a drafter's foot look even larger than it is.

Scotch-bottom shoes for the front feet are made full and rounding at the toe and front quarters and have a toe clip to help anchor the shoe to the foot. Low, flat, heel calks may be used on the front shoes if a horse happens to be very shallow-footed.

Scotch-bottom shoes for the rear feet usually feature a heel calk on the

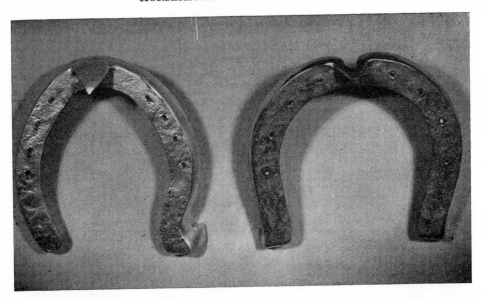

Typical Scotch-bottom shoes for draft horses that are to be shown. The shoe at the right is a front shoe. The shoe at the left is a hind shoe. Note the fullness at the toe and front quarters of the shoe as well as the width at the heels. The rear nail holes are punched just slightly rearward of the center of the wings of the shoe. This permits expansion at the heels when the feet are on the ground. Notice that the front shoe has a drawn toe clip and that the hind shoe has a welded or brazed toe clip. The drawn clip makes the nicer job. The hind shoe weighs 48 ounces. The front shoe weighs 50 ounces. Photograph courtesy Photography Department, The Ohio State University.

outside wing of the shoe. These outside heel calks raise the outside buttress of the rear feet, tend to push the hocks closer together, and aid a horse in collecting himself on the move.

The inside branches of Scotch-bottom shoes on both front and rear feet should be fitted snug to keep a horse from treading on them and tramping them off. Scotch-bottom shoes for the hind feet also feature a toe clip which, along with the nails, helps to hold the shoe securely in position. Usually, the clips on both front and rear shoes are drawn upward from the outside web of the toe of the shoe. Drawn clips make a neater job of shoeing than do welded or braised clips.

In getting the feet of the drafter ready for show, it is good practice to plate all prospective show horses six to eight weeks before the Scotch-bottom shoes are put on. At The Ohio State University, when preparing draft horses for show at the Ohio State Fair during the last week in August or the first week in September, we always make it a practice to shoe all of our entries with ordinary plate, not later than the first week or ten days of July. These show plates are plain in design, have small toe clips front and rear, and sometimes a low heel calk on the outside wing of the rear shoes if a horse

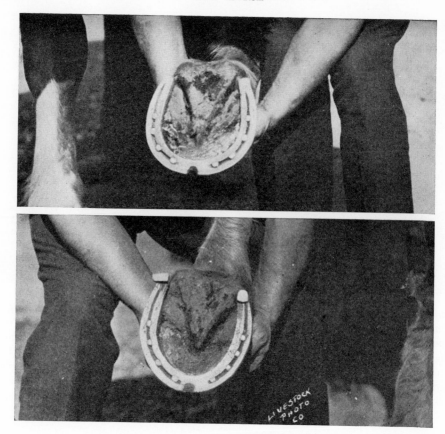

Scotch-bottom show shoe.
Front shoe above, hind shoe below. Note that the rear nails are driven just slightly rear-
ward of the center of the wings of the shoe. Also note the drawn toe clip. Photograph
courtesy Live Stock Photo Co.

needs to be pushed together a little at the hocks. Plates are used to protect
the feet, to keep them from breaking, and to permit sufficient growth of hoof
wall so that the feet will be amply large when the plates are removed and
replaced by the Scotch-bottom shoes. Six or seven weeks of hoof wall growth
gives a blacksmith opportunity to trim and shape the feet as they should be
shaped preparatory to nailing on the Scotch-bottom shoes for show day.

Questions

1. Thinking in terms of shape and quality, describe an ideal foot for a horse.
2. Contrast the way in which the feet of the draft horse and the feet of light-
legged horses commonly go wrong.
3. What are the objections to feet with narrow heels?

4. Name the functions of the hoof wall.

5. Why should the shoe be shaped to fit the foot rather than the foot to fit the shoe?

6. What factors determine the kind of shoe that a horse should wear? Cite specific examples in support of your answer.

7. Why do shoes for trotters and pacers differ more in design than do work horse shoes?

8. Compare the shape of the front and the rear feet of horses.

9. How can you distinguish between the left rear and the right rear shoes of horses?

10. What is the web of the shoe?

11. Usually, shoes are wider webbed at the toe than at the ends of the branches. Why?

12. Discuss the length of the wings of a front shoe in comparison with the length of the wings of a rear shoe.

13. How wide should the web of the shoe be?

14. Why should the hoof surface of the shoe be slightly concave or seated?

15. Why should the inside borders of shoes be snugly fitted?

16. Discuss the importance of the number, the depth, and the placement of the nail holes.

17. Why should the rear nails be driven but slightly rearward of the middle of the wings of the shoe?

18. What is the function of a toe clip or side clips as features of a shoe?

19. What is a drawn clip? a welded clip?

20. Define the terms "toe calk" and "heel calk."

21. Name and discuss briefly three kinds of toe calks.

22. What is the chief purpose of a three-calk shoe?

23. List five or six factors upon which the selection of the proper shoe depends.

24. Why is the length of the shoe in relation to the length of the foot important?

25. In the case of light-leg horses working at speed, shoes should be fitted snugly. Why?

26. Compare the weight of a racing shoe for a Thoroughbred with the weight of a Scotch-bottom show shoe for a drafter.

27. What is the advantage to some horses of a rolled toe shoe in front?

28. How does the white line of a horse's foot function as a guide to the blacksmith?

29. If a trotting colt has a good natural trot barefooted, how is he usually shod?

30. If a colt's action is low and he lacks knee action, suggest a method of shoeing to correct this fault.

31. After the use of weight to correct a faulty stride has accomplished the purpose, why should the weight be reduced?

32. What is a common cause of knuckling on rear ankles and pasterns?

33. If a prospective race colt is a pacer, how would you shoe him in front and behind?

34. Why are thin hoof walls a problem in shoeing?

35. Where should the additional weight be placed in a shoe to increase the length of stride?

36. Where should the added weight be placed in a shoe to increase height of stride?

37. What are the chief functions of shoes that are used on running race horses?

38. Why are rubber pads useful in the shoeing of some horses? Cite examples.

39. Describe a Scotch-bottom shoe for drafters.

40. Scotch-bottom shoes for the rear feet usually feature a heel calk on the outside wing of the shoe. Why?

41. Why should the inside branches of Scotch-bottom shoes be fitted very snugly?

42. About how many weeks of hoof wall growth are required in order that a blacksmith do a good job in fitting Scotch-bottom shoes?

23

Selling Purebred Horses

The Five Divisions of Horse Production

In the second chapter of this text, it was stated that for purposes of discussion the whole field of horse production consisted of five fields subdivided as follows: judging, breeding, feeding, miscellaneous management, and marketing, and selling. In this same chapter each of these five fields was regarded as a link in what was called "the horse production chain."

Then the conclusion was drawn that a breeder's success or failure might be accounted for in any one of these areas. Let us cite a few specific examples.

The Links of the Horse Production Chain

1. JUDGING   In many instances owners of both grade and purebred mares have made a big mistake when they purchased their foundation stock. Their incompetency as a judge of horses resulted in the purchase of mares whose individuality did not include the features which discriminating buyers insist upon when the offspring of these mares are offered for sale.

2. BREEDING   The selection of a breed-building sire is a difficult assignment. Many a breeder of purebreds has spent his life in the business and never owned a breed-building sire. By this I mean stallions whose stock horse prowess will help maintain the herd standards of excellence already attained or will improve them. The individuality of the stallion, like the individuality

of the mare, should feature those characteristics which buyers are sure to seek in the colts that are sired by the stallion.

Mr. W. H. Butler, formerly of Woodside Farms, Sandusky, Ohio, had two stallions, Giroust 78504 and Nectar 129726 (117636), prior to the time that he bought Laet, the horse that really established Woodside Farms as one of the leading Percheron nurseries of this country. The first two stallions failed to make a breed-building contribution at Woodside Farms and they have long since been forgotten. But Laet 133886, the breed builder, is a Percheron sire immortal.

3. FEEDING   It is in this field of horse production that many breeders fail. As a usual thing, the best horses are both well bred and well fed. Pedigree may be the reason why a newborn foal is a potential champion and in good hands might actually become one, but in poor hands the same foal might prove to be a disappointing failure.

The Percheron stallion Milaet is a splendid example to cite when breeding versus feeding, two important factors in attaining a championship, are discussed. On the day that Mr. William B. Murray of Wellington, Ohio, bought Milaet from a farmer in Muskingum County, Ohio, the horse had the same pedigree that he had when he was made grand champion Percheron stallion at Chicago in 1936. The farmer who owned the horse was a poor feeder, but Mr. Murray, who purchased the horse in a half-starved condition, was a good feeder. This example proves that horses whose pedigrees make them potential champions cannot become actual champions if neglected, half-starved, and badly managed.

4. MISCELLANEOUS MANAGEMENT   At a beef cattle breeders' barbecue, years ago, John Imboden, noted cattle feeder from the state of Illinois, said to the assembled cattlemen: "If you want to be disappointed in the cattle feeding business, buy cattle that have had better care than you intend to give them." Any good horseman knows that if you want to be disappointed in the horse business, all you have to do is to buy horses that have had better care than you intend to give them. This is true because there is no farm animal that will respond more quickly to care or to the lack of it than a horse.

One horseman treats his foals regularly for parasites. Another horseman fails to treat, and his foals become infested with parasites. One man believes in killing the bots, the roundworms, and the bloodworms and giving all the feed to his horses. The other breeder, who keeps on trying to feed the parasites and the horses together, is courting disaster. Let us, therefore, again paraphrase John Imboden's statement, for it is applicable in all fields of livestock production: "If you want to be disappointed in the horse business, buy horses which have had better care than you intend to give them."

Feeding vs. Breeding—Milaet. Photograph courtesy Mr. William B. Murray and Live Stock Photo Co.

5. MARKETING AND SELLING   Some people are failures as salesmen of purebred livestock. First of all, they fail to sell themselves to the prospective purchaser. Any owner whose horse is for sale has to sell himself to his customer before he can sell his horse. If the prospective customer lacks confidence in the owner of a horse, he is likely to purchase his horse elsewhere.

A horseman was heard to say of a certain horse dealer: "That fellow can't sell fifty-cent pieces for a quarter because people think that there is something wrong with the fifty-cent pieces which he has in his possession." Confidence in the owner of the horse that is for sale helps the prospective purchaser to decide that the horse is the one that he should buy. After all, the purchaser of a horse should be careful about purchases from sharp dealers because the horse business represents a slower turnover, a greater element of risk, a higher investment, and a more limited sales opportunity than does any phase of meat animal production.

The Present Status of the Work Horse Business

The Union Stock Yards and Transit Company of Chicago issues annually a summary booklet in which it lists the annual receipts of horses, cattle, sheep, and swine. Its figures showing the annual receipts of horses at

This beautiful chestnut pony with flaxen mane and tail is not only a saddle pony but also a harness show pony. He is owned by Mr. James Franceschini of Mt. Tremblant, Quebec. The little lad in cowboy regalia, a grandson of Mr. Franceschini, is in the incipient stage of becoming a horseman. Ponies such as this are in ready demand. Photograph courtesy Mr. Franceschini.

the Chicago yards over a period of eighty-five years indicate very clearly what has happened to the commercial horse business.

During the First World War, thousands of horses were used in the military service. It was during the First World War, in the year 1916, to be exact, that the Chicago market handled shipments of horses which totaled 193,290 head. In the year 1950, after a lapse of thirty-four years, this number on the Chicago market had dwindled to 246 head of horses.

The above figures prove a few things very conclusively. First, the years have brought kaleidoscopic changes in the horse business. Particularly does the statement apply to the status of the work horse. The trucks have driven work horses from the streets of our cities and the tractors have replaced them on the majority of farms where work horses are no longer considered an economic necessity.

As a consequence, the work horse market as it used to be has been destroyed. The lack of demand has battered prices downward. Auction sales of commercial horses are still held in a few places, but they have dwindled in number, consignors of horses to such sales have decreased, the horses offered are nondescript and plain in quality, the prices paid for them are low, with many shipments going to the killers at three cents a pound.

Light-Leg Horses Still in Demand

The only horses whose breeder and owner patronage has increased in spite of the great era of motor development are light-leg horses. I refer to the Thoroughbred, the Standardbred, the American Saddle Horse, and the Quarter Horse. In addition to the American Saddle Horse for pleasure and show, we may include hunters and jumpers, Tennessee Walking Horses, western stock horses, Palominos, and all kinds of parade horses. In other words, people have turned to saddle horses for recreation, exercise, and health in such numbers that more people are riding horseback today than ever in the history of the business.

The Jockey Club Thoroughbred Registry reports 8,800 registrations for 1950; the United States Trotting Association reports 4,561 Standardbred registrations; the American Saddle Horse Breeders Association reports 4,000 registrations; the American Quarter Horse Association reports 10,171 registrations; the Tennessee Walking Horse Breeders Association reports 2,000 registrations; the American Shetland Pony Club reports 1,121 registrations. Shetland ponies are in great demand by children. Many a Shetland pony today will bring as much as or more than a pair of work horses.

Light-Leg Horses at Private Treaty and Public Auction

Many thousands of light-leg horses change hands annually at both private treaty and public auction. No matter whether the sale be private or public, discriminating purchasers are in quest of horses that are both well bred and well made. If the pedigree gives to a Thoroughbred, a Standardbred, or an American Saddle Horse the right kind of identity, the horse, if he is a pleasing individual, will appeal to buyers. A Thoroughbred colt that is bred to run fast, a Standardbred trotter or pacer that is bred to trot or pace fast, and a saddle-bred colt that has ancestors which have proven their worth as show horses are all sure to attract many buyers and in most instances will sell themselves because the number of buyers seeking the best horses is always greater than the supply of top horses.

Some Noted Public Auctions

For many years, Thoroughbred, Standardbred, and American Saddle Horse breeders have patronized public auctions as a means of bringing consignors and purchasers together. The annual sale of Thoroughbred yearlings

Sparkling Aire 49537, winner of the National Futurity, Kentucky State Fair, 1950. This weanling filly is by Sparkling Waters and out of Ebony Aire by Oklahoma Peavine. One of the greatest type studies, standing still and in motion, that has ever proved to be the pacemaker in American show rings. She was bred and is owned by Dodge Stables, Lexington, Kentucky. With a pedigree and individuality like this filly has, the owner need not worry about making a sale. Photograph by John R. Horst, courtesy Dodge Stables.

at Saratoga, New York, is a fine example. The Keeneland summer and fall sales at Lexington, Kentucky, are patronized also by many breeders of Thoroughbreds who consign their yearlings annually.

Among the leading Standardbred sales held annually are the Harrisburg sale of yearlings at Harrisburg, Pennsylvania; the Tattersall Sales at Lexington; the Indianapolis Speed Sale at Indianapolis; and the Ohio Breeders' Sales Company auction, held each year at Delaware, during the week of the Grand Circuit Races.

Large Standardbred nurseries such as the Hanover Shoe Farms at Paoli, Pennsylvania, and the Village Farm at Langhorne, Pennsylvania, have consigned their colts to the Harrisburg sale.

Walnut Hall Farm and Gainesway Farms, Standardbred nurseries near Lexington, Kentucky, have sold their colts under the auspices of the Tattersall Sales Company. Sometimes the Walnut Hall colts have been sold at the farm. The Gainesway colts have usually been sold at the Tattersall Sales barn located at the Grand Circuit Speedway in Lexington.

Two of the leading consignment sales of saddle horses have been the annual Tattersall Sales at Lexington, and the Missouri Saddle Horse Sale Company, St. Louis. Usually there is a spring and summer sale of saddle horses at Tattersall. Mr. J. Truman Ward, breeder of saddle horses, Maryland Farm, Brentwood, Tennessee, has consigned his sale offering annually to the Tattersall Sales, where the patrons are given the opportunity each year to bid upon an offering from one of the leading saddle horse nurseries in the United States. Of course, both the Tattersall and St. Louis auctions have consignors from nearly all of the midwestern states. Occasionally Canadian consignors have patronized these auctions.

THE OHIO BREEDER SALES COMPANY AUCTION   This annual sale of Standardbred yearlings, during the Grand Circuit meeting at Delaware, Ohio, is the result of the steady expansion of the Standardbred horse industry in Ohio.

According to the registration figures of the United States Trotting Association, the four leading states in Standardbred registration in 1950 were Ohio, Illinois, Indiana, and New York. The two-year total (1948 and 1949) of weanling registrations in Ohio was 1,100 head. In 1950, 627 weanling Standardbreds were registered by breeders in Ohio.

In order that the yearling Standardbred crop in Ohio be disposed of with as little sale expense as possible, Ohio breeders formed a sales company under whose auspices for the last two years a sale of Standardbred yearlings has been held at Delaware, Ohio.

Mr. William B. Murray, Bonnie Brae Farms, Wellington, Ohio, has been president of the Ohio Breeders' Sales Company and has been one of its most ardent supporters. In the last four years Bonnie Brae Farms has consigned fifty head of yearlings to the Delaware sale. They sold for a total of $89,650.00 or an average of $1,793.00 a head. In 1949 and 1952, Bonnie Brae Farms consigned the high priced colt of the sale. In 1949, their top colt brought $5,600.00. In 1952, their top colt, Widower Abbey brought $5,200.00. Another Bonnie Brae colt, sold at the Harrisburg-Pennsylvania, sale in 1952, brought $3,400.00.

These figures are submitted to show what can be done in the Standardbred business under what may be termed average farm conditions. Bonnie Brae Farms is not a rich man's domain. Measured in terms of land and buildings, it is an average Ohio farm, but the plan of management which prevails is not average in any sense of the term. The brood mares and the stallions owned there are bred about as well as horses can be bred. That is to say, when a foal is dropped at Bonnie Brae Farms, it is a potential racing prospect.

The Widower, the sire of Meadow Rice, winner of the Little Brown Jug at Delaware, 1952. The Widower is owned and stands for service at Bonnie Brae Farms, Wellington, Ohio, a Standardbred nursery owned by William Murray and Son. In 1952, The Widower bred sixty-nine mares, service fee $350.00. There are sixty mares booked to The Widower for 1953 at a $500.00 service fee. Photograph courtesy *Harness Horse*, Harrisburg, Pa.

Meadow Rice, brown 3-year-old pacing stallion, with a race record of 1:58$\frac{1}{5}$. This record was made on a mile track August 28, 1952 at Duquoin, Illinois. On September 18, 1952 on a half mile track at Delaware, Ohio, Meadow Rice became the seventh winner of the Little Brown Jug pacing classic on a half mile track, winning the last two heats of the race in 2:02$\frac{1}{5}$ and 2:02$\frac{3}{5}$. The purse totaled $60,463.35 of which Meadow Rice won $30,231.66. Photograph courtesy *Harness Horse*, Harrisburg, Pa.

In addition to having a rich racing heritage, each colt at Bonnie Brae is well fed, so that when sale day arrives he is well grown and is presented in such rig that the customers in quest of a good colt will bid real money to get him. The man who owns Bonnie Brae Farms believes that the time to start to sell a Standardbred yearling is the time when the mare is bred, no matter whether the yearling is sold through an auction or by private treaty. Pedigree identity and pleasing individuality make customer appeal.

The Shows as Sales Windows for Horses

During the years 1918 to 1946, inclusive, The Ohio State University exhibited draft horses at the Ohio State Fair and the Chicago International. The prize winnings in these years totaled $21,818.37. The sales receipts, all sales by private treaty, totaled $118,866.50. The combined show winnings and sales receipts totaled $140,684.87.

Following is a partial breakdown of the above figures:

229 head of drafters (purebred and grade) brought	$111,366.50
2 grades brought	400.00
227 purebreds brought (Percherons and Belgians)	110,966.50
Average price	484.43
141 Percherons brought	71,279.00
Average price	505.52
86 Belgians brought	37,412.50
Average price for Belgians	435.02
Lowest-priced female (filly foal stifled)	25.00
Lowest-priced stallion (foal with bog spavins)	25.00
Highest price for mare	2,500.00
Highest price for stallion	3,000.00
116 head (all ages bred at The Ohio State University)	45,874.00
Average (all ages bred at The Ohio State University, many of them sold as foals, yearlings, and two-year-olds)	394.60

In twenty-two instances mares sold for $1,000 or more. In eleven instances mares sold for from $750 to $1,000 a head. Ninety-one head sold for $500 or more each.

In dozens of instances, the Percheron and Belgian sales listed above were consummated at the shows. The highest price for a draft stallion was for the Percheron stallion Hesitation Leon 216511. He was sold during the 1939 Chicago International for $3,000 to Mr. Frank Foster of Phoenixville,

Pennsylvania. The highest price for a draft mare was for the Percheron mare Miss Janet 205787. She was sold during the Ohio State Fair, 1937, for $2,500 to Mr. Harry McNair, Union Stock Yards, Chicago, Illinois.

Advertising as a Factor in Selling Horses

In making private treaty sales, the show window has proved to be a sales window for many an exhibitor. There are several reasons. First, it gives a winning horse a chance to identify himself on a competitive basis with other horses. Second, the shows are a means of bringing exhibitors and prospective purchasers together. The potential buyer has an opportunity at the leading shows to inspect a large number of animals at a minimum expenditure of time and money. Third, the shows—local, state, and national—are among the most effective advertising agencies of good livestock and furnish to breeders of the best purebred livestock—whether horses, cattle, sheep, or swine —an opportunity to identify themselves as leaders in their field. Years ago, for example, Colonel E. B. White of Selma Farms, Leesburg, Virginia, by virtue of his winnings at the leading shows, established the identity of Selma Farms as one of the leading Percheron nurseries in the United States.

Futurity Events as Sales Agencies

The term "futurity" in the case of draft and saddle horse shows, as well as in the case of racing events for speed horses, involves the nomination of in-foal mares whose colts, when dropped, will be kept eligible by the payment of entry fees to compete on show day or race day, as yearlings, two-year-olds, or three-year-olds, as the case may be, depending upon the specific rules which govern each futurity competition.

Futurity events at the shows and on the race track have catered to the needs of horse breeders in the following ways: First, they have emphasized in the minds of breeders the necessity of mating their mares to the best stallions available. Futurity shows have done much to help identify the best sires. Futurity colts, to win, must be both well bred and well fed. The breeder who wishes to win on show day must mate his mare with discrimination and then grow the colt. Second, futurity shows have taught breeders how to fit their colts. The underfitted, half-starved entries which appeared in number at the first futurity shows now appear infrequently. Exhibitors have learned that colts whose fitness is mute testimony of neglect have a tough row to hoe on Futurity Day. They have also learned the penalty of overfitting and feeding colts off in their legs.

Third, futurity shows bring colts together in numbers where prospective buyers may see them at a minimum expenditure of time and money. A great many yearlings which have participated in futurity shows have changed hands before the week is over. When colts sell as yearlings, their owners speed up the turnover in the horse business.

Fourth, the futurity show makes a strong appeal to the small breeder who may have only one colt to show, for the futurity classes afford him a splendid opportunity to advertise his offering.

Fifth, the futurity classes are a very important reason why breeders' organizations have pulled together successfully for many years. Such breeders' organizations have lived on because they exist for a definite purpose, the promotion of a futurity show. Therefore, breeders come back with their entries year after year, lean years and fat years alike. The futurity classes at the various shows and the futurity racing events have been the main jackscrews supporting the industry. On countless occasions, the seller has met the buyer at a futurity event and a deal has been made for a real colt prospect. Such events are a splendid example of the operation of the law of cumulative effect. Just a little energy, always expended in the right direction, may mean thousands of sales in a relatively few years.

Miscellaneous Methods of Advertising

Without question, the shows are one of the very best methods of advertising purebred livestock. But other methods are also very helpful: the local papers; the state and national breed publications; the use of circulars, folders, booklets, catalogues, and form letters, as well as billboard, roadside, and farm building advertisements. Of course, carefully worded letters, good photographs, and personal conferences are all effective factors in the consummation of sales.

The treatment of a prospective purchaser is most important. A good horse salesman must understand people as well as horses. There are very few instances where a salesman succeeds in selling a horse without first having sold himself to a prospective customer. Courteous treatment, promptness in correspondence, honest, conservative statements to prospective customers concerning the offering—all of these are factors which appeal to customers. Good horsemen will tell you that it is poor policy and bad sales psychology to present your offering to a prospective purchaser with an apology. There are three fundamental rules to keep in mind when selling horses: First, have the offering well bred, well made, and fit and ready for sale. Under such circumstances, customer appeal is not a problem. Second, a pretty good time to sell is the time that you have a customer. Third, a good time to sell is the time that you are making a profit. Any livestock project must be both productive and profitable if it is to be permanent.

Questions

1. Judging, breeding, feeding, miscellaneous management, and marketing and selling are the five links in the horse production chain. Why do the first four links of the chain constitute such important prerequisites to the last link? State your answers clearly.

2. Cite definite data to show how the business has been affected in the work horse area, as compared to the situation in the areas of light-leg horse production.

3. Discuss the importance of pedigree, individuality, and fitting as factors in making sales.

4. Name several noted Thoroughbred auctions in this country to which yearling colts are consigned annually for sale.

5. Name a few noted saddle horse auctions to which breeders consign regularly.

6. Name three or four noted Standardbred auctions through which hundreds of trotters and pacers are sold annually.

7. Discuss the show window as a sales window for horses.

8. List the advantages of futurity events as effective sales agencies.

9. List the advantages to the breeder of selling his colts as yearlings.

10. There are many miscellaneous forms of advertising horses for sale. List all of them that you can.

Index

Note: A page reference in *italics* indicates an illustration. Names of horses are given in SMALL CAPITALS.